Nobel Prize
Winners
in
CHEMISTRY
1901-1961

A Volume in The Life of Science Library
Number 41

REVISED EDITION

Nobel Prize Winners in CHEMISTRY

1901-1961

by

Eduard Farber

Abelard-Schuman

London   New York   Toronto

Photographs and selections from the Nobel Prize Lectures have been reproduced (and translated) by permission of the Royal Swedish Academy of Science, Stockholm.

LONDON
Abelard-Schuman
Limited
8 King Street

NEW YORK
Abelard-Schuman
Limited
6 West 57th Street

TORONTO
Abelard-Schuman
Canada Limited
896 Queen Street

Printed in the United States of America

INTRODUCTION

THE BEGINNING of the twentieth century was also the beginning of the functioning of the Nobel Foundation, created to carry out Dr. Alfred Nobel's will. Since then to the end of 1950, fifty-three chemists have received Nobel prizes in chemistry. Every year, except 1916, 17, 24, 33, 40, 41, and 42, candidates for the prize were selected and proposed by an international group of the most outstanding men in chemistry. This group comprised about 300 at the start, about 450 now. From the list of candidates which increased from ten in the early years to 70 recently, the Nobel Committee of the Royal Swedish Academy of Science selects the winners. The prize amounted to $41,800 in 1901, declined to $31,700 in 1950, and rose again to the present $49,600. While the monetary value of the prize has decreased, its importance and prestige have grown during the years. The appreciation and encouragement given to the men who made what their colleagues considered the greatest contribution to the advance of chemistry stimulates the progress of science and humanity.

The purpose of this book is to bring the knowledge of life and work of the Nobel Prize winners to a larger public. The original plan was suggested by Mr. Henry Schuman, and in my discussions with him the plan took the present form. A short biography is followed by a quotation from the prize-winner's description of his work, and an explanation of the importance of this work is added.

In the biographical sketches I have endeavoured to give more than a chronology of education and professional positions. Our understanding of scientific discoveries and industrial applications would be enhanced if we could know more about the human factor, the origin of the interest and the conditions for the achievement. Biographical sources are richer for the older than for the more recent laureates who may be willing to admit their preference for mountain climbing over violin playing but not much more about their feelings and incentives.

The selection from the prize-winner's description of his work was most frequently taken from his lecture delivered upon acceptance of the prize. For publications in French, German, and Swedish I have tried to give translations which retain the original form of expression. Usually, I have included at least a brief section in which the background of the new discovery is mentioned. Additional comments are inserted where the complexity of the material seemed to require explanations beyond those given by the laureate. Frequent references to preceding chapters are given to indicate connecting lines of thought and experiment.

The importance of the new discovery is described by showing its influence on the further development of theory and practice. This influence can be very broad so that it forms a new basis for chemical thinking, or it can be very specific so that it leads to the solution of a definite practical problem. In many instances, the award was given for the finding of a new light which illuminates many fields of our search. It has been my purpose to avoid any exaggeration in justifying the critical enthusiasm without which great work is not produced.

Thus, the book represents a collection of the stories of great events in the chemistry of our century, their origin in great personalities, and their role in our lives. This story will be more complete when taken together with that of the Nobel prizes in physics and physiology, some of which could just as well have been assigned to chemistry. In telling such a story for a wide public, it has to be based upon a certain standard of experience. This standard is hard to define but directly connected with a standard of living. Atoms, chlorophyll, vitamins, fertilizers are involved in both. Because more results of scientific work enter the sphere of our practical living, more people will want to know what makes chemistry advance and how chemists achieve their tasks. Although the present book shows only some of the peaks and by no means a systematically complete history of twentieth century chemistry, it may help some readers to find the way to their goals from the inspiring example of previous achievements.

In the present revised edition the story, which previously ended with 1950, is extended to include 1961. An appropriate bibliography has been added.

The general arrangement has been retained. In the chapters of the first edition, the biographical sketches have been brought up to date and the descriptions of the prize-winning work have been amplified with a view to provide more background for the recent developments. In the eleven new chapters, the excerpts from the fourteen Nobel Prize Lectures are, in general, larger than the previous ones. I hope the Laureates will accept my apologies for reprinting only selected parts of their important presentations. For the full stories the reader will have to consult the publications by the Nobel Foundation, most of them reprinted in *Science,* and to the references given in the appended bibliography.

My thanks are extended to the Royal Swedish Academy of Science for permission to reprint the selections from the Nobel Prize Lectures, and to Professor Melvin Calvin for revising the part on 1961.

Eduard Farber

Washington, D.C.
March 1962

CONTENTS

1901
JACOBUS HENRICUS VAN'T HOFF
(1852–1911)

"For the discovery of laws of chemical dynamics and of osmotic pressure."

BIOGRAPHICAL SKETCH

JACOBUS VAN'T HOFF WAS BORN ON AUGUST 30, 1852, IN Rotterdam. Although he decided to study chemistry, his interests were not limited to it; mathematics, poetry, and medicine attracted him strongly. His studies began in Delft, Holland, and were concluded in Utrecht, in 1874. In between, he spent a few months in Bonn, where the noted chemist Kekulé took little notice of him, and in Paris, under Adolphe Wurtz, where his first scientific conception took shape. Upon his return to Utrecht, he published an eleven-page booklet: "Proposal to extend the presently used chemical structural formulae into space, connected with a remark concerning the relationship between optical rotation and chemical constitution of organic compounds." In this "proposal" he started from older attempts to represent atoms by geometric symbols and combined them with Kekulé's teaching of a quadrivalent carbon atom. J. Wislicenus (Würzburg) gave his enthusiastic endorsement to van't Hoff's theory that substances which show optical rotation do so because of the asymmetric structure of their molecules, and the University of Amsterdam thereupon offered him its professorship in chemistry.

1

During twenty years (1877-1896) in Amsterdam van't Hoff enriched science by the development of other relationships—those between the physical and chemical concepts of energy, and those between the botanical-physiological concepts of osmosis and the chemical state of substances in solutions. For this work he received the Nobel Prize for 1901, the first year in which the Nobel Prizes were distributed.

Tired by twenty years of teaching, van't Hoff accepted a call to the Prussian Academy of Sciences in 1896, where he concentrated his investigations on the salts found in the mines of Stassfurt, the richest source of potassium salts used as fertilizers.

In his student days, van't Hoff had been more interested in theories than in experiments. Later he learned to combine these two sources of chemical progress.

DESCRIPTION OF THE PRIZE-WINNING WORK*

"Now, what physical chemistry in the latest period has done, or has claimed to do, did not consist in the introduction of new apparatus or of a new method of observation. The most recent development of physical chemistry has been characterized rather by the establishment of comprehensive principles which fertilize the whole foundation of the science, and promise to furnish nourishment for a large part of the chemistry of the future.

"There are in the main two foundations on which the recent development of physical chemistry rests: the extension of the law of Avogadro, and thermodynamics.

"The extension of Avogadro's principle consists in this: that for a given substance the osmotic pressure is equal in value to the gaseous pressure, provided the temperatures and concentrations, that is the quantities in unit volume, are the same. From that it follows immediately that two solutions of different bodies containing equal numbers of molecules in equal volumes, provided they are at the same temperature, exercise the same osmotic pressure. Not

---

* From J. H. van't Hoff, *Physical Chemistry in the Service of the Sciences* (Chicago: University of Chicago Press, 1903). Lectures delivered June 20-24, 1901, at the University of Chicago.

only so, but when the molecular weight is known, this pressure, like the gaseous pressure, can be calculated with ease.

"[This law] claims strict accuracy, both in the original and extended forms, only when the dilution is very great, or, in other words, only under conditions which cannot be realized practically. Nevertheless, at dilutions which correspond to that of atmospheric air, that is to say, in the case of gases at a pressure of one atmosphere and in the case of solutions of an analogous concentration (about one-tenth normal *), the deviations in most cases where the principles find application are insignificant.

"So much for the first principle, which . . . is often named the theory of solutions. The second concerns the application of thermodynamics, and particularly of conservation of work or energy, and of the Carnot-Clausius principle to chemical questions.

"It may be applied by carrying out so-called reversible cycles of operations or by the introduction of abstract physical conceptions and mathematical functions, such as entropy, as is done by physicists like Gibbs, Planck, and Duhem. I am convinced that, for the chemist, the first form, in which reversible cycles are employed, is the most advantageous. Briefly stated, a cycle consists in a series of changes in course of which the original condition is reached. Thus, for example, we permit ice to evaporate, condense the vapor to water, and then freeze the water.

"The equation $\dfrac{dK}{dt} = \dfrac{W}{2\,T^2}$

(W = heat developed in the reaction at T = absolute temperature) connects the equilibrium constant K with the heat W developed by the reaction. This equation has been tested and confirmed by experiment.

"A corollary of this law shows how the chemical equilibrium changes with temperature, i.e. how at rising temperature more of one compound is formed at the expense of the other, and vice versa. This corollary states: at a low temperature, more of that product is always formed, which is produced with a development of heat."

---

* A solution containing one tenth of an equivalent weight in one liter—e.g., 4.6 grams of ethyl alcohol per liter.

CONSEQUENCES IN THEORY
AND PRACTICE

Van't Hoff's work represents the culmination of a century of endeavors to find a scientific meaning of affinity, the "love" and "hatred" between chemical substances. He brings together, in mathematical form, heat of reaction, chemical affinity, and temperature of chemical change. The mathematical form has the alluring qualities of being simple and universal, but both these qualities are obtained by the substitution of an idealized symbol for the realities of chemical substances and behaviors. The completely reversible cycle of chemical change, for which he once gave the dissecting and cooking of a goose as the opposite example, is one of van't Hoff's idealizations. He was conscious of the fact that the ideal state, which lends itself to such mathematical treatment, does not exist. Nevertheless, he showed its amazing consequences. Relationships are revealed between vapor pressure and concentration of solutions. The influence of the dissolved substances on raising the boiling point and lowering the freezing point of the solvent can be calculated. The way in which chemical reactions change direction by changing temperature or pressure can be foreseen. The word "equilibrium" becomes just another expression for relationships of compounds and their components to controllable conditions. These relationships provide a general knowledge of what to do in order to achieve specific, desired results. The practical value of idealized theory thus becomes apparent, and van't Hoff demonstrated this practical value in his last years through his work on the equilibria that caused the composition of the salt deposits from the ocean, described in his two books of 1905 and 1909. A natural sodium-magnesium sulfate, discovered by W. Kubierschky in 1901, was named Vanthoffite.

1902
EMIL FISCHER
(1852–1919)

"For his syntheses in the groups of sugars and purines."

BIOGRAPHICAL SKETCH

EMIL FISCHER WAS GRADUATED, AT THE HEAD OF HIS CLASS, FROM the Gymnasium of Bonn in 1869. He could have joined his father's thriving and expanding business in real estate and industrial enterprises, but he desired to study physics and mathematics. Sickness (stomach disorders) prevented him from entering the University of Bonn until Easter of 1871. Dissatisfied with the poor conditions of instruction there, he changed to Strasbourg, where his teachers were Adolf von Baeyer in chemistry, Paul Groth in mineralogy, and Adolph Kundt in physics.

Fischer received his doctor's degree in 1874. In the year following, he published his discovery and investigation of a new organic compound which was to form a powerful tool in his later research on sugars. He called it phenyl-hydrazine. Hydrazine was the name he gave to an inorganic compound of two nitrogen atoms linked with each other and each carrying two hydrogen atoms. In the new substance, one of the hydrogens was replaced by the phenyl group, which is benzol minus one hydrogen atom. He found that phenyl-hydrazine combines with simple sugars, such as glucose or fructose, and that these new derivatives of the sugars could be easily purified and identified.

Fischer continued this investigation after he joined Baeyer in Munich in 1875, and pursued it when he went to Erlangen in 1882, to Würzburg three years later, and finally to Berlin in 1892. The general plan of work was always carefully prepared, but unexpected results were followed through to wherever they might lead. Such strategy was successfully applied to the investigation of uric acid, which in snakes is a normal product of excretion but which in humans causes certain kinds of rheumatism. Uric acid had interested Baeyer; Fischer expanded the latter's research, and in doing so he elucidated the chemical structure of caffein and theobromine. These substances can be regarded as derived from a basic substance which he called purine, which means the pure basic material of uric acid (purum uricum).

This investigation was rounded out in 1899. When Fischer received the Nobel prize for his sugar and purine research in 1902, he had already begun the systematic approach to the chemistry of proteins. Again combining premeditation with alertness to the unexpected, and with the help of numerous students and assistants from many countries, he developed new and improved methods of analysis. When the basic constituents of some proteins had been found and their chemical structure cleared up, synthesis according to plan followed. Thus he built large molecules of proteinlike substances in well-controlled steps. His summary, given in a lecture in 1906, led to exaggerated reports that the riddle of life had been solved; Fischer deplored them.

Fischer's work on tannins was barely concluded when the First World War broke out. Contrary to widespread assumptions, the production of chemicals and food materials had not been organized in Germany when the war started. Emil Fischer, the recognized leader of German chemistry, was charged with creating such organization.

Depressed by the loss of two of his three sons, one of them a war casualty, and by the outcome of the war for Germany, Emil Fischer succumbed in 1919 to his old ailment.

DESCRIPTION OF THE PRIZE-WINNING WORK*

This following passage from Fischer's Nobel Prize lecture is selected because it shows the connection between his researches on sugar and on proteins. The basic connection was his interest in the chemistry of life. Glucuronic acid, which, in the laboratory, is produced by oxidizing the carbon number six to convert its alcoholic group into an acidic group, occurs as a product of metabolism in animals. Plants and animals have special chemical tools by means of which they produce chemical changes of sugars and their derivatives, such as the glucosides. These tools are the ferments. They are delicate in stability and sensitive to changes of temperature. They are easily destroyed by certain chemical influences which act like poisons, yet they are sufficiently powerful under their own conditions to convert many thousand times their own weight of physiologically specific substances. Emil Fischer had tried to correlate this exceptional activity with the intricate arrangement of the atoms in a molecule of sugar or protein.

The most common sugars consist of chains of six carbon atoms, each connected with an oxygen atom. Five of these oxygen atoms carry hydrogen besides, in the linkage which is characteristic of alcohols. One of the oxygens, however, is in the more reactive form in which it exists in formaldehyde. The carbon atom carrying this aldehydic oxygen is usually numbered as one. Combinations of this atom with alcohols are designated as glucosides. The alcoholic groups connected with the other carbons can be reacted with acids, like all alcohols, and esters are thus formed. Fischer found that certain tanning substances contain gallic acid thus esterified with sugars. Again, he confirmed his analysis by synthesis.

"Now the synthesis in this field has been directed to new problems. Of the simple derivatives of glucose, the physiologist knows glucuronic acid best, since the animal organism makes use of this acid to render harmless such poisonous substances as carbolic acid, chloral, and turpentine. Its configuration, its relationships to glucose, and a likely explanation for its production in the body were easily made clear by the synthetic method. Great difficulties were found with glucosamine, a peculiar nitrogen-containing substance which was first obtained from lobster shells, but which we now

---

* Translated from *Les Prix Nobel en 1902*.

know is widely distributed in the animal world. Its synthesis, which I succeeded in carrying out only in the last few weeks, shows that glucosamine is an intermediary between glucose and the alpha-amino acids and thus forms one of the long-sought bridges between carbohydrates and proteins.

"Of general interest are the results obtained with the glucosides, which are widely spread over the plant world and which are to be considered as compounds of sugars with other substances of very different natures. Examples are amygdalin, a component of bitter almonds, or salicin, a fever remedy of the older medicine.

"Ferments, called enzymes in more recent times, have so prominent a place among the chemical tools of the living organism that it can be postulated that the chemical conversions in the living cell are predominantly bound to the collaboration of the enzymes. The examination of the artificial glucosides has shown the result that the effect of the enzymes depends to a high degree upon the geometric structure of the subjected molecule, that the two must fit together like lock and key. Consequently, the organism can carry out very special chemical conversions with their help, such as can never be achieved with the common agents."

CONSEQUENCES IN THEORY
AND PRACTICE

The chemical tool for sugar research, which Emil Fischer discovered seventy-five years ago, is still being used. Many modifications have been made, and a number of further applications have been found. Glucuronic acid, in which he was so greatly interested, is acquiring new prominence because of remarkable medicinal effects which have recently been observed.

Ribose is one of the carbohydrates which Fischer investigated purely for its systematic role, as an example of a specific configuration of atoms in a sugar molecule. This sugar has since been recognized as an important part of highly active substances in blood and muscle. It is there combined with adenine, one of the purines. This compound is perhaps the only really valuable substance in the famous Liebig's meat extract, a concentrated "soup" for which high nutritional value had been claimed.

In Fischer's notation of 1893, the structural and sterical relationships are as follows:

	CHO		CHO		CHO		CHO
	H │ OH		H │ OH		H │ OH	HO │ H
	HO │ H		HO │ H		HO │ H	HO │ H
d-glucose	H │ OH	HO │ H	HO │ H	HO │ H	HO │ H
	H │ OH		H │ OH		HO │ H	HO │ H
	CH₂OH		CH₂OH		CH₂OH	CH₂OH
			l-xylose		l-arabinose	l-ribose

For the importance of ribose and deoxyribose in nucleic acids and enzymes see the chapter on the Nobel prize for 1957.

Fischer himself drew practical conclusions from his scientific work by synthesizing veronal (1904) and, together with Joseph von Mering, introducing it as a hypnoticum. The patent for which they applied included the whole series of barbiturates.

By the addition of hydrogen to the aldehydic oxygen in simple sugars the oxygen is reduced to an alcoholic group. This reaction was of considerable help in elucidating the fine structure of sugars. It has become an industrial operation for producing sugar alcohols on a large commercial scale. Certain compounds of these alcohols with acids (esters) are widely used as wetting agents and detergents.

Since Fischer's work on sugars and purines is closely related to that on proteins, it may also be mentioned here that the amino acids, which he found to be the building stones of the proteins, are being produced and used for special nutritive purposes.

1 9 0 3
SVANTE AUGUST ARRHENIUS
(1859–1927)

"For his theory of electrolytic dissociation."

BIOGRAPHICAL SKETCH

SVANTE ARRHENIUS WAS BORN IN WIK, NEAR LAKE MÄLAR, Sweden. He learned to read at the age of three and became ardently interested in mathematics and physics in early school years. Although he began his studies at the University of Uppsala, he carried out his actual research work in Stockholm, returning to Uppsala to receive his doctor's degree in 1884.

At that time the physicist, Friedrich Kohlrausch, in Würzburg, had developed a convenient method for measuring the electrical conductivity of solutions. The electrical conductivity of a length of metal could be easily determined. When two pieces of the same metal are immersed in pure water, current will not pass from one to the other; in this respect pure water is an insulator. The addition of a salt or an acid to the water imparts conductivity to it. It had been assumed that the electric current was transported through the solution by becoming attached to the molecules of the dissolved substance, which were thereby split into carriers of positive and negative electricity. Faraday had given these carriers the name "ions," and those substances which form ions for the transportation of electric current were called "electrolytes."

When Arrhenius measured the change of conductivity caused by changing the concentration of an electrolyte, he arrived at the con-

10

clusion that a part of the electrolyte is active and another inactive as a carrier for electricity. As dilution increases, the active parts increase, until at infinitely great dilution all of the electrolyte is split, or dissociated, into the active parts. This dissociated state exists independently of the passage of electricity through the solution. Arrhenius' dissertation of 1884 interested Wilhelm Ostwald (see pp. 37-41) so greatly that the latter went to Uppsala to discuss the meaning and application of these results with Arrhenius. Swedish academic circles thus learned of the importance of this work and facilitated the academic career of their young countryman. Travels brought him to Ostwald in Riga, Kohlrausch in Würzburg, Boltzmann in Graz, and van't Hoff in Amsterdam. The electrolytic theory took definite shape in these years. It formed the basis for extended work, but Arrhenius, having become professor in Stockholm, in 1891, was chiefly interested in the widest application of the fundamental theory of chemical reactions. E. A. von Behring and Paul Ehrlich arrived at an explanation for the action of poisons (toxins) in the living organism and its ability to neutralize their effects by elaborating antitoxins. Arrhenius sought the general, or physical-chemical, laws which govern organismic changes. He found that these reactions follow the same laws as all "ordinary" chemical reactions, and that there is no essential difference between those in the test tube and those in the human body. Here again was a theme which could have captured all his energies, but Arrhenius' curiosity reached out further. He developed a theory of cosmic physics, in which the pressure of light-radiation sent particles, even germs of living organisms, through space and thus connected all the world.

In 1905 Arrhenius assumed the directorship of the Nobel Institute for Physical Chemistry, a fitting position for a man of such universal interests.

DESCRIPTION OF THE PRIZE-WINNING WORK*

"The conductivity depends upon the velocity with which the ions (Zn and SO_4) of the molecules ($ZnSO_4$) are carried through the liquid by the electric force, i.e. the potential difference. If this potential difference remains constant, the velocity depends only on the friction that the ions in their passage through the liquid exert on the surrounding molecules. As these, at higher dilutions, are only water molecules, it might be expected that the conductivity would remain constant and independent of the dilution if it be supposed that all the molecules, $ZnSO_4$, take part in the electric transportation. As experiment now teaches us that the molar conductivity increases with dilution, even if this is very high (1,000 molecules or more of water to one molecule of $ZnSO_4$) we are led to the hypothesis that not all, but only part of, the $ZnSO_4$ molecules take part in the transportation of electricity. This part increases with the dilution in the same proportion as the molecular conductivity k. The limiting value k^∞ is approached at infinite dilution and corresponds to the limit that all molecules conduct electricity. The conducting part of the molecules I called the active part. It may evidently be calculated as the quotient $k : k^\infty$.

"The most far reaching conclusion of the conception of active molecules was the explanation of the heat of neutralization. As this is much more easily understood by means of the theory of electric dissociation I anticipate this for a moment. According to this theory, strong acids and bases, as well as salts, are at great dilution (nearly) completely dissociated into their ions, e.g. HCl in $\overset{+}{H}$ and $\overset{-}{Cl}$, NaOH into $\overset{+}{Na}$ and $\overset{-}{OH}$, NaCl into $\overset{+}{Na}$ and $\overset{-}{Cl}$. But water is (nearly) not dissociated at all. Therefore the reaction of neutralization at mixing a strong acid, e.g. HCl, with a strong base, e.g.

---

* From Arrhenius' Nobel Prize acceptance lecture, published in the *Proceedings of the Royal Institution of Great Britain*, Vol. XVII (1904), pp. 553 ff. Given in his own English version. He uses as examples zinc sulfate, $ZnSO_4$; hydrochloric acid, HCl; and sodium hydroxide, NaOH. The ions are indicated by placing a + or − sign on top of the symbol for the substance.

NaOH, both in great dilution, may be represented by the following equation:

$$(\overset{+}{H} + \overset{-}{Cl}) + (\overset{+}{Na} + \overset{-}{OH}) = (\overset{+}{Na} + \overset{-}{Cl}) + HOH$$

or

$$\overset{+}{H} + \overset{-}{OH} = HOH$$

"The whole reaction is equivalent to the formation of water out of both the ions, $\overset{+}{H}$ and $\overset{-}{OH}$, and evidently independent of the nature of the strong acid and of the strong base. The heat of any reaction of this kind must, therefore, always be the same for equivalent quantities of any strong acids and bases. In reality, it is found to be 13,600 calories in all cases. This thermal equality was the most prominent feature that thermo-chemistry had discovered.

"It was now asked in what respect the active state of the electrolytes differs from the inactive one. On this question I gave an answer in 1887.

"The active molecules of the salts are divided into their ions. These are wholly free and behave just as other molecules in the solutions.

"An important role is played by the water which may be regarded as a weak acid or base. By its electrolytical dissociation it causes the hydrolysis of salts of weak acids and bases.

"For physiological chemistry this question is of greatest importance, as is confirmed by the experimental results of Sjogvist and others. Also for the explanation of volcanic phenomena, the concurrence between water and silicic acid at different temperatures has found an application."

CONSEQUENCES IN THEORY AND PRACTICE

At first Arrhenius found considerable resistance to his theory. It was argued that sodium is known to decompose water violently, and that chlorine has a penetrating odor. How could these elements be contained in a quiet, odorless solution? The answer was connected with the electrical charge. Not sodium itself but its positively charged atoms, not chlorine itself but its negatively charged atoms were present in these solutions of sodium chloride. This split of one molecule into two parts explained the fact that the osmotic pressure was found to be much higher than calculated for the combined substance, and the change of osmotic pressure with dilution indicated the relative amount of dissociation. The chemical activity of all strong acids in dilute solutions turned out to be the same in Ostwald's measurements; the new theory accounted for that. The hydrogen ions were the active part in chemical reactions as they were in electrical conductivity. Soon the discovery of the electron as the unit of electrical charge further justified Arrhenius' theory. The positive ion of sodium now became an atom which had lost one of its electrons to the chlorine atom, which thus acquired its negative charge.

When it was discovered that X-rays make a gas at normal pressure conductive for electricity, J. J. Thomson explained that the exposure to X-rays "does for the gas much what is done by the solvent for the salts dissolved in liquid electrolytes."

Facts of many kinds—heat of reaction, color, osmotic pressure, and chemical affinity—thus found a unifying explanation. In the enthusiasm about the beauty of this idealization the discoverer of the theory and his immediate followers went too far. The influence of the nature of the electrolyte made itself known in refined experiments. The idealization might be acceptable for very highly dilute solutions; for more concentrated ones it oversimplified things. The theory proved to be a first approximation to the real behavior of electrolytes. Its basis, however, the dissociation of acids, bases, and salts into parts of opposite electrical charge, remained fruitful. The exchange of electrons became the fundamental explanation of chemical bonding.

1 9 0 4
WILLIAM RAMSAY
(1852–1916)

*"For the discovery of gaseous, indifferent elements
in the air and the determination of their place in the
periodic system."*

BIOGRAPHICAL SKETCH

SIR WILLIAM RAMSAY DESCRIBED THE ORIGIN OF HIS INTEREST
in chemistry as follows: "My grandfather on my Father's side,
William Ramsay, was a chemical manufacturer in Glasgow; he
came from a long line of dyers, who carried on their work in Had-
dington, a small country town in the east of Scotland. He was the
first, I believe, to distill wood for the production of pyroligneous
acid; and he purified it by 'torrefying' the acetate of lime formed
by its neutralization, and distilling with oil of vitriol. He also was
the first to manufacture bichrome; and for many years, he and his
partners, the Messrs Turnbull, made 'Turnbull's Blue.'

"My mother's Father was a medical man, practicing in Edin-
burgh. He was the author of a series of textbooks, one of which
was entitled 'Colloquium Chymica.' Hence I inherited the taste for
Chemistry from my ancestors on both sides of the family."

Ramsay obtained his doctor's degree in Tübingen in 1872 for
work on ortho-toluic acid and its derivatives, carried out under
Rudolf Fittig (1835-1910). For more than ten years, after his
return to Glasgow and as professor in Bristol (1880), he continued
organic chemical research. The new developments in physical chem-

15

istry found his active interest, particularly after he took over the chair in inorganic chemistry at the University College, London, in 1887. When Lord Rayleigh described the discrepancy in specific gravities between nitrogen from ammonia and nitrogen from air, Ramsay was prepared to suggest an answer. ". . . in my copy of Cavendish's life, published by the Cavendish Society in 1849, opposite his statement that on passing electric sparks through a mixture of nitrogen with excess of oxygen, he had obtained a small residue, amounting to not more than 1/125th of the whole, I find that I had written the words 'look into this.' It must have been the latent memory of this circumstance which led me, in 1894, to suggest to Lord Rayleigh a reason for the high density which he had found for atmospheric nitrogen." The result of his "looking into this" was the discovery of a new element, argon, which he soon followed with the discovery of neon, krypton, and xenon. He identified as helium the gas developed from certain uranium minerals when they were treated with acids.

The great experimental skill developed in this research later permitted Ramsay (with R. Whytlaw-Gray) to separate and weigh tiny quantities of the radioactive gas emitted by radium and to determine its atomic weight. His ideas about radioactive decomposition (*Elements and Electrons,* London, 1912) were not generally accepted at that time.

DESCRIPTION OF THE PRIZE-WINNING WORK *

"Helium, like argon, is a gas, sparingly soluble in water, withstanding the action of oxygen in presence of caustic soda, under the influence of the electric discharge, as well as of red-hot magnesium. Like argon, the ratio of its specific heat at constant volume to that at constant pressure shows it to be a monatomic element, the atom and the molecule being the same; and its density was found both by Langlet and myself to be nearly 2; it is therefore the lightest gas known, with the exception of hydrogen. These properties in common made it evident that helium and argon belong to the same

---

* From *Les Prix Nobel en 1904.*

natural family; and it was also obvious that there must exist at least three other elements of the same class; this is evident on inspection of the periodic table where the following elements are in apposition:

Hydrogen (?)	Fluorine	Chlorine	Bromine	Iodine
1	19	35.5	80	127
Helium	?	Argon	?	?
4	20	40	82	132
Lithium	Sodium	Potassium	Rubidium	Caesium
7	23	39	85	133

"While 15 litres of argon were being purified, Dr. Hampson had succeeded in perfecting his machine; and he placed at our disposal about a litre of liquid air. After 'playing' with it, so as to familiarize ourselves with its properties, there remained in the vessel about 100 cubic centimetres. I suggested that we should allow this portion to evaporate almost entirely away, and that we should collect the last 10 cubic centimetres by allowing it to boil off into a gas-holder. This was done; and after removal of oxygen and nitrogen, there remained 26 cubic centimetres of a gas which showed, besides the spectrum of argon, a bright yellow and a bright green line, of wavelengths 5571, and 5570.5 respectively. Although the density of the new gas, which we named 'krypton,' or 'hidden,' was found to be only 22.5, we conjectured that, when purified, it would turn out to be forty times as heavy as hydrogen, implying the atomic weight 80, for our earlier experiments established the fact that, like argon, its molecular and atomic weights were identical.

"An account of this discovery was communicated to the Royal Society on June 3rd, 98; and no time was lost in examining the argon by liquefaction and fractional distillation. On June 13th, we were able to announce that the lower boiling portions of the 15 litres of argon contained a gas which we called 'neon,' or 'new.' It showed a spectrum characterized by a brilliant flame coloured light, consisting of many red, orange, and yellow lines.

"In September 98, the discovery of another gas was announced; it was separated from krypton by fractionation, and possessed a still higher boiling point. We named it 'xenon,' or the 'stranger.'

"The amounts of neon and helium in air have once been measured; the former is contained in air in the proportion of 1 volume in 81,000; the latter, 1 volume in 245,000. The amounts of krypton and xenon are very much smaller, not more than 1 part of krypton by volume can be separated from 20,000,000 of air; and the amount of xenon in air by volume is not more than 1 part in 170,000,000."

CONSEQUENCES IN THEORY AND PRACTICE

Helium, neon, argon, krypton, and xenon are alike in their chemical inertness. The discovery of this group of "noble gases" was in part predicted from the regularities of the periodic system, and it enlarged this system by an entire new group. It is the group of elements with valency O. These exceptional chemical elements which have no chemical reactivity formed the perfect transitions from the end of one period to the beginning of the next in the periodic system. These new links in the chain of elements permitted the erection of a theory of atomic structure which Niels Bohr began to build in 1913.

The methods developed by Ramsay and his associates became increasingly important as work with minute quantities of substances was required in radioactivity and biochemistry. On the other hand, the principles on which the separation of the gases were based soon found applications in industrial production. Helium, neon, and argon did not remain chemical curiosities of which only one or two scientific laboratories possessed a small supply. Helium, of which rich sources were discovered in mineral deposits, replaced the dangerously inflammable hydrogen as the gas with which balloons were filled. Helium or argon forms the protective gas under which magnesium, aluminum, and stainless steel are welded; because of the inert gas amosphere, the metals are not oxidized in spite of the high temperature. Neon, argon, and krypton are used in fluorescent lamps and in "neon" signs. The electric discharge through neon, its mixtures with mercury, or traces of krypton produce intense light at low temperature and with high efficiency.

1 9 0 5
ADOLF VON BAEYER
(1835–1917)

*"For his researches on organic dyestuffs and hydro-
aromatic compounds."*

BIOGRAPHICAL SKETCH

ADOLF BAEYER WAS BORN IN BERLIN. HIS FATHER, AT THAT TIME
a captain in the Prussian General Staff, later became a general and
after retiring was made president of the Geodetic Institute of
Prussia. His mother was the daughter of a famous jurist and literary
historian. Baeyer's inclination to chemistry was developed at an
early age. In his lecture on indigo synthesis, in 1900, he mentioned
that as a boy he was greatly impressed with "the strange behavior
and peculiar odor" of the dyestuff from the East Indies. Berlin had
no laboratory for instruction in chemistry; Baeyer therefore went
to Heidelberg, in 1856, to study under Bunsen. There he met
Friedrich August Kekulé (1829-1896) and, after being graduated
in 1858 with a thesis on organic arsenic compounds, followed him
to Ghent, Belgium. Baeyer considered himself a self-taught chemist, although Bunsen introduced him to laboratory practice and
Kekulé to theory.

In 1860, Baeyer found a modest position at the Trade Academy
(Gewerbe Institut) in Berlin. Uric acid became his main theme of
research; he derived from it an interesting acid which he called
barbituric acid, because his best girl friend's name was Barbara.
Barbituric acid and other products of the oxidation of uric acid

supplied him with analogies by means of which to distinguish between the products obtained from indigo. This king of all dyestuffs contains oxygen. It was therefore to be considered as the oxidation product of a "mother-substance" which Baeyer stated to be a substance somewhat related to aniline and called indole. It was relatively easy to obtain an oxidized indole, called oxindole, and the next more highly oxidized indole, called isatin, from indigo. Comparing indole with benzene, oxindole could be considered analogous to phenol, although there is an important difference between them. Phenol is derived from benzene by substituting hydroxyl for the hydrogen of one of the six carbon atoms. The adjacent carbon atom, called the ortho-position, is also substituted in indole. Without having to depend on indigo, isatin could be prepared from a benzene molecule in which one carbon had its hydrogen replaced by a nitric acid residue (nitro-group), and the adjacent carbon atom by a residue of acetic acid, or its neighbor in the chemical system, propionic acid.

Baeyer's work on indigo synthesis extended over the years 1865 to 1883. From 1872-1875 he was at the newly organized University of Strasbourg and from 1875 on he was in Munich as the successor to Liebig. He continued to teach and to experiment into his eightieth year. Chemistry to him was experimenting with one of the simplest of tools, the test tube. Richard Willstätter used to tell the story that Baeyer once invited Emil Fischer to inspect a wonderful apparatus he had built—it consisted of a test tube held in a clamp over a small Bunsen burner. With this tool Baeyer disclosed fundamental relationships for products of benzene and terpenes (hydroaromatic substances), for dyestuffs, and for a new class of compounds in which oxygen displays four instead of the conventional two chemical valences.

Fundamentally, Baeyer was averse to theorizing. However, he developed two very general concepts which remained valid, although with subsequent refinements. One of these concepts referred to the basic chemical reactions by which plants convert carbon dioxide and water into sugars and starch; the other was derived from van't Hoff's theory of the tetrahedron as the model for the carbon atom with its four valences. When carbon atoms combine to form rings, according to Baeyer's theory, the angle of these valences is more or less deflected, and a "strain" is set up which is decisive for the degree of stability of these structures.

DESCRIPTION OF THE PRIZE-WINNING WORK*

"In order to find the mother-substance of indigo I started from oxindole, which contains only one oxygen atom and behaves like a phenol. The problem of producing indole was thus reduced to that of converting phenol into benzene. This analogy was of little use, since this task, simple as it is in theory, can be solved only in ways which are forbidden for the easily resinifying oxindole. After a half year's fruitless work I talked of my predicament with my colleague Stahlschmidt, who, at that time, lectured on technical chemistry at the Trade Academy. I learned from him that zinc dust, which had formerly been used only as a paint ingredient, now served as an industrial reducing agent. I immediately tried an experiment; but oxindole withstood all efforts, until, in despair, I heated it with zinc dust in a combustion tube to near glowing temperature. Now (1866) I finally had in my hands the mother-substance of indigo, and I rejoiced the way Emil Fischer may have done when he found purine, the mother-substance of uric acid, after fifteen years' work.

"Artificial indigo first saw the light of the world in 1870, when I, together with my student Emmerling, converted isatin into the dyestuff by recation with phosphorus-containing trichloride of phosphorus. At that time, isatin was obtainable only from indigo, so that the synthesis became a complete one only when I produced isatin artificially from phenyl-acetic acid, on June 6, 1878.

"By the reduction of isatin to oxindol, just that oxygen atom, which must be retained for the formation of indigo, is substituted by hydrogen. Phosphorus chloride, however, does not touch this oxygen and, by eliminating the other, leads directly to indigo, as shown by the following formulas:

---

* From the lecture "Über Die Geschichte der Indigo Synthese" (On the History of Indigo Synthesis), in *Berichte der Deutschen Chemischen Gesellschaft* (1900); reprinted in *Gesammelte Werke* (Braunschweig: Friedr. Vieweg und Sohn. 1905), Vol. II.

$$C_6H_4{<}_{NH}^{CO}{>}CO \qquad\qquad C_6H_4{<}_{NH}^{CH_2}{>}CO$$

Isatin.   Oxindol.

$$C_6H_4{<}_{NH}^{CO}{>}C\boxed{O \quad\quad O}C{<}_{NH}^{CO}{>}C_6H_4$$

Indigo.

"In 1878 and '79 I developed further the method of indigo synthesis from isatin and found that it is based upon the reduction of isatin chloride, which is formed first. The method also permitted the production of substituted indigoes, such as dibromo, tetrabromo, dinitro, and diamido indigo, and gave particularly high yields for tetrabromo indigo.

"The reduction of isatin chloride consists, in all probability, in the addition of two hydrogen atoms, yielding a chlorinated indoxyl, which can then split off hydrogen chloride and go over into indigo:

$$C_6H_4{<}_{N}^{CO}{\geqslant}C.Cl \qquad\qquad C_6H_4{<}_{NH}^{CO}{>}C\boxed{\begin{matrix}H\\Cl\end{matrix}}$$

"This indoxyl, an isomer of oxindol, was discovered in 1879, simultaneously by Baumann and Tiemann. To them belongs the merit of having discovered indoxyl and its easy transition to indigo. At first, however, I had fought against them, and I acknowledged the correctness of their findings only two years later, when I had synthesized indoxyl and proved its identity with the substance obtained from dog's urine.

"In the course of experiments to obtain ortho-nitro-phenyl-acetaldehyde I boiled the bromide of ortho-nitro-cinnamic acid with alkalies and I observed that some indigo was formed thereby. The further prosecution of this discovery led to the discovery of ortho-nitro-phenyl-propiolic acid and to the production of indigo from it. The first patent on this invention was filed on March 19, 1880, and the first scientific publication appeared in December of the same year."

CONSEQUENCES IN THEORY
AND PRACTICE

Baeyer's long, systematic work on the constitution and synthesis of indigo began with the accidental finding of a method for getting at the core of certain compounds. This method of heating the compound with finely divided zinc metal proved to be of great importance. At Baeyer's insistence, Carl Graebe applied the method to the famous red dyestuff alizarin and thus discovered its chemical skeleton. An industry for manufacture of alizarin grew out of this laboratory finding in a short time, and the success of this enterprise encouraged chemical manufacturers to persist in the costly efforts toward the technical synthesis of indigo. On the basis of Baeyer's work, but not following his specific steps, indigo was finally made from aniline and acetic acid. The impact on industry and agriculture was world-wide. In Bengal, over a half million acres of land had been devoted to the culture of the indigo plant. At the end of the nineteenth century, the chemical factory began to replace the indigo plantation, and the German chemical industry, staffed partly with men who had received their chemical training from Baeyer, came into its dominant position.

In 1883, Baeyer announced that he had determined the place of every atom in the molecule of indigo. A correction was found necessary forty years later. Baeyer's clear picture of the dyestuff molecule, as modified by other chemists, made possible the production of valuable derived coloring substances. Among them was an indigo derivative containing two atoms of bromine, a purple dyestuff which is identical with that secreted by a snail (*Murex brandaris*). This was the purple used in antiquity.

1 9 0 6
HENRI MOISSAN
(1852–1907)

*"For his research on the isolation of the element
fluorine and for placing at the service of science the
electric furnace which bears his name."*

BIOGRAPHICAL SKETCH

HENRI MOISSAN WAS BORN IN PARIS AND STUDIED CHEMISTRY
there while working in a pharmacy. His chemistry professor,
Dehérain, helped to convince him that his field was pure science.
After publishing a thesis on the respiration of leaves in the dark,
in 1876, he turned to inorganic chemistry, at that time a somewhat neglected branch. First he investigated a peculiar form of
iron, a finely divided powder which ignites readily and is, therefore, called pyrophorous. On June 20, 1888, after four years of
work, he announced the isolation of the element fluorine. This was
only the beginning of his research on this highly reactive and poisonous element. He investigated organic compounds from methyl-
fluoride to carbon tetrafluoride, and showed that the hexafluoride
of sulfur is nearly as stable and inert as nitrogen.

All this was done under rather poor laboratory conditions. No
wonder Moissan later declared that fluorine may have shortened
his life by ten years. Later, as professor at the Faculty of Sciences
of the University of Paris (from 1900 on) he obtained better
facilities.

In 1892 Moissan found a particularly practical arrangement for

24

an electric oven in which he made calcium carbide without any thought of its industrial possibilities. Tungsten metal and a steel in which carbon was replaced by boron were prepared in this oven.

From geological studies Moissan concluded that diamond must have been formed from a liquid or pasty mass. "This carbon must have crystallized under the action of a strong pressure; the iron was in a liquid state and owing to rapid cooling, due to some cause, there was a violent contraction of the mass and the carbon passed from a density of 2 to 3.5, giving the diamond."

In his later years Moissan devoted much time to his book on inorganic chemistry, which comprises five large volumes.

DESCRIPTION OF THE PRIZE-WINNING WORK*

"Our first model of electric furnace, shown to the Academy of Sciences in December 1892, was of quicklime. It was composed of two well-dressed blocks of lime laid one on the other. The lower piece contained a longitudinal groove through which passed the two electrodes, and in the center was a small cavity which served as a crucible. The depth of this cavity can vary and contains a layer several centimeters thick of the substance which is to be heated by the arc. It is also possible to introduce into this cavity a small carbon crucible containing the material to be heated. The upper block is slightly hollowed in the part which lies directly over the arc, and as the intense heat of the current soon melts the surface of the lime and gives to it a high polish there is formed a dome which reflects all the heat on the small cavity which contains the crucible.

"This apparatus is a reverberatory electrical furnace with movable electrodes. This last point is of importance, as the moving of the electrodes gives an easy means of establishing the arc, for lengthening or shortening at will, and in a word, it materially simplifies the conduct of the experiment.

"Many experimenters have hitherto used the electric arc to obtain high temperatures, but those who have preceded me have not

---

* The first excerpt is from *The Electric Furnace,* translated by Victor Lenher (Easton, Pa.: The Chemical Publishing Co., 1904), pp. 5 and 21; the second is from *Smithsonian Institution Reports for 1897,* pp. 268 ff.

separated the electrolytic action of the current from the thermal.

"The models of furnaces have allowed us to readily attain temperatures bordering on at least 3,500° C.

"*Synthetic diamonds:* 200 grams of soft Swedish iron cut into cylinders, 1 cm to 2 cm in length and about 1 cm in diameter were placed in a carbon crucible and completely covered with sugar carbon. It was heated from three to six minutes with a current of 35 amperes at 60 volts. The cover of the furnace was raised and, with the hand wrapped with a cloth, the edge of the crucible was grasped with a pair of iron tongs and was plunged into a vessel filled with cold water. The crucible and contents remained at red heat for several minutes, with evolution of bubbles of gas which burst at the surface without taking fire. The temperature fell rapidly, the light faded and the experiment was ended."

* * *

"I prepared at first pure anhydrous hydrofluoric acid, and found, as shown by Faraday and by Gore, that it was a nonconductor.

"In order to make the acid a conductor there is added to it before the experiment a little of the dried and fused fluohydrate of potassium fluoride, about 2 grams to 10 cubic centimeters of the liquid. Under these conditions the decomposition takes place continuously, and we obtain at the negative pole a gas which burns with a colorless flame, and which has all the characteristics of hydrogen. At the positive pole there is a colorless gas of a very disagreeable, penetrating odor, resembling that of hydrochlorous acid, and irritating to the mucous membrane of the throat and the eyes. The new gas is endowed with very energetic properties—for instance, sulfur inflames upon contact with it.

"Crystallized silicon, even when cold, kindles immediately upon contact with the gas, and burns with much brilliancy, sometimes giving off sparks."

CONSEQUENCES IN THEORY AND PRACTICE

The most spectacular of Moissan's successes was the artificial production of diamond. He developed the method which, as he speculated, nature had used, the rapid cooling of molten iron containing carbon, so that a hard outer shell kept the still liquid iron under high pressure while it was cooling. William Crookes reported that he had seen the artificial making of diamonds by Moissan (reprinted in the Annual Reports of the Smithsonian Institution for 1897, p. 227). However, serious doubts were raised later on, and only recently has a successful method been developed. Interesting as this discovery was, his work on calcium carbide and fluorine had much greater practical consequences. In the year of his death, 1907, the production of calcium carbide already totaled about 165,000 tons. Twenty years later, this figure was about quadrupled, and many more products made in the electric furnace had been added—aluminum, phosphorus, metal alloys, silicon carbide (carborundum).

The development of fluorine as a chemical raw material was much slower. Fluorinated polymers of ethylene came into use in 1939; Teflon, a tetra-fluoro-ethylene plastic, followed in this country shortly afterward. Methane, reacted with chlorine and fluorine, found wide application as a refrigerant (freon). Fluorinated acetic acid, a deadly internal poison, is the basis for a rodenticide.

1 9 0 7
EDUARD BUCHNER
(1860–1917)

"For his biochemical researches and his discovery of
cell-less fermentation."

BIOGRAPHICAL SKETCH

EDUARD BUCHNER BEGAN STUDYING CHEMISTRY IN HIS NATIVE
Munich, but he had to interrupt his studies for financial reasons.
His older brother Hans helped him to return to science in 1884.
Chemistry, under Baeyer, and botany, under Carl von Nägeli,
were his main subjects, and Hans directed his attention to problems involved in fermentation. Buchner's first publication, which
appeared in 1885, dealt with the influence of oxygen on fermentations. He received his doctor's degree in 1888 and continued to
work as Baeyer's assistant for five years. Fermentation was still his
favorite subject, although his superiors told him that nothing
new could be expected in the direction which he intended to follow, grinding yeast finely to see what the destruction of the cell
structure would do to its activity. Hans Buchner at that time hoped
to obtain medically valuable proteins from the digestion of bacteria
with alkalies; he was therefore also interested in cell juices pressed
out of bacteria or yeast. Eduard Buchner continued experiments
with such juices during vacation from his teaching of analytical
and pharmaceutical chemistry in Tübingen. In 1896 he made a
fundamental observation. He had used concentrated sugar solutions to act as a conserving agent in pressing juice from yeast, and

28

he discovered that a slow fermentation started; he soon established that no yeast cells were present in this fermentation, and that yeast killed by treatment with alcohol and acetone still functioned to ferment sugars. In January 1897 he reported on alcoholic fermentation without yeast cells. He found much opposition to his views. A professorship at the agricultural college in Berlin, in 1898, gave him the means to extend his biochemical work. Buchner died as a major in the German army in Rumania.

DESCRIPTION OF THE PRIZE-WINNING WORK *

"Yeast cells are to be considered as small bubbles containing a semiliquid mass, called protoplasma, which is enclosed in a relatively tough cell membrane.

"As far as the microscope shows, these membranes are uniform, yet they must be pierced by fine holes through which food materials enter and excretions leave the cell.

"In order to investigate the cell content, it was necessary to remove the membrane and the plasma tube. Chemically active solvents or the use of high temperatures had to be avoided. Finally, it was important to complete the process in the shortest time to exclude changes during the preparation.

"Marie von Manassein, in Wiesner's institute in Vienna, showed perhaps for the first time in 1872 that the difficulties in grinding yeast disappear when quartz powder or sand is added. Then the pestle finds the required points of attack. In this manner microorganisms were ground by Adolph Mayer, A. Fernbach, and Amthor, before I started my experiments.

"When yeast is mixed with an equal weight of quartz sand and one fifth of its weight of kieselguhr, the initially dust-dry mass can be ground within a few minutes by placing it into a large mortar and using a heavy pestle on a long handle. The mass becomes dark gray and plastic, like dough.

"When this thick dough is wrapped in strong cloth and put into a hydraulic press, a liquid juice seeps out under a pressure which is

---

* Translated from *Les Prix Nobel en 1907*.

gradually increased to 90 kg./sq. cm. (about 1250 lbs./sq. in.). Within a few hours, 500 cu. cm. of liquid can be obtained from 1000 grams of yeast, so that considerably more than half of the cell content is pressed out.

"The press juice loses its effectiveness very rapidly at room temperature. I have been able to explain this strange behavior by the presence of a proteolytic enzyme, the endotryptase, which had first been discovered by M. Hahn through the liquefying action on gelatine. Indeed, the fermentation capacity of the press juice is diminished still more rapidly, when digestive enzymes are added, e.g. raw pancreatine or tryptase. The fermentation agent in the juice is destroyed by a digestive enzyme, similarly to the high-molecular proteins, which also disappear on storing the press juice. Thus, old press juice that does not produce fermentation can be heated to boiling without thereby causing flocculation.

"Summarizing the results of all our experiments, it can be stated that the fermenting activity has been separated from the living yeast cells.

"The cells of plants and animals appear, with increasing distinctness, as factories where in separate workshops all kinds of products are produced. The foremen in this work are the enzymes."

CONSEQUENCES IN THEORY
AND PRACTICE

Fermentation has always held a prominent position in chemistry. The ability of a small amount of "ferment" to convert large quantities of plant materials was considered by the alchemists as the model for the action of the magic philosophers' stone. That the action is exerted by a living organism was a discovery of the nineteenth century. This finding was used as a strong argument in favor of vitalistic theories which attributed fermentation to the action of a force which is the exclusive property of life. In opposition, the mechanistic theories claimed that the molecules of sugars are torn apart by vibrations accompanying the decomposition of organisms. The extreme positions were held to be irreconcilable. They broke down only slowly, as the experimental approach showed that neither vitalism nor mechanism had a definite meaning unless the problem were stated in specific relationships. When Buchner declared that he could ferment sugar without living cells, he felt that he had disproved vitalism. The situation was similar to that which had existed just about sixty years before Buchner's discovery, when the German chemist Wöhler stated that he could make urea without a living organism. Vitalists did not give up their position then, and they defended it against Buchner now. Max Rubner, a leading physiologist, offered direct proof that fermentation was a vital, not an enzymatic, process. The proof consisted in the fact that tannin has an inhibiting effect on juice or macerated cell suspensions but does not prevent the fermentation caused by living cells. For Eduard Buchner, the explanation was obvious: the enzyme which causes fermentation, zymase, does not leave the living cell and cannot, therefore, be damaged by tannin. Zymase goes into solution only after the cell has been killed or its wall disrupted, and then tannin can act upon it.

The new concept of fermentation as an enzyme action stimulated the manufacturing of yeast and alcohol. It was a great advantage to understand that nutritive substances, such as ammonia salts and peptones, and even phosphoric acid salts, contributed to the formation of zymase, and that this beneficial enzyme had to be protected against destruction by a digestive enzyme, peptase. The mystery of yeast action was dissolved into controllable factors. Further investigation disclosed that the number of actions and factors was much greater than had been foreseen.

1908
ERNEST RUTHERFORD
(1871–1937)

"For his investigation into the disintegration of the elements and the chemistry of radioactive substances."

BIOGRAPHICAL SKETCH

ERNEST RUTHERFORD WAS BORN TO ENGLISH PARENTS IN Nelson, New Zealand. His excellence at school won him a scholarship to the University of New Zealand, which at that time had seven professors and about 150 students. For his B.Sc. in 1894 he prepared an investigation of "the magnetization of iron by high-frequency discharges." In this work, which was stimulated by the new discoveries of Hertz, Rutherford showed, among other things, that the magnetization is only skin deep and can be removed from a magnetized iron needle by dissolution of the surface layer in acid. He won fame with his oscillators and detectors at J. J. Thomson's laboratory at Cambridge, where he began work in 1895. Three years later, J. J. Thomson recommended him for the professorship at McGill University, Montreal. Frederick Soddy joined Rutherford there in work on radioactive disintegrations. From 1907 on he was professor at the University of Manchester. The competition with Ramsay in London was sometimes rather keen. During the First World War, Rutherford applied his experiences with oscillators and detectors to problems of submarine detection. In 1919 he discovered the "artificial disintegration" of nitrogen; under the impact of alpha radiation, nitrogen, although an element, is decomposed and hydrogen is formed.

Rutherford felt very strongly that professors should spend more time thinking than doing, and he urged the professional men "to take an interest in the administration of their own affairs or else the professional civil servant would step in—and then, the Lord help you!"

DESCRIPTION OF THE PRIZE-WINNING WORK*

"The study of the properties of the alpha rays has played a notable part in the development of radioactivity and has become instrumental in bringing to light a number of facts and relationships of the first importance.

"While the evidence as a whole strongly supported the view that the alpha particle was a helium atom, it was found exceedingly difficult to obtain a decisive experimental proof of the relation. If it could be shown experimentally that the alpha particle did in reality carry two unit charges, the proof of the relation would be greatly strengthened. For this purpose an electrical method was devised by Rutherford and Geiger for counting directly the alpha particles expelled from a radioactive substance. The ionization produced in a gas by a single alpha particle is exceedingly small and would be difficult to detect electrically except by a very refined method. Recourse was had to an automatic method of magnifying the ionization produced by an alpha particle. For this purpose it was arranged that the alpha particles should be fired through a small opening into a vessel containing air or other gas at a low pressure, exposed to an electric field near the sparking value. Under these conditions the ions produced by the passage of the alpha particles through the gas generate a large number of fresh ions by collision. In this way it was found possible to magnify the electric effect due to an alpha particle several thousand times.

"This method was developed into an accurate method of counting the number of alpha particles fired in a known time through

* From *Les Prix Nobel en 1908*.

the small aperture of the testing vessel. From this was deduced the total number of alpha particles expelled per second from any thin film of radioactive matter. In this way it was shown that 3.4×10^{10} alpha particles are expelled per second from one gram of radium itself and from each of its alpha ray products in equilibrium with it.

"We have seen that there is every reason to believe that the alpha particles, so freely expelled from the great majority of radioactive substances, are electric in mass and constitution and must consist of atoms of helium. We are consequently driven to the conclusion that the atoms of the primary radioactive elements like uranium and thorium must be built up in part at least of atoms of helium. These atoms are released at definite stages of the transformation at a rate independent of control by laboratory forces.

"It is very remarkable that a chemically inert element like helium should play such a prominent part in the constitution of the atomic system of uranium and thorium and radium. It may well be that this property of helium of forming complex atoms is in some way connected with its inability to enter into ordinary chemical combinations."

CONSEQUENCES IN THEORY AND PRACTICE

At one time the smallest particle of matter, which could not be further divided, was represented as a solid ball. This model, drawn from experiences with visible and weighable materials, was useful in explaining certain chemical reactions. An entirely different model became necessary when optical and electrical properties had to be considered. First of all, the atom had to be divided into positively and negatively charged electric parts. One of the next steps was to account for the negatively charged part as a number of small points compared with the relatively large extent of the positive part of the atom, as J. J. Thomson did. The decay of radioactive elements caused Rutherford to think in terms of more definite structures. The disintegration of these elements is accompanied by the emission of positively charged helium atoms and negatively charged particles of almost no mass, the electrons. The atom, concluded Rutherford, is not a last unit of matter. It is composed of an arrangement of subatomic particles. In radioactive elements this arrangement is unstable. The unstable atom reaches stability by unloading itself of particles which can form the atoms of other elements. These particles come out of a positive nucleus, in which the mass of the atom is concentrated, and out of an atmosphere of electrons which surround the nucleus like a number of shells, in distances which are vast compared with the size of the nucleus.

The apparatus for counting the alpha particles, which Rutherford developed together with H. Geiger, made it possible to derive the mathematical formulation of the decay process. The basic assumption was similar to that used for any chemical reaction, which presupposes that the number of atoms reacting, or decaying, per unit of time (second or minute) is proportional to the number of existing atoms.

The concept of the atom as consisting of a small, very heavy nucleus surrounded by electrons circulating at specific, relatively wide distances from the center, was further developed by Niels Bohr and many others. It is the fundamental concept of nuclear physics. The mathematical formulation of the disintegration of atoms made it possible, in many cases, to identify substances (by correlation with their characteristic radiations) which existed in quantities too small to permit any other identification. The time within which the number of originally present active atoms is reduced to half, the "half-life" of a radioactive element, can readily be derived from the basic mathematical relationship.

1 9 0 9
WILHELM OSTWALD
(1853–1932)

"For his work on catalysis and on the conditions of chemical equilibrium and velocities of chemical reactions."

BIOGRAPHICAL SKETCH

WILHELM OSTWALD BECAME INTERESTED IN CHEMICAL EXPERI-mentation at an early age. As an eleven-year-old he made his own fireworks and contraptions for transparent pictures. At the University of Dorpat he read Julius Thomsen's measurements of the heat connected with chemical reactions. The thought suddenly occurred to him that any other property could serve as well to indicate the actual conditions of the substances in a watery solution. The simplest property, within the means of his instrumentation, appeared to be density. He was so convinced of the general importance of the method that he created the name "volume chemistry" to designate a field of equal rank with thermochemistry.

These investigations, together with measurements of another physical property, optical refraction, served Ostwald as the theme of his doctoral thesis (1878). His driving goal was to learn more about the nature of chemical affinity. As fu]¹ professor in Riga, from 1882 on, he widened the search for an answer with investigations in chemical dynamics, the measurement of the rate at which chemical change takes place. Calculations based on the velocity with which acids split esters into alcohols and organic acids led to the same relative values for affinity as did previous results obtained volumetrically.

These special investigations were undertaken from the point of view of their general meaning. They offered a new basis for all of chemistry and required a rewriting of much of its contents. Ostwald had scarcely undertaken the task of writing a new textbook, in 1883, when Svante Arrhenius' work on affinity and electrical conductivity and van't Hoff's views of the analogy between solutions and gases opened still wider horizons. Ostwald welcomed them enthusiastically.

At the University of Leipzig, where he began his work in 1887 with two students, Ostwald soon created a focal point of the new field of physical chemistry. Physical-chemical experiments were instituted as a regular part of the chemistry curriculum. Analytical chemistry was lucidly described by Ostwald from the new standpoint in his book of 1893. About sixty years before this time, Berzelius had introduced the name "catalysis" for the action of substances which influence chemical reactions without taking part in them. Through Ostwald's work this strange action now became accessible to measurement and connection with affinity. The most important practical consequence was his discovery, in 1901, of a method for obtaining nitric acid by burning ammonia in the presence of platinum.

Ostwald's relations with administrators and colleagues at the University of Leipzig deteriorated. His resignation from the professorship in 1906 gave him freedom to devote himself to his many general interests—painting and the measurement of colors, the organization of science and international cooperation, the role of energy ("energy is everything"), and the monistic structure of universal life. For several years he published "monistic Sunday sermons" every Sunday.

Of his many publications Ostwald liked his book on electrochemistry (1895) best; it was the only one of his books which saw only one edition.

In the early years of his career, somebody gave him the advice not to generalize too quickly. He never heeded this advice. As the creator of a new system in chemistry, and in other respects, Ostwald may be called the German Lavoisier.

DESCRIPTION OF THE PRIZE-WINNING
WORK*

"Initially I was exclusively busy with the task of finding a quantitative measure for the concept of chemical affinity, which is so important and was then so indefinite, and I had considered . . . using both static or equilibrium methods and dynamic methods based upon the measurement of velocities of reactions.

"I remembered from the literature of organic chemistry, which I had to follow for my teaching job, several cases where esters had been split by strong acids, like hydrochloric or sulfuric acid, in concentrated form into acid and alcohol. In order to be able to work with aqueous solutions I turned to those esters which are sufficiently soluble in water, and I still remember today the joyful excitement with which I pursued the increase in acidity in a solution of the common acetic ether with hydrochloric acid added (1883).

"This is not the place to describe the development of the problem of affinity and, specifically, the measurement of the 'strength' of acids which at that time were the intended objects of my investigations. Suffice it to say that the connection between static and dynamic methods really came to light and the 'strength' was recognized as a general property of the specific acid, independent of the nature of the particular reaction. Soon afterward the inversion of sugar was investigated from the same point of view, with the immediate result that this classical reaction also was quantitatively determined by the same property of the acids, as had been expected on the basis of previous results.

"Thus, the close connection between the strength of the acids and their catalytic action came undeniably to the fore, and I searched for other acid catalyses so as to study this relationship more broadly. These experiments showed, in contrast to previous ones, that the reacting substances themselves exerted an action of measurable velocity upon each other, even before the foreign substance was added. At present, one would say that the reaction was

* Translated from *Les Prix Nobel en 1909.*

accelerated by the presence of hydrogen ions already existing in the reacting substances; at that time such explanation was not yet possible, since the work was carried out in 1887, just before the theory of free ions had been formulated and communicated to the world. Thus, I was irresistibly urged to the conclusion that the essence of catalysis is not to be sought in the origination of a reaction but in its acceleration. In the corresponding publication of 1888 I gave the proper mathematical formulae explicitly; they are perhaps implicitly contained in the methyl acetate paper of 1883."

CONSEQUENCES IN THEORY AND PRACTICE

The inversion of sugar is a change of saccharose (beet or cane sugar) under the influence of small amounts of acids. The optical rotation is reversed in this reaction, and the crystallizable sugar is converted into a noncrystallizable mixture of its components, glucose and fructose. The reaction, dreaded by the manufacturer of crystal sugar, was deliberately carried out for the production of an artificial honey. On the basis of Ostwald's work on catalysis it was found that the inversion could be obtained at high sugar concentrations with a minimum of acid.

Ostwald rediscovered and redefined catalysis. Although his original intention was purely and very broadly scientific, he saw the great importance of its technical applications. He failed in his attempts to produce ammonia by a catalyzed reaction of its elements, nitrogen and hydrogen, but he succeeded in achieving its catalytic oxidation to nitric acid. The catalytic ammonia synthesis became a reality soon afterward. Sufficient raw material for the new nitric acid process thus was available. The extent and fury of the First World War would have been impossible without this method of manufacturing a basic material from which all important explosives are derived.

The revived interest in catalysis was a powerful stimulant for the chemical industry. Mineral oil is converted into improved motor fuel and natural gas into a host of chemicals by catalytic processes. The production of synthetic methanol, developed with the aid of a pupil of Ostwald's by catalytic combination of carbon processes. The production of synthetic methanol by catalytic combination of carbon monoxide and hydrogen, had profound repercussions in the old wood distillation industry.

Many of these developments in the theory and industrial application of catalysis were in considerable measure due to men from Ostwald's laboratory like Max Bodenstein and Alwin Mittasch.

The synthesis of simple inorganic and organic compounds by catalysis was followed by the production of synthetic resins of specified molecular size and composition by means of many kinds of catalysts under selected conditions of temperature and pressure.

The measurement of physical properties to gain insight into rate and extent of chemical reactions has become the basis for the design of industrial plants.

1 9 1 0
OTTO WALLACH
(1847–1931)

*"For his initiative work in the field of alicyclic
substances."*

BIOGRAPHICAL SKETCH

OTTO WALLACH WAS BORN IN KÖNIGSBERG, EAST PRUSSIA. HE
received his doctor's degree at the University of Göttingen, in 1869.
From there, he went to Bonn, where Kekulé offered him a "scientific artist's life." One of the advantages of Bonn, for him, was
the proximity to the Dutch and Belgian art treasures. After a brief
interlude in the chemical industry he returned to Bonn, where he
became extraordinary professor in 1876 and was in charge of instruction in pharmacy from 1879 on.

In his courses of instruction Wallach had to give lectures about
ethereal oils and became interested in this subject. Kekulé told
him that these oils are mixtures which no chemist could hope to
disentangle. Nevertheless, Wallach began a systematic study of
this whole class of pharmaceutically used oils. They were routinely
made by distillations of selected plant leaves, petals, bark, and
fruits. He separated pure substances from them by careful redis-
tillations, identifying the products by their physical properties and
following transitions between some of them. Most of these substances were similar in their basic structure, a ring of six carbon
atoms which differed from that present in benzene by a higher
hydrogen content. The ring, or cycle, of most of these "terpenes"

is formed of saturated carbon atoms, like those in the "fatty," or aliphatic, substances. They were, therefore, called alicyclic. Wallach continued these studies in Göttingen, from 1889 to 1915, the year in which he retired to devote himself more exclusively to his interests in art.

"Wallach's highest ideal was not theory, not the formula, but carefully and reliably performed experiment." *

DESCRIPTION OF THE PRIZE-WINNING WORK†

"By appropriate conversion of the hydrocarbons into oxygen-containing compounds, and conversely of oxygen-containing compounds into hydrocarbons, we succeeded in connecting by transformations a very great number of the terpene-like substances which occur in ethereal oils and to trace the genetic relationships of the several compounds.

"Pure empiricism reigned in the manufacture of ethereal oils up until about twenty-five years ago. The fragrant components of plants were merely distilled and the distillate brought to market. In this process, the products obtained were not always handled rationally, in the absence of all knowledge of their chemical nature, and the doors were wide open for every kind of falsification. When this was carried out with only some skill, the consumer was helpless against it.

"This has now been changed thoroughly. Thanks to the possibility of distinctly characterizing the single components of the ethereal oils, we now possess a sufficient analytical system to detect falsifications and to guard against them. Besides purely chemical methods we have, for these examinations, the physical properties such as boiling point, density, refraction, and optical rotation, which have been determined during the work on terpene compounds with utmost care.

"Another progress consists in our having learned to evaluate

---

* Leopold Ruzicka in his biography of Wallach in the *Journal of the Chemical Society* (London), 1932, p. 1596.
† Translated from *Les Prix Nobel en 1910.*

correctly the single parts of the oils on the basis of our new knowledge.

"Among the oils which are particularly preferred as odoriferous materials, the most common are mixtures of substances which cooperate in producing the effect. Unexpectedly it was found that in especially fragrant natural oils there are, in very small quantities, extremely bad-smelling substances which nevertheless are also decisive for the odor. These are products of the decomposition of plant proteins, closely related to those which are formed from animal proteins during digestion and which cause the repugnant odor of the feces. Among these substances is indole. This is found, for example, as Dr. Albrecht Hesse has proved . . . as a characteristic component in oil of jasmine.

"Insight of this and similar kind, which could be attained only through the progress of scientific research, has been utilized particularly in that branch of the industry which is concerned with the artificial composition of perfumes.

"We now are in a position to prepare substances which are analogues of natural odoriferous materials. We are able to predict, within certain limits, that synthetically produced substances of specific molecular structure will have the odor of peppermint, camphor, carroway, or lilac.

"Already the chemical synthesis of camphor is a complete success, whereas up to now we were nearly completely dependent upon the production of the island of Formosa and the good will of the Japanese.

"One would think that plants of the same genus would all produce the same, or at least similar, oils, but this is not at all the case.

"Thus, botanically closely related plants form entirely different products, and conversely, unrelated plants sometimes form the same products."

CONSEQUENCES IN THEORY AND PRACTICE

Wallach solved the task which Kekulé had considered hopelessly difficult, by separating pure substances out of the ethereal plant distillates and showing chemical relationships among them. A common principle of chemical structure was thus discovered which linked substances such as those contained in turpentine with isoprene, the simple hydrocarbon obtained by depolymerizing natural rubber. A unity of chemical building principles in nature became visible. It attracted later investigators, among them Leopold Ruzicka (see pp. 171-174).

Wallach did not base his conclusions on syntheses, as Tiemann and Semmler did, and he was not interested in the industrial applications of his scientific findings. Former students of his brought the scientific foundation to the industry of perfumery.

Wallach's elucidation of the terpenes was of considerable help in the scientific development of an apparently quite unrelated field. The biologically important carotinoids were found to contain a terpenelike structure as a part of their more complicated molecule.

1 9 1 1
MARIE SKLODOWSKA CURIE
(1867–1934)

"For her services to the advancement of chemistry by the discovery of the elements radium and polonium, by the isolation of radium and the study of the nature and compounds of this remarkable element."

BIOGRAPHICAL SKETCH

MARIE SKLODOWSKA WAS BORN IN WARSAW, THE CAPITAL OF that part of Poland which was then under Russian domination. She received most of her education in science from her father who was professor of science and languages at a high school. She later wrote of this period: "Literature interested me as much as sociology and science." (Quoted by Eve Curie in her biography of her mother, New York, 1943, p. 71.)

In 1891, the money saved from several years of teaching as a governess and an invitation from her elder sister enabled her to go to Paris to continue her studies. She met Pierre Curie, professor at the school of physics of the Sorbonne, in 1894 and married him the following year. From measurements of radiation she concluded, in early 1898, that pitchblende might contain an element which is much more radioactive than uranium. Then began the systematic search for this element in cooperation with her husband and with André Debierne; in 1902 radium was prepared as a pure salt. The following year, she received her doctor's degree from the Sorbonne and, together with her husband, one half of the Nobel Prize for Physics.

45

After Pierre Curie died in a traffic accident, in 1906, Mme. Curie was offered his chair at the Sorbonne, where she had been "chief of work" since 1904. A radium institute was organized for her work in 1914. During the First World War she was active in hospital work and in nurses' training.

When she received the gift of the women of America, one gram of radium, in 1921, she was already suffering from the effects of exposure to radium rays, which gradually attacked her nerves and blood.

DESCRIPTION OF THE PRIZE-WINNING WORK*

"We gradually developed a new method of search for new elements, a method which is based upon radioactivity considered as an atomic property of matter. Every chemical separation is followed by a measurement of the activity of the products obtained. This gives an account of the way in which the active substance behaves from the chemical point of view. This method has found general application; it is somewhat analogous to spectral analysis. Owing to the great variety of radiations emitted, the method should be refined and extended so that it permits one not only to discover radioactive substances but also to distinguish them from one another with certainty.

"By the use of the indicated method it has been established that it is actually possible to concentrate the activity by chemical operations. We have ascertained that there are in pitchblende at least two new radioactive bodies; one of them, which accompanies bismuth, has received the name polonium, while the other, which accompanies barium, has been called radium.

"We had the conviction that the substances which we had discovered were new chemical elements. This conviction was based solely on the atomic character of radioactivity. From the chemical point of view, however, everything in the beginning looked as if our new substances were pure bismuth or pure barium respectively. It was essential to demonstrate that the radioactivity is bound to

---

* Translated from *Les Prix Nobel en 1911.*

traces of elements which are neither bismuth nor barium. These hypothetical new elements, therefore, had to be isolated. This isolation has been completely achieved for radium. It took several years of continued effort to do that. Radium in the form of a pure salt is, today, a product manufactured by an industry; for no other new radioactive substance have such definite results been obtained.

"The best radium mineral is pitchblende from St. Joachimsthal, which has long been used for extracting salts of uranium. After these have been removed, the residual mineral contains radium and polonium. We have usually started from this residue as the raw material.

"The first treatment consists in extracting the radium-bearing barium and the polonium-containing bismuth.

"From a ton of residue, we obtain 10 to 20 kilograms of crude barium sulfate with radium. This sulfate is purified and converted to chlorides. Now, the radium is still present only in a proportion of about 3 in 100,000.

"For separating the radium from the barium, I have employed a method of fractional crystallization of the chloride (the bromide could also be used). The salt of radium, being less soluble than that of barium, accumulates in the crystals. This fractionation is a long and methodic operation to eliminate more and more of the barium. In order to arrive at a very pure salt, I may have had to carry out several thousand crystallizations. The progress of the fractionation is controlled by measuring the radioactivity.

"The radioactivity of radium in its pure salts is about five million times as great as the radioactivity of an equal weight of uranium. Because of this radioactivity the salts have a spontaneous luminescence. I should also like to mention that radium constantly develops energy which, measured as heat produced, corresponds to an hourly 118 calories per gram of radium.

"We are now used to work with substances which manifest their presence to us only by their radioactive properties, and which we can, nevertheless, measure, dissolve, reprecipitate from their solutions, or deposit by electrolysis. This is a particular kind of chemistry for which the electrometer, not the balance, is used as the common tool and which could well be called the chemistry of the imponderable."

CONSEQUENCES IN THEORY
AND PRACTICE

The discovery of radium was perhaps more important than the discovery of any other element since oxygen. The very concept of element had to be changed, and a new "force" of matter had to be recognized. Radium made its presence known by imparting an increased electrical conductivity to the surrounding air. This characteristic property served as the guide for Marie Curie in her efforts to remove all ordinary matter from the uranium ore and so to separate the radioactive substance. The method of determining the presence of radium was similar to that of analysis by optical spectrum in the great sensitivity to smallest amounts of the substances involved. For the optical analysis, however, the substance had to be heated to high temperatures, so that part of the heat was transformed into emitted light. Radium carries its electrical activity with it at all temperatures, undiminished even at the temperature of liquid air. It is a source of energy which manifests itself in strange kinds of a cold glow connected with a lasting development of heat. Radium diminishes slowly, at a rate from which it can be calculated that freshly isolated radium will be almost two-thirds transformed into nonradioactive substances in about 2450 years.

Although one ton of pitchblende gave only about one tenth of a gram of pure radium in the form of its chloride salt, radium is widely distributed in tiniest quantities. It is accompanied by a still more powerful radiator of energy, the element polonium, which Marie Curie and A. Debierne isolated and named in honor of Poland. The radiation emitted from these elements has a strong influence on living organisms. The water of many springs is radioactive, and much of its medical value was attributed to this fact. More concentrated forms of radioactive materials were applied in medicine soon after the discovery of radium. On the other hand, as in the early work on Röntgen rays, many investigators suffered from the ill effects of uncontrolled doses of radiation.

Institutes for the study of radioactivity were founded in practically all the research centers of the world.

1912
VICTOR GRIGNARD
(1871–1935)

"For the discovery of the so-called Grignard reagent, which has greatly helped in the development of organic chemistry during these last years."
(*The award for 1912 was shared with Paul Sabatier; see below, pp. 51-55*)

BIOGRAPHICAL SKETCH

François Auguste Victor Grignard was born in Cherbourg, where his father was a sailmaker, "a simple man with much common sense and a practical mind." He made good grades as a student, but chemistry seemed to him incoherent, just a collection of single facts to be memorized. The beauty of chemical experimentation gradually impressed him, however, during his studies at the University of Lyons. His chemistry professor, Philippe Antoine Barbier (1848-1922), was working on reactions in which the methyl group, CH_3, is introduced into organic compounds. Such reactions had been carried out with the iodine derivative of methane, methyl iodide, CH_3I. Zinc had earlier been found to form very reactive organic compounds, and this metal had been added to further the methylation reaction. Barbier replaced it by magnesium. The results were satisfactory, and he asked Grignard to continue this research. Grignard found that methyl iodide reacts very well with magnesium metal when ether is added. Every trace of water had to be excluded. Once the compound was formed, it could be used immediately, without being separated from the solution in ether, for further reactions.

Grignard published the results of this investigation as his doctoral thesis in 1901. The new method aroused great interest. Publications on organo-magnesium compounds soon began to appear from many laboratories; in 1905, there were already over 200 such publications, and the number rose to about 6000 in the year of Grignard's death. He became professor in Lyons in 1906, then in Nancy in 1910, and he remained there with interruptions during the war years. He did war work on the production of toluene from heavy oils by cracking, in spite of a great burden of administrative duties.

Grignard was not quite satisfied with the decision of the Nobel Prize Committee; he felt that Sabatier should have shared the prize with Senderens (see p. 53), and that afterward a prize should have been divided between him and his former teacher, Barbier.

F. G. Mann said of Grignard: "Certainly his own output of original work was not large, but no other man has initiated the means whereby so vast a field of synthetic chemistry has subsequently been developed." *

DESCRIPTION OF THE PRIZE-WINNING WORK †

"The preparation of the organo-magnesium ethers is, in general, extremely simple. The apparatus is just a round-bottomed flask connected with a good ascending condenser and with a dropping funnel with stopcock, but it is indispensable that everything be absolutely dry.

"One atomic weight of magnesium, in the form of fine filings, is placed into the flask. On the other hand, one molecular weight of the halogenated hydrocarbon to be used—for example, methyl iodide—is dissolved in an almost equal volume of perfectly dry ether which was kept over sodium. Of this mixture, 25-30 c.c. are

---

* *Chemistry and Industry,* October 15, 1955, p. 1338.

---

† Translated from "Le magnesium en chimie organique," *Bulletin de la Société Chimique de France,* Vol. XIII (1913), p. 1.

added to the magnesium. A lively reaction begins after a very short time. Then, 250-300 c.c. of ether are added, and the reaction is kept going by addition of the rest of the reaction mixture drop by drop. The reaction is completed by short heating, if necessary. Under these conditions the magnesium disappears completely. In general, a clear or slightly colored solution is obtained, in which, however, very fine particles of iron, an impurity in the magnesium, produce a momentary haze of slate color.

"The compound, prepared as just indicated, shows all the characteristics of organo-metallic compounds; it changes rapidly in air, absorbs oxygen and carbon dioxide, is decomposed violently by water, and reacts strongly with almost all functional groups. These operations can usually be carried out without any change in the apparatus. It suffices to add, through the dropping funnel, the antagonistic compound dissolved in a convenient quantity of water-free ether. Thus, either a solution or an oily or crystalline separation is obtained, and the reaction is completed, if necessary, by a more or less prolonged heating. After that, all that remains to be done is to hydrolyze the compound."

PAUL SABATIER
(1854–1941)

"For his method of hydrogenating organic compounds in the presence of finely divided metals."
(*The award for 1912 was shared with Victor Grignard; see above, pp. 49-51*)

BIOGRAPHICAL SKETCH

PAUL SABATIER WAS BORN IN CARCASSONNE, IN SOUTHERN France. After graduation from the famous Ecole Normale, where he studied physics, he became assistant to Marcelin Berthelot (1827-1907) in Paris. His doctoral thesis dealt with sulfur compounds of metals, and he continued to work on inorganic compounds as professor in Toulouse. At first he lectured there on physics; the border line of physics and chemistry interested him most. Investigations on the heat connected with chemical reactions show the influence of his old master, Berthelot, which can also be detected in Sabatier's research on reactions with hydrogen. Berthelot had discovered that alcohol vapor, in contact with a redhot iron surface, forms a permanent gas which he called acetylene. It contains only two hydrogen atoms for two carbons. When carbon is chemically saturated with hydrogen, one carbon atom binds four hydrogens, as in methane, CH_4. When two carbons are combined, as in ethane, the number of hydrogens is six, C_2H_6. Acetylene is, therefore, highly unsaturated, as the symbol C_2H_2 shows. By the addition of hydrogen, a process called hydrogenation, ethane can be obtained by way of an intermediately unsaturated compound, ethylene, C_2H_4. In 1897, Sabatier and his colleague, the Abbé Jean-Baptiste Senderens (1856-1936) found that finely divided metals furthered the reaction of such unsaturated substances with hydrogen. The metal had to be freshly prepared from its oxide or salt, because a peculiar influence was exerted by the surface of the metal. The behavior of benzene in this reaction was of especial interest. Benzene is different from the methane series; it contains six carbon atoms linked with one another into a closed hexagon, and each connected with one hydrogen atom. Hydrogenation in the presence of nickel added six hydrogen atoms to the molecule without opening the carbon-to-carbon bonds.

Sabatier declined offers to go to the Sorbonne as Moissan's successor. He remained in Toulouse and published books on catalysis in organic chemistry and on agricultural chemistry.

DESCRIPTION OF THE PRIZE-WINNING WORK*

Moissan (see pp. 24-27) and Moureu found that freshly reduced nickel, cobalt, iron, or platinum begin to glow when acetylene is present. A decomposition occurs with formation of carbon, of a gas which

---

* Translated from Les Prix Nobel en 1912.

Moissan thought was hydrogen, and of liquid condensates containing benzene and other aromatic substances.

"I thought, and I still think . . . that the real cause of the catalytic action of porous platinum is not a simple phenomenon of physical condensation which produces a local rise in temperature, but that it is a real chemical combination on the surface of the metal with the free gas.

"In the experiments of Moissan and Moureu, I attributed the decomposition of the acetylene to an affinity of the metal either for acetylene itself or for its constituents, carbon or hydrogen, which it could easily detach from the endothermic molecule of this hydrocarbon.

"Having ascertained that Moissan did not intend to continue the study of this reaction, I thought of taking it up myself and, first, I tried with Senderens an analogous experiment with ethylene.

"When one directs a stream of ethylene on to nickel, cobalt, or iron which has been freshly reduced and is kept at around 300° C, one observes a vivid incandescence of the metal with voluminous deposition of char from the destruction of ethylene. However, the gas which comes out of the apparatus is not hydrogen; it is mostly composed of ethane.

"This latter could originate only in a hydrogenation of undestroyed ethylene, and without a doubt this hydrogenation was provoked by the metal.

"In effect, if one passes a mixture of ethylene and hydrogen over a column of reduced nickel, the ethylene is changed into ethane, and the metal can serve indefinitely to produce the same transformation (June 1897).

"At the end of 1900, success was decisive and, with Senderens, I recognized that, in contact with nickel at about 180° C, benzol can be completely changed into cyclohexane. Since then I have had absolute confidence in the generality of the method of which we announced the principle in early 1901: Pass the vapors of the substance, together with an excess of hydrogen, over freshly reduced nickel kept at a convenient temperature (150-200° C).

"Direct hydrogenation permits one to convert vapors of liquid fatty acids (oleic acid) into solid acids (stearic acid), and it has been found that this reaction, which is easily carried out, can be applied to the oils themselves, with the metal catalyst kept in suspension in the presence of hydrogen gas, which changes the oils into solid fats. This is actually being done by a powerful industry in England and Germany.

"What explanation can we give for the hydrogenation by catalysis? I suggest that hydrogen acts upon the metal by rapidly combining with it on its surface. The hydride thus formed dissociates easily and rapidly, and if it is put into the presence of substances that can utilize the hydrogen, the hydride yields its hydrogen, regenerating the metal which starts again to produce the same effect endlessly.

"The distinction I made between several kinds of activity of the nickel would lead to assume several states of combination. For example, well prepared and unaltered nickel could give the perhydride Ni H_2 that is capable of hydrogenating benzene. On the other hand, nickel prepared at too high a temperature or a little

$$\begin{matrix} Ni - H \\ | \\ Ni - H \end{matrix}$$

poisoned would only give a lower hydride, such as   which

cannot act on benzene but is active with ethylenic hydrocarbons or nitrated derivatives.

"If this theory is correct, we can conclude that nickel and the other active metals (copper, cobalt, iron, platinum) should combine not only with free hydrogen, but should take hydrogen out of substances that can furnish it and that, therefore, these metals should be catalysts for dehydrogenations. This is actually true; finely divided copper produces very readily, at between 250° and 300°, the dehydrogenation of primary alcohols to aldehydes, of secondary alcohols to ketones, and offers a practical method that is very advantageous for carrying out these transformations."

CONSEQUENCES IN THEORY
AND PRACTICE

Both Grignard's and Sabatier's methods, now about a half-century old, use metals to obtain reactions of carbon compounds. In Grignard's method, magnesium is combined with an organic halogen compound. The metal, which has great affinity for chlorine, bromine, or iodine, accepts the organic radical to which these halogens are attached a little unwillingly. The presence of ether facilitates the reaction, because it offers at least an opportunity for the magnesium to attach oxygen to itself, even if this oxygen is strongly bound to the carbon atoms in the molecule of ether. When a more reactive, freer oxygen is offered, the magnesium compound in Grignard's reagent readily combines with it in releasing the organic radical for further reactions. A great number of combinations are thus opened up for obtaining new bonds between carbon atoms by the intermediary action of the magnesium-organic halogen substances. Carbon dioxide is easily introduced into a hydrocarbon, converting it into the corresponding organic acid. On the other hand, the organic acids in fats, which are there combined with glycerine, can be reduced to alcohols. After the rules for these manifold combinations were established, new substances could be produced with the possibility of predicting the constitution of the expected products. Medicines, perfumes, and detergents were among the new products.

The theory of hydrogenation led to the use of these metallic catalysts for dehydrogenating reactions, as in the production of aldehydes from alcohols with copper at 250-300°C.

In Sabatier's method, nickel forms a fleeting association with hydrogen and with the unsaturated substance which then receives the hydrogen into more permanent bond. Soon after its discovery, the method was applied to convert low-melting fats into more saturated, higher-melting, and thus "hardened" substitutes for butter.

Magnesium and nickel remained the foremost agents in these two methods, although the question was frequently raised whether other metals could not offer specific advantages in some cases. Lithium has such effects when substituted for magnesium. Nickel alloys and mixtures in distribution on silicic carriers have acquired technical importance. Both the Grignard and Sabatier reactions are widely used in research and industrial production.

1913
ALFRED WERNER
(1866–1919)

"In recognition of his work on the linkage of atoms in molecules, by which he has thrown fresh light on old problems and opened up new fields of research, particularly in inorganic chemistry."

BIOGRAPHICAL SKETCH

ALFRED WERNER, LIKE OSTWALD AND BAEYER, DEVELOPED AN active interest in chemical experiments at an early age. He installed a laboratory in the barn of his parents' property in Muhlhausen (Alsace). His study of chemistry began in Karlsruhe and continued in Zurich. There Arthur Hantzsch had found certain nitrogen-containing organic substances which differ in properties although they have the same analytical composition. The explanation for this particular case of isomerism was developed by Werner in his doctoral thesis, in 1890. He extended van't Hoff's theory of the tetrahedral carbon atom and modified it for nitrogen.

Werner's "contributions to the constitution of inorganic compounds" started in 1893 and were continued through twenty publications. Physical measurements showed optical and electrical differences between complex compounds and gave access to their inner structure. Geometric models were still helpful in visualizing the structures, but they were models of a higher order than the previous ones. Werner did not need the guidance which these models afforded. He lived so intensely with these substances that he understood their relationships and natures by their appearances.

Certain complex compounds of metals such as cobalt (Co), chromium (Cr), or rhodium (Rh) with oxalic acid residues (C_2O_4) should be nonidentical with their mirror images. Characteristic of such compounds is the asymmetry which van't Hoff saw as the cause of their property of turning the plane of polarized light. It was a wonderful confirmation of Werner's theory when he found optically active complexes in which one of these metals formed the center.

Werner became full professor at the Technische Hochschule in Zurich before he was thirty (in 1895). At times he had 25 graduate students working under his direction for the doctor's degree in his relatively small laboratory. A new chemical institute was built for him in Zurich in 1909; he taught and worked there until, in 1915, his fatal sickness began to show itself.

DESCRIPTION OF THE PRIZE-WINNING WORK*

"Elementary atoms, even when they are saturated in the sense of the old theory of valence, still have sufficient chemical affinity at their disposal to bind other atoms and atom groups, which themselves seemed to be saturated. New atom compounds of a definite nature are thus formed. This rule is, today, so well founded in experiments on a great number of molecular compounds that we are justified in taking it as a starting point for further developments.

"One of the first questions to be answered is concerned with the number of atoms which can be directly bound to an atom in the center of a complex molecule. It was found that this number, called maximum coordination number, depends upon the nature of the elementary atoms which are combined. Up to now the maximum coordination numbers four, six, and eight have been observed. This corresponds to the theoretically possible symmetrical arrangement of a number of points around a center in such a manner that the distances between neighboring points are equal. However, the composition of the complex chemical compounds does not always

---

* Translated from *Les Prix Nobel en 1913*.

have to correspond to the maximum coordination numbers, because there are coordinatively unsaturated atoms just as there are valence-unsaturated ones.

"The most recent investigations have shown that there is no fundamental difference between principal valences (which cause the bond in compounds of the first order) and auxiliary valences (as I called those valences which cause the formation of complex compounds). The two kinds of valences have precisely equal importance for the strength with which the atoms hold together in the molecule.

"So far we have considered only the affinity relationships between the atoms in a coordination compound, and we have disregarded the relative position of these atoms in the molecules. The question now is directed to the manner in which the six groups A, forming the complex radicals MeA_6 with the central atom Me, are arranged in space around this central atom. This question can be answered experimentally by comparing the actually found isomerisms with the several possibilities of spatial arrangements.

"Compounds with complex radicals $\left[Me \begin{array}{c} B_2 \\ A_4 \end{array} \right]$ actually occur in two isomeric forms, never in three.

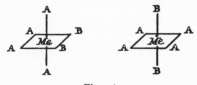

Fig. 2.

"The explanation of isomerisms, which were found first in the platinum series and then in the cobalt series, has required long years of work. Today we know twenty different series of compounds of cobalt with the described isomerism, and for chromium similar isomerisms have been proven by P. Pfeiffer. The differences in the properties of the isomeric compounds are so great that it is frequently possible to distinguish them by their appearance. Characteristically different are, for example, the dichloro compounds ($Cl_2Me\ A_4$)X_2, of which the cobalt and the chromium series have the one set of isomers green, the other violet.

"The octahedrical distribution of the six groups around the central atom leads to the conclusion that compounds with complex radicals $\left[Co\begin{smallmatrix} A_3 \\ B_3 \end{smallmatrix} \right]$ must exist in two stereoisomeric forms, depending on whether the three groups B are situated in a plane or in a crosscut of the octahedron (Fig. 3). This too has recently been confirmed.

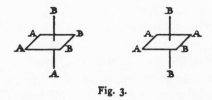

Fig. 3.

"If the six groups which are combined with the central atom are not identically the same, it is possible to construct molecular configurations which are not identical with their mirror image. Compounds with such molecular configurations could, therefore, be expected to exist in optically active mirror-image isomers.

"We have, therefore, tried to separate such compounds into optically active isomers. This has actually been achieved in many cases. . . . Most recently, we have separated into active forms and thereby definitely established the constitution of metal-trioxalic acids of the general formulae

$$[Co(C_2O_4)_3]\ R_3;\quad [Cr(C_2O_4)_3]\ R_3;\quad [Rh(C_2O_4)_3]\ R_3."$$

CONSEQUENCES IN THEORY AND PRACTICE

Werner's theories advanced chemistry beyond concepts which had become too rigid. In some respects, as in his distinction between primary and auxiliary valences, he had to reach compromises. Few chemists of his time were ready to follow him when he assumed multiple valences even for the traditional unit of hydrogen.

Recent developments have, independently, led back to Werner; in Linus Pauling's words: "It has been recognized in recent years that under certain conditions an atom of hydrogen is attracted by strong forces to two atoms, instead of only one, so that it may be considered to be acting as a bond between them. This is called the hydrogen bond.' "

Inorganic chemistry was the model upon which organic chemistry developed. By the end of the nineteenth century, the interest in inorganic chemistry which had been stimulated at the beginning of the century had faded. Werner's work contributed to a vigorous new growth in this field, and soon organic chemistry was in a position to help its sister science. The investigation of the arrangement of the atoms in the space occupied by the molecule, a topic of stereochemistry, developed as a branch of inorganic chemistry.

With the new laboratory experiences, complex compounds were soon found in many minerals. Methods of separating metals from their ores and of preparing gold and platinum metals were improved on the basis of the new concepts in inorganic chemistry.

Further confirmation of Werner's basic thoughts came from the study of crystallized substances by means of X-rays, for which Max von Laue received the Nobel prize in Physics one year after Werner, and the Braggs, father and son, in 1915.

1914
THEODORE WILLIAM RICHARDS
(1868–1928)

*"For his exact determinations of the atomic weights
of a great number of chemical elements."*

BIOGRAPHICAL SKETCH

THEODORE W. RICHARDS WAS BORN IN GERMANTOWN, PA. HIS
father was a painter, his mother a poet. The son soon proved to be
an artist in chemical experimentation. He studied at Harvard,
where Professor Josiah Parsons Cooke entrusted him with the
delicate task of redetermining the atomic weight of oxygen. He
found a value of 15.869 with a possible error of plus or minus
0.0017, compared to hydrogen as the unit. This was the subject of
his doctoral thesis in 1888. He completed his studies in Germany
and returned to Harvard in 1894 to become assistant professor. A
full professorship was offered by Göttingen University in 1901;
he declined, and Harvard thereupon gave him a full professorship
with reduced teaching duties.

Highest accuracy in determining atomic weights and heat values
in neutralization and combustion led to many corrections of previously accepted measurements. When K. Fajans in Munich needed
a definite comparison of the atomic weights of lead from ordinary
deposits and from radioactive transformation of uranium, he sent
the samples to Richards (1913). Richards expanded this investiga-

tion to research on atomic weights of elements from varied sources
and of varied geological background. In his words, "the success
in a precise chemical or physico-chemical measurement lies in so
choosing the particular substance and process and so checking every
operation by parallel experiments that both chemical and physical
errors may be avoided as effectively as possible; and this choice
often involves much study and above all sound common sense. The
precautions must be of a consistent order of refinement. Far more
depends upon this intelligent choice of conditions than upon a mere
mechanical execution of the operations, although that too is important."

DESCRIPTION OF THE PRIZE-WINNING WORK*

"Sodium bromide had been prepared in a state of very great
purity for the purpose of determining the transition temperature
of its hydrated crystals. Such a transition temperature, especially of
a substance with small heat of transition, is very sensitive to impurity. This sodium bromide, which gave a very constant transition
point, was analyzed with precision as a matter of routine. To my
amazement more bromine was found in it than corresponded to the
atomic weights as determined by Stas. The only reasonable explanation seemed to be that Stas' atomic weight of sodium was too high.
Such an iconoclastic conclusion, however, needed verification in
other ways. Especially Stas' experiments with common salt must be
repeated, for sodium chloride was the chief substance upon which
his atomic weight of sodium rested. The research was not an easy
one, and because it involved the disproving of results among the
most carefully obtained in the whole field of chemistry, it de-
manded unusual precautions and meticulous care. The story is long,
and can only briefly be summarized here. We found that not only
the atomic weight of sodium, but also that of chlorine, was in error.
Indeed the error in the latter was partly responsible for that in the
former: for Stas, because of an unsuspected impurity in his silver,
had obtained less silver chloride from a specimen of the metal than

---

*From *Les Prix Nobel en 1914-1918.*

really should have been produced by it. This led him to an atomic weight of chlorine distinctly too small, and to values for sodium and silver distinctly too large. The excessive value for silver was augmented still further by the fact that his method of precipitating the silver chloride by placing fused common salt in a solution of silver nitrate tended to cause impurity in the precipitate. But these are technical details. . . . The higher atomic weight of chlorine has been amply justified by others in many ways. . . .

"The next important contribution, involving a new method and a somewhat new problem, was that in which lithium and silver were compared directly with oxygen through the analysis of lithium perchlorate and the precipitation of the chlorine in lithium chloride by silver. These two processes together give a new means of comparing oxygen with silver—an eventuality much to be desired, because many atomic weights are determined by reference to silver, and all are stated in relation to oxygen.

"Years ago my present colleague, Gregory P. Baxter, and I had worked upon the atomic weight of terrestrial iron, and found it to have a value distinctly lower than that usually assigned to it. In connection with never-ceasing curiosity as to the constancy of the atomic weights, I wondered later whether or not iron in meteorites, possibly having its birth far beyond the limits of the solar system, might have a different atomic weight from ordinary iron. Baxter kindly consented to investigate this question and, with characteristic ease, using methods similar to those used upon terrestrial iron, he found that the iron from meteorites has precisely the same atomic weight as this metal smelted on the earth. The outcome, although not unexpected, is, nevertheless, of interest, and thrills one who appreciates it with an added realization of the unity of the universe."

CONSEQUENCES IN THEORY AND PRACTICE

Richards' improved methods gave atomic weights which were accurate to the third decimal. It may seem strange that this development came at a time when atomic weight had lost its meaning as an absolute constant. A paradox of great consequence in the history of science is here illustrated. By the time experimentation reaches a stage such that it can provide a thorough test for a scientific idea, this idea has often changed. Because Richards succeeded in determining atomic weights with such precision and reliability, it could be proved that an element may consist of several species which are identical except in weight. Radioactive transformation of uranium results in a metal of atomic weight 206 which is chemically identical with common lead of atomic weight 207.21. These species of lead are isotopes (see p. 81).

One of the most important of Richards' investigations was the first one, concerning the atomic weights of hydrogen and oxygen. When it was discovered, in 1929, that oxygen contains isotopes, the most accurate methods of measuring the atomic weight of hydrogen had to be interpreted as indicating the existence of a "heavy" hydrogen (see p. 137).

The International Committee on Atomic Weights was the first organization of international scientific cooperation, created for the unified critical survey of atomic weights. This organization, which published annual tables of the accepted figures, later including those of the isotopes, has survived the two world wars.

1 9 1 5
RICHARD WILLSTÄTTER
(1872–1942)

"For research on coloring matter in the vegetable kingdom, principally on chlorophyll."

BIOGRAPHICAL SKETCH

RICHARD WILLSTÄTTER WAS BORN IN KARLSRUHE, BADEN, GERmany; he went to school there and in Nuremberg, with equally good results in mathematics, literature, and languages. In his autobiography, he said of himself: "I lacked the intensity of one natural ability, especially of one-sided natural ability; I had to create a partial equivalent for it by a one-sided life occupation during the important decades." Chemistry was his choice for study. His strong inclination toward physiology and medicine found its way into his later work. After completing his courses in Munich, he was drawn into the field of alkaloid chemistry by Alfred Einhorn, the discoverer of novocaine. In many years of research Willstätter elucidated the chemical structure of tropine, the basic part of the molecules of atropine and cocaine. He found methods for separating intermediate substances of delicate stability in the oxidation of benzene and naphthalene derivatives. This enabled him to give a chemical explanation for the black dyestuff which is produced by oxidizing aniline.

In 1905 Willstätter left Munich, where he had become associate professor in 1902, for a professorship in Zurich. There he began his work on chlorophyll. His principal idea was to use gentle methods of splitting the molecule gradually by acid and then by alkali, and to recover, identify, and combine the products. Chlorophyll was found to contain about 3 percent of magnesium, held by chemical bond to four nitrogen atoms which themselves are parts of a cycle closed by carbon atoms. Later Willstätter discovered that iron is held in a similar position in the molecule of hemoglobin, the red dyestuff of blood.

It was necessary to bring the living plant into the laboratory if the real chemistry of its most important constituents was to be investigated. The methods of investigation had to be refined so as to imitate the means by which the plant carries out chemical changes. Willstätter pronounced this principle and followed it in his work on plant dyestuffs and enzymes.

This work was in part interrupted during the First World War. Willstätter had accepted a call to the Kaiser Wilhelm Institut in Berlin-Dahlem in 1911. Actually, he had only about twenty months of productive time there before returning to Munich in 1916. One of his remarkable achievements during this time was the development of an effective gas mask which contained three layers of active absorbents.

The process of assimilation was one of the first themes which Willstätter developed in Munich (from 1917 on). He now approached the chemistry of enzyme action, which had begun to occupy him in Zurich, in a new, systematic way. Saccharase, the sugar-splitting enzyme, was obtained in a form 4000 times purer than its raw material, dried yeast, and the oxygen-splitting enzyme peroxydase was purified to 12,000 times the activity of the dried plant root in which it occurs. This was a triumph of Willstätter's chemical viewpoint over a somewhat nebulous, but widespread, biological explanation.

Willstätter resigned from his professorship at Munich in 1924, as a protest against anti-Semitic forces at the university. However, he remained active in research for the chemical industry, to which he gave medically used substances such as avertin, a narcoticum, and as an adviser to professional organizations. After heartbreaking difficulties caused by the Nazi regime, he left Germany for Switzerland in 1939.

DESCRIPTION OF THE PRIZE-WINNING
WORK*

"The same characteristics which serve for comparing the dye-stuffs from any kind of leaves also enable us to decide whether the chlorophyll remains unchanged in the fine details of its molecule during the preparatory work. Thus, this characterization was the basis for preparing chlorophyll itself in a pure and unharmed state and for confirming, by its analysis, the conclusions which had first been reached by investigation of its derivatives. The isolation of chlorophyll relied on colorimetric measurement of the degree of purity of its solutions and depended upon the systematic raising of purity by methods of distribution between several immiscible solvents such as petroleum ether and aqueous alcohol. By this method, colorless admixtures and the yellow pigments of the leaves were removed. The association of these yellow pigments, the carotinoids, with green dyestuffs seemed to indicate a special physiological role of these substances which are conspicuous by their great affinity to oxygen. Therefore, these yellow substances also were prepared in pure form and analyzed. Two easily crystallizing, nitrogen-free pigments occur in every green part of the plant and in many yellow ones. One of them, identical with the long-known carotene of carrots, is an unsaturated hydrocarbon of the formula $C_{40}H_{56}$. Its partner, xanthophyll, was not previously known in substance, although it predominates in leaves; according to composition and properties it is an oxide of carotene, $C_{40}H_{56}O_2$. Only in the phaeophyceae carotene and xanthophyll are accompanied and repressed in quantity by a third oxygen-rich carotinoid, fucoxanthin, which can be isolated in crystal form and which is composed of $C_{40}H_{56}O_6$.

"While chlorophyll in plant extracts is accompanied by 8 to 15 times its weight in other substances, solutions of 70 percent pure chlorophyll can be obtained by operations of partition. From there, a surprising observation helped to solve the problem. When this substance has reached a certain degree of purity it reveals its true solubility relationships, which before were distorted by the admix-

---

* Translated from *Les Prix Nobel en 1914-1918.*

tures. Pure chlorophyll is not soluble in petroleum ether and sepa-
rates out of the alcoholic solvent when the alcohol is washed away.
The procedure permits the isolation of pure chlorophyll in good
yields from dried or fresh leaves as easily as that of any other plant
substance, such as alkaloids or sugars.

"This pure chlorophyll is, however, not yet a uniform substance.
(It consists of about 3 moles of the blue-green chlorophyll a and
one mole of the yellow-green component b.)

"Chlorophyll, that is to say, each of the two components, combines in a colloid state with carbon dioxide to form a dissociable
addition compound. This observation can form the basis for a
theory of assimilation which assumes that the light which is absorbed does its chemical work in the chlorophyll molecule itself,
of which carbon dioxide has become a part by attachment to the
magnesium complex. This chemical work consists in rearranging
the valences of the carbon dioxide into a form suitable for volun-
tary decomposition, which occurs in such a manner that all the
oxygen of the carbon dioxide is liberated.

"The isolation of the anthocyanins in pure form and their analysis are based upon their basic nature and were achieved by preparing well crystallized salts with hydrochloric or picric acid. These
acidic compounds are red, the alkali salts are blue, and the violet
neutral forms are to be understood as inner salts, as phenol-
betaines. Many variations of flower colors are caused solely by the
occurrence of these three forms.

"Anthocyanins proved to be glucosides in which the real dyestuffs, compounds with phenolic hydroxyl groups, are paired with
one or two (or even more) sugars, with glucose, galactose, and
rhamnose."

"The constitution of the sugar-free substances, the anthocyanidins, is made clear by the decomposition in melting alkali: the
molecule is disrupted into two parts, into phloroglucinol or one
of its methyl ethers, and an aromatic oxy acid, namely, para-
oxybenzoic, protocatechuic, or gallic acid or a methyl ether of these
phenolic acids.

"Disregarding some variants, which consist in differences of the
methyl ether groups and the sugar components with the various
ways of their attachments, most of the anthocyans can be derived

from only three closely related anthocyanidins, pelargonidin, cyanidin, and delphinidin, hydroxylated phenyl compounds of benzopyrrylium, which was synthesized by Decker and von Fellenberg:

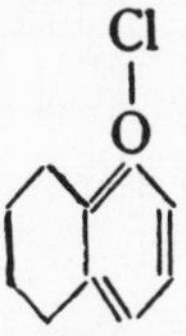

Benzopyryliumchloride

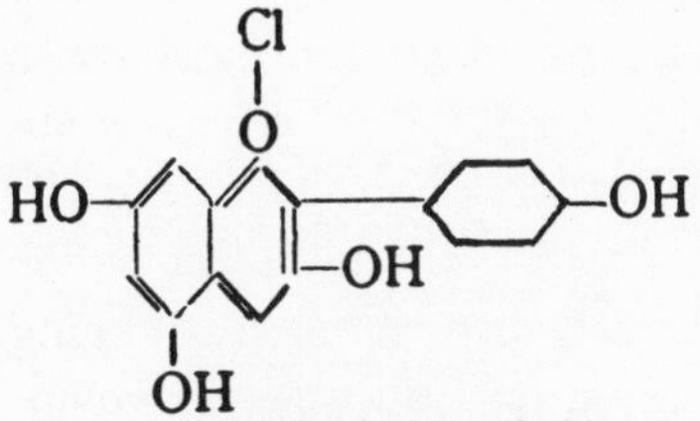

Pelargonidinchloride

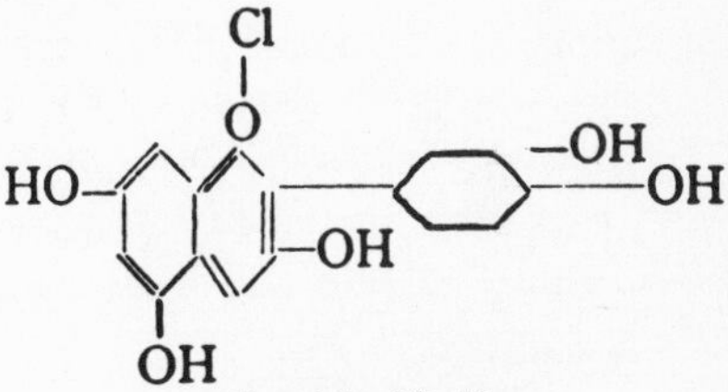

Cyanidinchloride

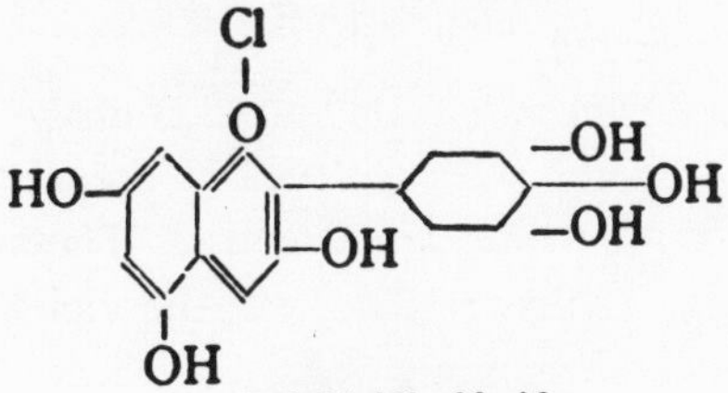

Delphinidinchloride

CONSEQUENCES IN THEORY AND PRACTICE

The separation of dyestuffs from leaves was accomplished by new methods, and the chemical investigation of the molecular composition showed new principles of chemical constitution. One of the methods was based upon the earlier discovery of Mikhail Tswett. Tswett filtered a solution containing leaf extracts through a glass tube filled with calcium carbonate powder and observed that only the carotenes came through in the filtrate, while others of the dissolved dyestuffs were withheld on the surface of the powder. This method of separating a mixture of substances by means of the gentle forces of adsorption was varied and refined by Willstätter. New adsorbing materials were prepared, and the solvents were selected which gave the best effect. This method of chromatography has become an indispensable tool in the laboratory and in the manufacturing plant.

The discovery of the specific sensitivities of chlorophyll, of the influence of impurities on its solubilities, of the reaction with ethyl alcohol under the action of a special enzyme present in the leaf, of the ease with which its magnesium is lost and replaced by other metals, served to improve the technical preparation of this substance. Valuable properties, including those responsible for its medical use, could thus be kept unharmed during the industrial manufacturing processes.

Carotinoids were laboratory curiosities until it was found that some of them are closely related to vitamin A. One of the carotenes occurring in carrots is a direct precursor of this growth-promoting vitamin and is used as a growth promoter by the human organism.

Extracts from flower petals had long been used in the laboratory for their property of changing color in relation to the acidic and alkaline reactions of solutions. Willstätter's work explained the chemical basis for such use and, at the same time, disclosed the common pattern of anthocyanins, the flower pigments.

1 9 1 6 – 1 9 1 7

No Award

1918
FRITZ HABER
(1868–1934)

*"For the synthesis of ammonia from its elements,
nitrogen and hydrogen."*

BIOGRAPHICAL SKETCH

AFTER FINISHING HIS STUDIES IN HIS NATIVE BRESLAU, FRITZ
Haber made an unsuccessful attempt at working in his father's
business. At the recommendation of a friend, he then went to
Karlsruhe. He liked the connection between industry and science
which he found there at the Technische Hochschule, a university
preparing its students for technical positions. He began, in 1893, to
investigate the decomposition of organic compounds at high temperatures, called pyrolysis. Marcelin Berthelot, the foremost French
chemist of this time, had worked in this field. Haber was soon able
to correct Berthelot's arbitrary generalizations by his intimate
studies. Pyrolysis reactions could have offered enough work for a
busy lifetime. Haber, however, was attracted by the influence of
electricity on organic substances. The connecting links between the
two fields were gas reactions and chemical energetics. Walther
Nernst had just developed the theory that the electrochemical driving force, when gases are involved, is determined by the effective
concentration of the gases in or on the electrode, the metal which
serves to introduce electrical current into a solution. By regulating
this driving force, the voltage, in particular chemical reactions,
Haber demonstrated the several steps in which these reactions can

take place. An example of great technical interest was the reduction of nitro-benzol to aniline, in which the two oxygen atoms of the former are exchanged gradually by two hydrogen atoms.

Starting from this success, Haber wrote a book on the entire field of technical electrochemistry and its scientific basis. In a similar way, he brought science and technology together in a book on the energy relationships in gas reactions.

Haber did not have to wait long for recognition of his efforts; his own Hochschule made him full professor in 1906. At this time, he had already begun to investigate the possibility of synthesizing ammonia from its elements. Karl Engler, the great authority in chemical technology, interested the Badische Anilin und Soda Fabrik (the forerunner of the I.G.), in near-by Ludwigshafen, in the project, and on July 2, 1909, Carl Bosch (see p. 123) and Alwin Mittasch (b. 1869, director of the BASF) came to Karlsruhe to witness the making of the first 100 grams of synthetic ammonia by Haber and his assistants.

When the Kaiser Wilhelm Institute for Chemistry was founded, Haber was elected its first director. From 1911 to the fatal year 1933, he remained in Berlin-Dahlem, widening the activities of the Institute, and in the early years of the war organizing chemical warfare. He directed the first use of gas—it was chlorine—in 1915. The French army reciprocated with the deadly phosgene the following year.

In 1919 Haber remembered Arrhenius' estimate that there are eight billion tons of gold in the seas. He organized an expedition to try to recover some of this gold, hoping that this would be a way in which chemistry could supply Germany with the means to pay the reparations. The result was completely disappointing. Heartbroken, he did not even carry out Richard Willstätter's friendly advice to convert the failure into an interesting book.

Later on, Haber came back to the work with which he had started, deepening it by experiment and thought concerning chemical chain reactions at high temperatures and under the influence of catalysts.

Haber's outstanding combination of wide knowledge with keen insight and splendid ideas made the Institute a center of varied research. His efforts in the interest of young scientists helped greatly in the postwar recovery of German chemistry. Nevertheless, the "awakened" Germany of 1933 had no use for him, because he was born a Jew. He died, broken in health and in spirit, in exile in Switzerland.

DESCRIPTION OF THE PRIZE-WINNING WORK*

"The colleagues' interest in the preparation of ammonia from the elements is based on the fact that a simple result is achieved by unusual means. The interest of a wider circle has its source in the recognition that ammonia synthesis on a large scale represents a useful, at present even the most useful, way to satisfy an economic need. This practical usefulness was not the preconceived goal of my experiments. I was not in doubt that my laboratory work could furnish no more than a scientific statement of the foundations and a knowledge of the experimental equipment, and that much had to be added to this result in order to attain economic success on an industrial scale.

"In the course of this research (on the equilibria) I returned in 1908, together with my young friend and collaborator Robert Le Rossignol . . . , to the task of ammonia synthesis, which I had abandoned three years before. Immediately before this time I had become acquainted with the liquefaction of air; at the same time I had received insight into the industry of formate manufacture, where flowing carbon monoxide is reacted with alkali under heat and pressure, and now I no longer deemed it impossible to manufacture ammonia under high pressure and at high temperature. However, the unfavorable opinion of the experts taught me that an impressive progress was necessary in order to awaken technical interest in the subject.

"It was clear in the beginning that it was advantageous to resort to high pressure. This produced a favorable position of the equilibrium, and the same could be expected for the reaction velocity. The compressor at our disposal permitted the densification of the gases to 200 atmospheres and thereby determined the working

---

* Translated from *Les Prix Nobel en 1914-1918.*

pressure which could not conveniently be exceeded in the large series of experiments. In the neighborhood of these pressures, the metals with which we had become familiar during our measurements of the equilibria, first manganese, then iron, easily gave a rapid combination of nitrogen with hydrogen at above 700° C. For an impressive result, it was necessary to find contacts which produced a rapid conversion between 500 and 600° C. We hit upon the idea of searching the sixth, seventh, and eighth groups of the periodic system, in which the top metals chromium, manganese, iron, and nickel are excellent catalysts, for metals which are still more active, and we discovered them in uranium and osmium. With their aid, at 200 atmospheres, the two requirements could be met which we believed had to be asked of a technically convincing execution of the experiment; one of these requirements related to the content [of the gas] in ammonia, the other to the amount of ammonia produced per cubic centimeter of the contact space and per hour. With a content of 5 percent the recycling apparatus of 1905 gave no longer only the demonstration of a mode of combination, but a method of preparation. At a yield of several grams of ammonia per hour and cubic centimeter of heated high-pressure space, the dimensions of this space could remain so small that the objections of industry, in our opinion, had to disappear.

"Finally, it was necessary to build a recycling apparatus which could serve as a model for the technical performance.

"Of the characteristics of our laboratory work, the following are retained in today's large-scale operations: the working pressure of about 200 atmospheres, the working temperature of around 500-600° C, the recirculation under continuing high pressure, the feature of heat transfer from exhaust gas to incoming gas."

CONSEQUENCES IN THEORY AND PRACTICE

The synthesis of ammonia has been attempted since the time, toward the end of the eighteenth century, when it was known that ammonia is a compound of nitrogen and hydrogen. The failure of these attempts would have deterred new efforts had not the theory of energy in chemical reactions led not only to the proof that this synthesis should be possible but, in addition, to the prediction of promising conditions for it. That the prediction was found correct showed the great value of the theory as a practical tool. Since it was necessary to have special vessels, pipes, valves, and so on, engineering for high-pressure reactions became an important field.

Four years after Haber had demonstrated the production of 100 grams of synthetic ammonia, industrial production was 6500 tons (metric) per year. The figure was doubled during each following year; 200,000 tons were produced in 1918.

From the start this development had the twofold purpose of sustaining life and of destroying it. As the basis for plant nutrients, it increased crop yields and gave more abundant food supplies. As the starting material for producing nitric acid, synthetic ammonia made possible the manufacture of larger amounts of highly explosive substances not only for mining and quarrying operations but also for ammunition.

Important modifications of the Haber process were developed in France, Italy, and the United States. With all these methods, about 5.5 million tons of nitrogen were converted into chemical compounds in 1948. For the year 1961, the capacity of synthetic ammonia plants in the United States was estimated at 5.9 million tons.

1 9 1 9

No Award

1 9 2 0
WALTHER NERNST
(1864–1941)

"For his thermochemical work."

BIOGRAPHICAL SKETCH

WALTHER NERNST WAS BORN IN BRIESEN, WEST PRUSSIA. HE studied, mainly physics and mathematics, at several universities before he was graduated in Würzburg, in 1887, with a thesis on electromotive forces which are produced by magnetism in heated metal plates. His interest in the relationships between electric and caloric energies was extended to include chemical affinity after he met Wilhelm Ostwald (see pp. 36-40) in Graz, in 1887, and later joined him in Leipzig. Ever since Volta had made his discovery, in 1801, how to explain the electric potential, or "voltage," of an electrochemical battery had been a controversial problem. Nernst found a very lucid solution. He considered the metal electrode as a reservoir of electrically charged metal atoms, which Faraday had called ions. These ions stand under a certain pressure in the metal, the "electrolytic pressure of dissolution." In the liquid surrounding the metal, the same ions are present and exert osmotic pressure. When the metal dissolves, the ions expand from the pressure of dissolution to that osmotic pressure which is determined by the concentration of the ions in solution. This causes the voltage, and the electric charge of the dissolving ions carries the current.

In 1891, Nernst wrote a survey of theoretical chemistry as the introduction to O. Dammer's handbook of inorganic chemistry. Two years later, he enlarged it into a separate book with the characteristic title *Theoretische Chemie vom Standpunkte der Avogadroschen Regel und der Thermodynamik* (Theoretical Chemistry from the Standpoint of Avogadro's Rule and Thermodynamics). He thought, as he stated in the Foreword, that "a period of quiet but successful elaboration has arrived for the physico-chemical scientist; not only are the ideas available, but they have also matured to a certain conclusiveness." He did not feel that he had been wrong in this thought when he wrote the Foreword to the tenth edition in 1921: "Theoretical physics at the present time produces, besides a wealth of durable material, one-day hypotheses rather plentifully, and thus I have found myself induced either to à waiting attitude or to outright rejection." In the first edition of his great textbook he discussed the Principle of Maximum Work which M. Berthelot had formulated in 1867: "Every chemical change which takes place without the aid of external energy tends to the production of that which is accompanied by the development of the maximum amount of heat." This so-called third principle of thermodynamics can be expressed as an equation between A, the maximum work, and Q, the heat of reaction: $A = Q$. The two older laws of energy show, however, that a distinction must be made between A and the change of the total energy U of a system, and $U = A - Q$. Nernst concluded that Berthelot's principle holds true at the lowest possible temperature, the absolute zero or $-273°$ C. He saw a "sound core" in this principle which some day might be extracted from its shell. Thirteen years later he had fulfilled this prediction; his new heat theorem was developed in 1906 and in his Silliman lectures of 1907.

His "Third Law" of thermodynamics states that at absolute zero of temperature, $T = 0$, the entropy of every substance in perfect equilibrium is zero, $S_0 = 0$. Pressure, volume, surface tension, all become independent of temperature at $T = 0$.

In his research work on chemistry of solutions, on relations between compressibility and atomic volume, and many other subjects, he was more successful than in his technical inventions. The Nernst Lamp, which used a ceramic body, might have assumed importance had not the new tantalum and tungsten lamps been developed. His electrical piano, which replaced the sounding board with radio amplifiers, did not find favor with musicians.

As professor in Berlin, from 1905 on, and as director of the Institute for Experimental Physics in Berlin, from 1924 to 1933, he had many fruitful contacts with industry. His scientific genius enabled him to understand industrial developments. He felt that Röntgen would have furthered science and industry more if he had patented his discovery.

DESCRIPTION OF THE PRIZE-WINNING WORK *

"In these researches I found, to begin with, distinct relations between the position of the chemical equilibrium and the development of heat of a particular reaction, but this was true only when reactions were compared in which the change of the number of molecules was the same. This change is the same, e.g. for the two reactions

$$Cl_2 + H_2 = 2HCl \qquad 2NO = N_2 + O_2$$

since in both cases the number of molecules remains unchanged in the reaction. Incidentally the two reactions above have about the same development of heat, and thus the position of the equilibrium is at least approximately the same. This relationship disappears when the two reactions are compared with chemical processes which take place with a change of the number of molecules, like

$$2H_2 + O_2 = 2H_2O$$

and it reappears when the dissociation of water vapor is compared with the analogous dissociation of carbon dioxide.

"I then pursued these questions in long-winded and wearisome calculations and I believe I clarified them, in principle, by the publication of my *Calculation of Chemical Equilibria from Thermal Measurements* (1906). The simple rule at which I arrived at that time can be expressed in the words that in all cases affinity and heat development become identical at low temperatures. And it is essen-

---

* Translated from *Les Prix Nobel en 1920.*

tial that this occur not as an intersection between affinity and heat development at the absolute zero of temperature, but in such a manner that they become equal to each other before reaching the absolute zero point; in other words, the two curves are tangential to each other near the absolute zero point.

"In generalizing this rule—that is to say, in applying it not only to chemical processes but to all occurrences—we obtain the new heat theorem which leads to a series of quite far-reaching consequences.

"1. The maximum work which is obtainable from a process can be calculated from the evolution of heat in this process, provided the latter is known over a range down to the lowest temperatures.

"2. This can also be expressed by saying that the evolution of heat at any one temperature and the specific heats of the substances involved over a range down to very low temperatures must be given.

"3. The specific heats must be rigorously additive at very low temperatures; in other words, the evolution of heat must always be independent of the temperature at low temperatures.

"It is in the nature of things that the foregoing rules, while applicable to all natural processes, are especially useful for chemical events. It is here that Berthelot, as is well known, believed that chemical affinity is equal to the heat developed; however, this assumption, although correct in many cases, could not be sustained. We now recognize clearly in which cases the Berthelot assumption is correct. For very great heat values and with restriction to condensed systems, the influence of specific heat becomes relatively small, and Berthelot's rule is right in usually sufficient approximation when the temperatures are not too high. It often fails completely for processes with little evolution of heat—for example, for the simple process of melting.

"In conclusion I may point out that Eggert, Saha, and others have used my heat theorem successfully for the answers to astrophysical questions."

CONSEQUENCES IN THEORY
AND PRACTICE

One's first impression is likely to be that Nernst's heat theorem is concerned with events at a temperature range which is far remote from that of nearly all our scientific and industrial operations. It seems irrelevant to ordinary conditions that at —273° C the entropy of every substance is zero, or that volume and surface tension become independent of the temperature. However, the relationship between the greatest amount of work which we can obtain from a process and the amount of heat which is developed in its course is of far-reaching practical importance. The recognition that work and heat approach the same value as the temperature is reduced to absolute zero can be extended from this limit-state to more practical conditions. This requires a judicious evaluation which may appear like a trick-conversion of the absolute into its relative counterpart. The use of this evaluation was decisive in the work on ammonia synthesis (see pp. 71-75). A first group of results was in conflict with the predictions of the new theory; this caused a re-examination and led to figures which now held much more promise that a technical process might be developed.

Conflicts between the new theory and measurements were also discovered in electrochemical investigations which were of fundamental importance for technical processes. The maximum of work which the combustion of hydrocarbons—e.g., gasoline—generates can be calculated and evaluated according to the new theory. For properties of the nucleus of the atom the new theory leads to predictions at temperatures of a very high order, where even gravitation and radioactivity should lose their usual independence of temperature.

Nernst's heat theorem removes an indefiniteness which is contained in the second law of energetics and thus broadens the possible extent of general thermodynamics.

1921

FREDERICK SODDY

(1877-1956)

*"For his contributions to the chemistry of radio-
active substances and his investigations into the
origin and nature of isotopes."*

BIOGRAPHICAL SKETCH

FREDERICK SODDY WAS BORN IN EASTBOURNE, SUSSEX. FROM
Oxford University he went to Montreal, in 1899, to join Ernest
Rutherford (see pp. 32-35) at McGill University. Three years
of most fruitful collaboration resulted in the general theory of
radioactive disintegration and a new conception of the atom as a
structure built from a positive nucleus surrounded by negative electrons. The instability of this structure is the cause of radioactivity.

After Soddy returned to England, in 1902, a certain competition
developed between him and Rutherford, particularly with regard to
the publication of a book on radioactive chemistry. An amiable
solution was reached, and Soddy deferred his publication until
after Rutherford's book had appeared.

The position of the new radioactive elements in the system of
chemistry was the object of much research at that time. All the
known elements had been arranged in the sequence of their atomic
weights and grouped according to their chemical analogies and
similarities. There seemed to be no place in this system, the periodic
table of the elements, for some of the products of radioactive transformation. On the other hand, no means for separating such new

81

elements from similar, ordinary ones was found. Soddy concluded that there were elements which belonged in the same place as the older ones, and he indicated this property in the name "isotope," meaning something like "the same place."

Soddy was greatly interested in the general conditions for the growth of science. As professor in Aberdeen (1909-1919) he collected some of his addresses in a book under the title *Science and Life* (London, 1920).

Soddy became professor at Oxford University in 1919 and retired from this famous institution in 1936.

DESCRIPTION OF THE PRIZE-WINNING WORK*

"Auer von Welsbach also, in 1910, carried out a masterly technical separation of ionium and actinium of the 'hydrate' fraction obtained from 30,000 kg of Joachimsthal pitchblende in the manufacture of radium, and prepared a very concentrated ionium preparation, upon the spectrum and atomic weight of which other investigators subsequently worked. He failed completely to separate the ionium from the thorium although many fresh methods were tried.

"Hershfinkel tried numerous methods to concentrate radium D (radiolead) from lead and failed completely. Three years later, Paneth and von Hevesy tried twenty different methods, also completely without result, and upon this failure they based their valuable and elegant method of using the radio elements as indicators. For example, in the present case, the solubility of very insoluble lead compounds was determined by adding radium D to the lead and determining the almost unweighable quantities of lead dissolved by radioactive methods. This use has wide applicability in chemical problems.

"On broader and quite general philosophical grounds, and without in the least postulating a continuation of the genetic series of the radioelements throughout the Periodic System I arrived at the conclusions reached by Strömholm and Svedberg (that the Men-

* From *Les Prix Nobel en 1921*.

delejeff scheme is only an approximate rule as concerns atomic weight, but does not possess the exactness of a natural law; this would not be surprising if the elements of the scheme were mixtures of several homogeneous elements of similar but not completely identical atomic weight).

"It was certain that among the groups of chemically identical radioelements differences of atomic weight of whole units must exist. Thus from the atomic weights of the parent elements and the number of α-particles expelled, the atomic weights of ionium (230) and radio-thorium (228) must differ by 2 and 4 units, respectively, from that of the chemically identical thorium (232). Once one enquired what evidence the chemist had for the real homogeneity of the elements as distinct from their chemical homogeneity, the conclusion followed at once that if all the elements were mixtures in constant proportions of chemical identities differing stepwise by whole units in atomic mass, the chemist with his methods must have remained unaware of it.

"The expulsion of two + charges as an α-particle and of two electrons as β-particles from the nucleus causes the element to come back to the original place it occupied in the Periodic Table. It follows therefore that the place in the Periodic Table is an expression of the net nuclear charge—that is of the difference between the number of positive and negative charges in the nucleus. Thus the chemically identical elements—or isotopes, as I called them for the first time in this (1913) letter to Nature, because they occupy *the same place* in the Periodic Table—are elements with the same algebraic or net nuclear charge, but with different numbers of + and — charges in the nucleus. On the view that the concentrated positive charge is the massive part in the atom structure, since positive electricity has never been observed free possessing less than the mass of an atom, the atomic weight of the isotope is a function of the *total* number of positive charges in the nucleus and the chemical character a function of the *net* number."

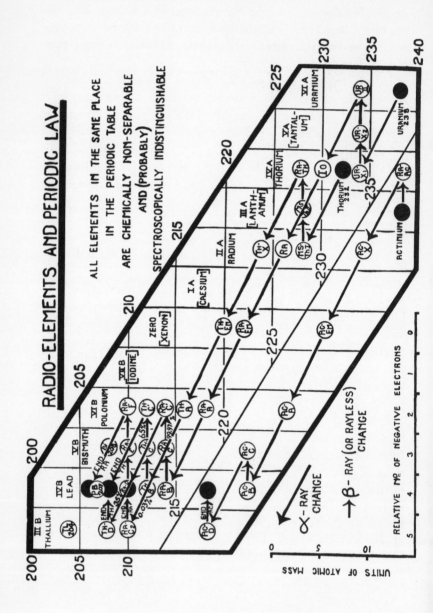

RADIO-ELEMENTS AND PERIODIC LAW

ALL ELEMENTS IN THE SAME PLACE
IN THE PERIODIC TABLE
ARE CHEMICALLY NON-SEPARABLE
AND (PROBABLY)
SPECTROSCOPICALLY INDISTINGUISHABLE

From British Association for the Advancement
of Science, Report 1913, p. 446.

CONSEQUENCES IN THEORY
AND PRACTICE

The chemical definition of elements, clearly conceived toward the end of the eighteenth century, characterized them as being indestructible and inseparable units of matter. The first of these characteristics had to be abandoned at the end of the nineteenth century, when the chemistry of radioactive disintegration was developed; the second characteristic was modified by the experience of isotopy, at the beginning of our century. The occurrence of isotopes was soon shown not to be limited to radioactively produced elements. Aston (see pp. 86-90) demonstrated that amply.

B. B. Boltwood (1870-1927), of Yale University, one of the first to prove that ionium and thorium cannot be separated by chemical means, developed the idea that the new findings could serve to indicate geological age of rocks. Soddy, in his *Science and Life,* described this very clearly: "To-day we know that radioactive minerals are in reality geological clocks, and they record more accurately than in any other way the age of the stratum in which they occur. In a uranium mineral, for example, each 1 per cent. of lead in terms of the quantity of uranium signifies the lapse of a period of 80,000,000 years. . . . On the other hand, every cubic centimeter of helium per gram of uranium in a uranium mineral signifies 9,000,000 years, and—as here helium, being a gas which forms no compounds, cannot have been initially present, and as, moreover, some will have escaped—the age of the mineral by this method is a minimum, whereas the age by lead content may be too high. The carboniferous rocks tested by this new method appear to have an age of some 350,000,000 and the oldest Archean rocks of over 1,500,000,000 years."

1 9 2 2
FRANCIS WILLIAM ASTON
(1877–1945)

"For his discovery, by means of his mass spectrograph, of the isotopes of a large number of non-radioactive elements, as well as for his discovery of the whole-number rule."

BIOGRAPHICAL SKETCH

FRANCIS WILLIAM ASTON WAS BORN IN HARBORNE, ENGLAND. When graduated from high school, in 1893, he received highest honors in mathematics and was the first in his class in sciences. He entered Mason College, which later became the University of Birmingham, in the same year. He worked with P. F. Frankland, professor at Birmingham, on optical properties of complex organic substances and published the results in 1901 in his first scientific paper. While employed with a brewing company, he continued experimenting with special equipment which he designed and built with great skill. Electrical discharge in glass tubes, evacuated by an automatic Toepler-type pump of his own construction, proved so interesting that he returned to the University to pursue his investigations. In 1910, he joined J. J. Thomson at Trinity College, Cambridge, for research on the special discharge tube which Thomson had developed. It consisted essentially of an evacuated glass bulb with the anode (positive pole of electricity) on one end and a narrow outlet to the cathode on the other. The positively charged particles passed from there through a magnetic field into a tube of very low pressure, where they described their paths on a photographic film. Aston changed this arrangement so that the particles which struck the photographic film were cleanly separated according to their relative masses, as light of different wave lengths is separated in an optical spectrum. The apparatus was therefore called a mass spectrograph.

The first apparatus which Aston constructed after returning from his war work as an aircraft engineer was an immediate success. This mass spectrograph of 1919 permitted measurements of relative masses with an accuracy of 1:1000; the third construction, in 1927, gave an accuracy of 1:100,000. The knowledge of exact values of atomic masses enables chemists who study atomic nuclei to synthesize elements, just as other chemists synthesize compounds from elementary substances; this was Aston's prediction in 1936.

Aston found his recreation in travel and sports, and his interest in music was so great that he served as music critic of the *Cambridge Review*. In the obituary notice of the Royal Society (*Proceedings of the Royal Society*, London) it is stated: "Aston's life was a chain of uninterrupted success."

DESCRIPTION OF THE PRIZE-WINNING WORK*

"When neon was introduced into the apparatus, 4 new lines made their appearance at 10, 11, 20, and 22. The first pair are second-order lines and are fainter than the other two. All 4 are well placed for direct comparison with the standard lines, and a series of consistent measurements showed that to within about one part in a thousand the atomic weights of the isotopes composing neon are 20 and 22 respectively. Ten per cent of the latter would bring the mean atomic weight to the accepted value of 20.20, and the relative intensity of the lines agrees well with this proportion. The isotopic constitution of neon was therefore settled beyond all doubt.

"The element chlorine was naturally the next to be analyzed, and the explanation of its fractional atomic weight was obvious from the first plate taken. Its mass spectrum is characterized by 4 strong first-order lines at 35, 36, 37, 38. There is no sign whatever of any line at 35.46. The simplest explanation of the group is to suppose that the lines 35 and 37 are due to the isotopic chlorines

* From *Les Prix Nobel en 1922.*

Table of Elements and Isotopes.

Element	Atomic number	Atomic weight	Minimum number of isotopes	Masses of isotopes in order of intensity
H	1	1,008	1	1,008
He	2	3,99	1	4
Li	3	6,94	2	7,6
Be	4	9,1	1	9
B	5	10,9	2	11, 10
C	6	12,00	1	12
N	7	14,01	1	14
O	8	16,00	1	16
F	9	19,00	1	19
Ne	10	20,20	2	20, 22
Na	11	23,00	1	23
Mg	12	24,32	3	24, 25, 26
Al	13	26,96	1	27
Si	14	28,3	2	28, 29, (30)
P	15	31,04	1	31
S	16	32,06	1	32
Cl	17	35,46	2	35, 37
A	18	39,88	2	40, 36
K	19	39,10	2	39, 41
Ca	20	40,07	(2)	40, 44
Fe	26	55,84	(1)	56, (54) ?
Ni	28	58,68	2	58, 60
Zn	30	65,37	(4)	64, 66, 68, 70
As	33	74,96	1	75
Se	34	79,2	6	80, 78, 76, 82, 77, 74
Br	35	79,92	2	79, 81
Kr	36	82,92	6	84, 86, 82, 83, 80, 78
Rb	37	85,45	2	85, 87
Sn	50	118,7	7 (8)	120, 118, 116, 124, 119, 117, 122, (121)
Sb	51	121,77	2	121, 123
I	53	126,92	1	127
X	54	130,2	7 (9)	129, 132, 131, 134, 136, 128, 130, (126), (124)
Cs	55	132,81	1	133
Hg	80	200,6	(6)	(197—200), 202, 204

(Numbers in brackets are provisional only.)

and lines 36 and 38 to their corresponding hydrochloric acids.

"The most important result of these measurements is that, with the exception of hydrogen, the weights of the atoms of all the elements measured, and therefore almost certainly of all elements, are whole numbers to the accuracy of experiments, namely about one part in a thousand.

"This enables the most sweeping simplification to be made in our ideas of mass. The original hypothesis of Prout, put forward in 1815, that all atoms were themselves built of atoms of protyle, a hypothetical element which he tried to identify with hydrogen, is now reestablished, with the modification that the primordial atoms are of two kinds: Protons and electrons, the atoms of positive and negative electricity.

"The Rutherford—Bohr atom consists essentially of a positively charged central nucleus around which revolve planetary electrons at distances great compared with the dimensions of the nucleus itself.

"As has been stated, the chemical properties of an element depend solely on its atomic number, which is the charge on its nucleus expressed in terms of the unit charge, e. A neutral atom of an element of atomic number N has a nucleus consisting of $K + N$ protons and K electrons, and around this nucleus revolve N electrons. The weight of an electron on the scale we are using is 0.0005, so that it may be neglected. The weight of this atom will therefore be $K + N$, so that if no restrictions are placed on the value of K any number of isotopes are possible.

"We know from Einstein's Theory of Relativity that mass and energy are interchangeable, and that in C.G.S. units a mass m at rest may be expressed as a quantity of energy mc^2 where c is the velocity of light. Even in the case of the smallest mass this energy is enormous.

"Take the case of one gramme atom of hydrogen, that is to say the quantity of hydrogen in 9 cu.cm. of water. If this is entirely transformed into helium, the energy liberated will be $0.0077 \times 9 \times 10^{20} = 6.93 \times 10^{18}$ ergs. Expressed in terms of heat this is 1.66×10^{11} calories, or in terms of work 200,000 kilowatt-hours. We have here at last a source of energy sufficient to account for the heat of the sun.

"Should the research worker of the future discover some means of releasing this energy in a form which could be employed the human race will have at its command powers beyond the dream of scientific fiction, but the remote possibility must always be considered that the energy once liberated will be completely uncontrollable and by its intense violence detonate all neighbouring substances. In this event the whole of the hydrogen on the earth might be transformed at once and the success of the experiment published at large to the universe as a new star."

CONSEQUENCES IN THEORY AND PRACTICE

A few black spots are found on developing a strip of photographic film, and it is concluded that it may some day be possible to convert our earth into a flaming star! The particular arrangement of that strip of film and the conclusion were results of only a few decades of intensive developments in chemistry, physics, and mathematics. The measurement of atomic weights had begun little more than a hundred years before Aston's method distinguished between atoms of different masses with such accuracy that the values could be used for far-reaching conclusions. They may have appeared entirely too far-reaching to many chemists in 1922 who felt that all this did not change the practical and industrial chemistry with which they were concerned. However, besides preparing the foundations for the later development of atomic energy, research by means of the mass spectrograph gradually became a method for analyzing difficult mixtures of substances.

A. J. Dempster had begun in 1918, in Chicago, to develop a mass spectrograph which used an incandescent platinum plate to convert the investigated salts into vapors and subjected them to electrostatic and electromagnetic fields. Dempster's instrument of 1935, with an electrical spark to produce ions of the elements, made possible the identification of 33 new isotopes in 17 elements. Today one can buy mass spectrographs from instrument dealers, and many laboratories use these instruments as highly refined and efficient tools—for example, in analyzing the complex mixtures of substances present in natural gas or mineral oil fractions.

1923
FRITZ PREGL
(1869–1930)

*"For his invention of the method of microanalysis of
organic substances."*

BIOGRAPHICAL SKETCH

FRITZ PREGL WAS BORN IN LAIBACH, AUSTRIA. AT FIRST HIS IN-
clination was toward medicine, and he became Dr. med. of the
University of Graz in 1893. While acting as an assistant in physiology and histology, he also studied chemistry. In 1904 he traveled
in Germany, spending a little time in Leipzig in Ostwald's institute and more time in Berlin, attracted by Emil Fischer.

When he returned to Graz the following year, Pregl undertook
physiological research, particularly on bile acids. The yields of pure
substances were so small that he had to decide whether to work
with very large quantities of raw materials or whether to find
methods through which he could carry out the necessary analytical
investigation with very small quantities of his valuable products.
He decided on the latter approach.

Pregl completed the elaboration of a method for determining
carbon, hydrogen, and nitrogen by careful combustion of very
small quantities during the years 1910-1913, when he was professor in Innsbruck. From 1913 to his death he remained at the
University of Graz, which he preferred to the larger University of
Vienna. He continued to refine the method in details and later
succeeded in making the combustion automatic. He applied the

microanalysis method extensively in his work on enzymes, sera, and bile acids. Besides, he showed the value of his method in forensic analysis, where minimal quantities of poisonous alkaloids could be measured with comparative ease.

DESCRIPTION OF THE PRIZE-WINNING WORK*

In order to determine the proportionate amounts of the elements in the molecule of an organic substance, it is burned under conditions which convert all the carbon into carbon dioxide and all the hydrogen into water, with complete absorption of the carbon dioxide in potassium hydroxide or a mixture of lime and soda, and of the water in calcium chloride. The change in weight of the absorbing materials then gives the quantities of the combustion products, and they can be calculated back to proportions of carbon and hydrogen in the analyzed substance. The combustion is carried out in a tube made of high-melting glass, of a length sufficient to accommodate the sample and copper oxide together with other substances which are necessary to complete the combustion. Nothing but carbon dioxide and water is permitted to reach the absorption system. Nitrogen, sulfur, and phosphorus, when present in the substance, are measured separately. The next step, after the elementary composition has been found, is to measure groups of elements, such as the carboxyl group, which is responsible for the acid character of the substance, or methoxyl, which consists of a methanol residue linked to the rest of the molecule by its oxygen atom, or methyl-imide, in which the oxygen group of methanol is replaced by an ammonia residue of the formula NH.

"When the substance which is to be analyzed contains nitrogen, halogen, or sulfur, its combustion gives rise to gaseous products which would erroneously be weighed and calculated as carbon dioxide, because these products are retained by the soda-lime used to absorb the carbon dioxide. In these cases, these products must at any cost be prevented from reaching the absorption apparatus.

"While macroanalysis recommends different fillings for its combustion tube, in correspondence with the composition of the different substances, I aimed at developing a filling which retains in

---

* Translated from *Les Prix Nobel en 1923*.

every case everything that is not carbon dioxide or water. I call this a universal filling. It consists of a mixture of copper oxide and lead chromate between two sections of silver and finally a section of lead superoxide with asbestos heated to 180°.

"By watching all conditions it is easy to obtain entirely accurate analyses with an amount of substance of 2-4 mg. The smallest quantity ever used was 1 mg, and the deviation still was within normally permitted limits of error. Thus we have reduced the quantity of substance required for an analysis quite extraordinarily, and when we consider that Liebig used half of one gram, originally even one gram of substance, while at the end of the last century 0.15-0.2 g were generally accepted as necessary, we may say that through the method of microanalysis the quantity required for an analysis has been reduced to a hundredth part of that customary as recently as ten years ago without reducing accuracy in the least. I can even state, and I see it with my own students, that much higher accuracy is asked for in microanalysis than was asked for formerly in macroanalysis, obviously for the reason that the fundamental conditions are much better and more completely fulfilled than is possible in macroanalysis. Besides, there are two other advantages. The first is the great economy in gas and reagents, and the second, perhaps still more valuable, is the economy of time. It is possible to obtain results in a third of the time required for macroanalysis.

"In addition to quantitative measurement of the elements in an organic substance, the quantitative content of certain atom groups is of greatest importance. I have, therefore, elaborated the determination of carboxyl groups acidimetrically with phenolphthalein as indicator, as well as the determination of the methoxyl and the methyl-imide group.

"Besides, the method of determining the molecular weight by boiling points has been made accessible to microanalysis. We are able to obtain reliable values with quantities of 7 mg of substance."

CONSEQUENCES IN THEORY
AND PRACTICE

Methods for identifying substances in very small quantities are not new in chemistry. Almost one hundred years ago, Bunsen and

Kirchhoff estimated that they could detect sodium or other metals which color a flame when present in quantities of a hundred-thousandth of a milligram. Certain sugars or proteins could be identified by colored products which they form in solution with special reagents. The exact determination of the composition of an organic substance with milligram quantities, however, was a new achievement. It fitted beautifully into the new development of physiological-chemical research. Substances present in extremely small proportions in plants or animals proved to have important biological functions. Only a few grams could be prepared from tons of the organic material. Research on pigments, vitamins, and hormones required microanalytical methods.

Radioactivity measurements indicated the presence of even smaller quantities. Thus it became necessary to continue on the way from macro- to microanalysis and to develop techniques for ultra-microanalysis.

The balances used to weigh micro-quantities at first were based on conventional principles; an example was the Kuhlmann balance, which made Pregl's work possible. For ultra-micro weighing, other principles had to be used.

1 9 2 4

No Award

1925
RICHARD ZSIGMONDY
(1865–1929)

"For his elucidation of the heterogeneous nature of colloid solutions and for the methods he has devised in this connection, which have since become of fundamental importance in modern colloid chemistry."

BIOGRAPHICAL SKETCH

RICHARD ZSIGMONDY WAS BORN IN VIENNA, WHERE HIS FATHER was a medical doctor and inventor of surgical instruments. Richard began to be interested in chemistry and physics at an early age. He studied in Vienna and Munich. Of great importance for his future work was the time he spent as an assistant to the physicist A. Kundt (1839-1894), in Berlin. Among the subjects of Kundt's research was the abnormal spectrum exhibited by substances of high specific absorptions of light. He interested Zsigmondy particularly in the luster colors produced when organic solutions of gold mixtures are spread on porcelain. The substances mixed with the gold have a great influence on the colors which develop after the coated porcelain is heated. When Zsigmondy returned to Austria to join the faculty at the University of Graz, he began to pursue the subject of gold colors systematically. It was an old subject—late alchemists had been interested in it. In 1679, Johann Kunckel started out to make gold and invented, instead, a secret method for producing ruby glass. Another alchemist, Andreas Cassius, discovered a wonderful purple pigment when he precipitated a gold solution by solutions of stannic chloride. In 1857 the English chemist Michael Faraday explained the color of ruby glass as caused by finely dispersed gold. He also experimented with solutions of gold salts which he transformed into deeply colored fine dispersions of the metal by the addition of a little phosphorus dissolved in ether. Such fine dispersions were called colloidal, an expression which had originally been used (by Graham) to indicate that solutions of animal glue or gelatin are in a class by themselves.

Zsigmondy continued these investigations when he joined the glass works of Schott in Jena, in 1897, and from 1900 to 1903 in his private laboratory. John Tyndall's method (1881) of making ultra-microscopically small particles visible by illumination at right angles to the line of observation formed the basis on which Zsigmondy, in 1903, together with the physicist Siedentopf, developed the ultra-microscope, a universal tool for detailed observation of colloids.

From 1907 on Zsigmondy was director of the Institute for Inorganic Chemistry at the University of Göttingen.

DESCRIPTION OF THE PRIZE-WINNING WORK*

"I investigated gold-ruby glass and certain ceramic colors which are based upon the finest dispersion of gold. It struck me particularly that closely related chemical compounds displayed fundamentally different effects on the production and appearance of these colors. This observation was the more astonishing since compounds of entirely opposite properties frequently have the same kind of effect on colors of gold in finest dispersions, or colloidal gold.

"These findings were not in accord with previous experiences in chemistry. Therefore, I sought to explore the cause of these observations in a way which was not purely chemical. Cassius' Purple served as the first special object of this research. At that time, the safest method for preparing deep-red colloidal gold was

---

* Translated from *Les Prix Nobel en 1924-1925.*

the use of formaldehyde. With this method I prepared a sufficient amount of pure, deep-red colloidal gold. With this gold I attempted the synthesis of Cassius' Purple, and when this experiment succeeded, the conception of Cassius' Purple as a mixture of finely divided gold with colloidal stannic acid was proved. Since, on the other hand, this purple behaves completely like a chemical substance, as Berzelius already had observed, I arrived at an important experience as to the understanding of colloidal precipitates. In order to avoid errors it is necessary to consider this experience in explaining colloidal systems. In summary it can be said that a colloidal mixture can behave like a chemical compound under certain circumstances and sometimes can be mistaken for it.

"Liquids of the same gold content can appear different to the ordinary observation; on the other hand, the intensity of the Faraday-Tyndall cone of light can vary in solutions which appear clear on mere direct inspection.

"For certain problems the simple observation of the cone of light under the microscope was insufficient. I endeavored, therefore, to develop microscopic observation for the light-cone to greatest efficiency.

"The method was, therefore, refined in collaboration with H. Siedentopf in Jena. An instrument of great efficiency was constructed, the slit-ultra-microscope, with which gold particles down to a diameter of a 10-millionth of a millimeter could be made visible in sunlight.

"The particles of gold in colloidal solutions have a negative electric charge, like the particles of many other irreversible colloids. The electrical charge on these colloids has great importance as the essential cause for their stability. If the charge is removed from the particles—e.g., by adding salts—the particles immediately combine and the system coagulates. This is visible for colloidal gold by the color change from red to blue. The ultra-microscope shows not only the color change of the single particles but also a considerable change of the number of particles.

"Coagulation can be interrupted at any time by the addition of protective colloids. Thus it is possible to determine the number of ultra-microns after each definite time interval, following the addition of the coagulant, and thus to measure the velocity of coagulation."

CONSEQUENCES IN THEORY
AND PRACTICE

Three states of matter have long been recognized: gas, solid, and liquid. A fourth state began to draw attention to itself about a hundred years ago, the state of fine dispersion; matter in this state may be in any one of the three fundamental states. A great many materials are found in this colloid state. Metals, salts, organic materials occur in finely dispersed forms, as fog or foam, as liquid or solid solution. They are found in the atmosphere, in natural waters, in rocks, in organisms. They are applied in medicine as salves or ointments, and in technical operations—e.g., as absorbent silica gel. Their large surfaces are seats of electrical charges and specific chemical actions. However, the colloid state is a delicate one, easily destroyed when not stabilized by protective colloids. Very small admixtures of certain foreign colloidal substances can protect a colloidal system; others can have the opposite effect.

The technically important cases in which colloidal dispersions are desired are almost as numerous as those in which they are harmful. For example, although oil emulsions of many kinds are produced by special efforts, the separation of oils from their emulsions is often required. In making or breaking colloid dispersions, the basic knowledge of their behavior is of great value. The ultramicroscope has, therefore, been improved in several ways. Siedentopf added the cardioid condenser, through which light is concentrated within the object at such an angle that only the light reflected from the colloidal particles reaches the eyepiece.

1 9 2 6
THEODOR SVEDBERG
(1884–   )

"For his work on disperse systems."

BIOGRAPHICAL SKETCH

THEODOR SVEDBERG WAS BORN IN VALBO, SWEDEN. HE STUDIED at the University of Uppsala. His doctoral thesis described a new method for preparing colloidal solutions of metals by dispersing them under the influence of electric currents of high frequency. When such currents were caused to flow between gold or nickel electrodes, the metal dispersed in the water. Observation under the ultra-microscope showed the fine particles of the metals. In 1909, a year after his graduation, he described these methods in a book of some 500 pages. Finely dispersed particles are in a constant state of motion or vibration. The Scottish botanist R. Brown had observed them, in 1827, on suspensions of pollen. Svedberg studied this "Brownian Movement" and saw in it the result of the movement of the molecules themselves which are impinging on the relatively coarser colloidal particles. These experimental studies were published in 1912 under the title *The Existence of the Molecules*.

In the same year, Svedberg became professor in Uppsala. He turned his attention to methods for increasing the pull of gravity on colloidal particles. This can be achieved by rotation at high speed in a centrifuge. Svedberg developed an ultra-centrifuge, partly as a result of work carried out while he was a guest researcher and lecturer in Madison, Wis., in 1922-1923. The main objects of research by means of the ultra-centrifuge were solutions of organic substances such as proteins and others characterized by the large size of their molecules. He is continuing this work as director of the Institute of Physical Chemistry at the University of Uppsala.

DESCRIPTION OF THE PRIZE-WINNING WORK*

"The procedure was based on the fact . . . that it should be possible to determine the mass of heavy molecules by measuring the sedimentation equilibrium in the ultra-centrifuge.

"When a solution is centrifuged in a closed cell for a sufficiently long time a state of equilibrium is finally reached when sedimentation and diffusion balance each other. To determine the molecular weight it is therefore necessary only to measure the relation between the concentration of the solution at two points situated x_1 and x_2 cm from the center of rotation and to know the temperature, the speed of the centrifuge, the partial specific volume of the solute and the density of the solvent.

"The formula holds only for dilute solutions. In the case of concentrated solutions the formula for the molecular weight will include the expression for the partial specific free energy of the solute.

"A small quantity of the solution to be studied, from 0.01 to 0.25 cc, is enclosed in a glass or quartz cell possessing plane parallel walls and rotated at constant temperature in a special centrifuge which permits photographing the solution when exposed to a centrifugal force up to 5,000 times the force of gravity. After equilibrium has been reached and the cell photographed, a series of solutions of different concentrations is photographed in the same cell shortly after starting the centrifuge, that is, before any marked sedimentation has set in. The plate carrying the photograph of the solution on its way to sedimentation equilibrium and after reaching it, as well as the scale of different concentrated solutions is then

* From "A Method for the Determination of the Molecular Weight of the Proteins," *Journal of the American Chemical Society*, Vol. XLVIII (1926), p. 430.

recorded by means of a self-registering micro-photometer. From the record thus obtained the curve giving the relation between concentration of the solution and distance from the center of rotation can easily be constructed.

"The eminent physiological importance of hemoglobin has made the determination of its molecular weight, which enters as a factor in the formula for the respiratory power of the blood, an urgent task. . . . The ordinary methods based upon freezing-point and vapor pressure determinations of course fail for a substance of such high molecular weight, and the previous attempts to measure the molecular weight of hemoglobin all deal with the measurement of osmotic pressure against a semi-permeable membrane.

"Our first experiments were made with dialyzed oxy-hemoglobin in pure aqueous solution and in 1% potassium chloride solution. They gave for the molecular weight of hemoglobin values which were between three and four times the minimum value of 16,700."

CONSEQUENCES IN THEORY AND PRACTICE

The separation of molecules from their solutions by the action of gravity seems to be the simplest and directest way to the determination of molecule weights. There are, however, many influences which have to be considered and evaluated in the light of a great amount of comparative data. The mass of the molecule is only one of the factors which enter into a calculation of the effect of gravity; shape and specific gravity of the substance have to be considered, and bonds with the solvent which in turn are influenced by the degree of acidity or alkalinity and by the presence of other substances—for example, salts. The equipment for obtaining high speeds of rotation was modified in many ways. The material from which the rotor was built had to be selected for its strength and weight, and the driving method was changed from electrical to turbines. The optical system for observing and photographing the sedimentation required much attention. Very small centrifuges, with rotors of only about 1 centimeter in diameter, could be run up to speeds of over a million rotations per minute. On the other hand, rotors of larger diameters, up to 20 centimeters, gave centrifugal forces up to 34,800 times gravity when driven at only 18,000 rotations per minute.

Molecular weights of proteins, viruses, and synthetic resins were measured by means of the ultra-centrifuge. Hemoglobin thus shows a molecule of 68,000 in higher vertebrates, 34,000 in certain bacteria, and 17,000 in the lowest class of vertebrates. Another blood pigment, hemocyanin, gave about 9 million. Cellulose appears to contain up to 2000 glucose units, according to some methods of measurement; in the ultra-centrifuge, much smaller molecular units can be observed, consisting of groups of 100 glucose residues. In the processes for manufacturing highly polymeric synthetic resins, the investigation of the sedimentation under great centrifugal force can serve as a guide to building the size and form of molecules which have the best technical value.

1927
HEINRICH WIELAND
(1877-1957)

"For his research on bile acids and analogous substances."

BIOGRAPHICAL SKETCH

HEINRICH WIELAND WAS BORN IN PFORZHEIM, BADEN. HIS father was a chemist. Heinrich studied chemistry at several universities in Germany and received his doctor's degree from the University of Munich in 1901. He became professor of organic chemistry there in 1913. After war work at the Kaiser Wilhelm Institut for Chemistry in 1917-1918 with Haber, he returned to academic research and teaching at Freiburg, in 1921. From 1926 on he has served as successor to Willstätter at Munich.

The new biochemistry which began to be shaped in the early part of this century attracted Wieland strongly. In his first Munich period he devoted much original work to the central process of oxidation in life. We breathe to supply oxygen to the blood, from which oxygen emerges loaded with carbon, as carbon dioxide, and with hydrogen, as water. The simplest chemical explanation of oxidation seemed to be an addition of oxygen. Wieland emphasized the role of hydrogen and showed that what is commonly conceived as oxidation may, in many important cases, be a dehydrogenation. Even when a metal is oxidized—when iron rusts, for example— the decisive process is a loss of hydrogen, because an intermediary compound is formed between metal and water.

$$Fe + H_2O \rightarrow Fe(H_2O) \rightarrow FeO + H_2$$
iron   water   hydrate   oxide hydrogen

In the "oxidation" of intermediate compounds in the organism, a transfer of hydrogen from the compound to an acceptor of hydrogen takes place.

Many years of work on alkaloids, bile acids, and highly toxic biological substances followed. While his friend Windaus (see pp. 107-110) studied digitalis glucosides, Wieland elucidated the chemical structure of heart-poisons of animal origin, particularly a toxin produced by certain toads. Together with C. Schöpf, he developed the chemical picture of pigments in the wings of butterflies and found analogous substances in fish skins. This apparently remote subject proved of great importance in the research on antianemic substances in liver.

DESCRIPTION OF THE PRIZE-WINNING WORK*

In his Nobel Prize lecture, Wieland described the way in which he located the atoms in the molecule of the most important of the acids obtained from bile, cholic acid. This way had many stations, marked by derived products for which the names were also derived from that of the parent substance, bile. A general plan had to be drawn; numbers were assigned to the 24 carbon atoms as they are supposed to follow one another, distributed over four rings of carbons and side chains of carbons attached to definite places of the rings. The molecule then had to be simplified by partial, well-controlled destruction, but sometimes it had to be made more complicated first—for example, by a Grignard reaction (see p. 51) to protect the hydroxyl groups. A few uncertainties remained at that time, but many of the artificially produced changes were "transparent" in giving a picture of the "inside" of the large molecules.

"The formula of cholic acid shows a structure built from four condensed carbon rings containing three branching side chains.

"The carboxyl group, which is responsible for the acidic character of the substance, is situated in one side chain. The three other oxygen atoms of cholic acid are distributed in the molecule as

---

* Translated from *Les Prix Nobel en 1927*.

alcoholic hydroxyl groups; in cholic acid they are placed at carbon
atoms number 3, 7, 12. Desoxycholic acid, $C_{24}H_{40}O_4$, lacks the
hydroxyl group at C-atom 12, and one of the OH-groups of litho-
cholic acid is bound to C 3. A cholic acid, $C_{24}H_{40}O_4$, which is
isomeric with desoxycholic acid has been isolated by Windaus and
myself from gall of several organisms, particularly goose, cattle,
and man. This cholic acid is designated by the names cheno-
desoxycholic acid and anthropo-desoxycholic acid. Although the
two discoverers are otherwise on excellent terms with each other,
no agreement has been reached with regard to uniform nomenclature. In this acid the two hydroxyl groups are situated at C 7
and C 12. As can be seen, the four most important cholic acids
are closely related to one another, not only regarding the fundamental skeleton, but also with regard to the distribution of their
hydroxyl groups.

"The first breach of the molecule has been made starting from
desoxycholic acid, which is split, by way of the diketo-acid, in ring
I. The two isomeric desoxybilianic acids are thus obtained.

"The cyclic ketone obtained from desoxybilianic acid was split
open, after several intermediate products, into a hexacarbonic acid,
$C_{23}H_{34}O_{12}$, in which only one ring was conserved and which was,
therefore, designated as solanellic acid. By decomposition of this
solanellic acid through heating, a new pentanone ring was obtained . . . and its further splitting led to an acid, $C_{22}H_{32}O_{12}$,
called biloidanic acid.

"All attempts to penetrate into the last ring of the molecule,
starting from biloidanic acid, remained without success.

"It will be seen that in the experiments described so far only
two carbon atoms had been removed from the large molecule in a
controlled transparent manner. The rule followed so far, to proceed
step by step, had to be abandoned, if the goal was to be approached
within a reasonable time.

"We started from the ester of cholanic acid, $C_{24}H_{40}O_2$, the
parent of the whole group, converted this into the diphenylated
carbinol by a Grignard reaction, and oxidized this product with
chromic acid. In this manner one C-atom after the other was split
off. Together with the third C-atom, the fourth split off, a proof
of its being connected with a CH_3-group. Beginning with the acid

$C_{20}H_{32}O_2$, the monotony of this process showed a welcome change. . . . The opening of the fourth ring was achieved. . . . This fourth ring was recognized as a five-carbon ring. . . . The relationship of the side chain to ring II (lactonization with the OH-group of C 7, condensation with the CO-group of the dehydro-acids) defines the place of the side chain at C 18.

"The present state of our knowledge of the formula for cholic acid is hypothetical insofar as the situation of the last two carbon atoms has not been determined accurately."

CONSEQUENCES IN THEORY AND PRACTICE

Shortly after presenting this picture of cholic acid Wieland had to change some of its details. New chemical analogies and the calculation of the relative distances of the carbon atoms from X-ray diagrams showed that carbon atoms 1 to 14 were connected in three benzene rings connected with one another by two carbons, and that only one five-carbon ring was attached to one of them, again by two carbon atoms. Various side chains on this skeleton account for differences among the main bile substances from different animals. The same skeleton was found in sterols from plants. Bufo-toxin from the toad *Bufo vulgaris* proved to be chemically related to scillaren, a toxin from squill, a plant from the class of lilies.

Bile acids have an important function in the digestion of food substances. With a little variation in their chemical structures, these beneficial substances become powerful poisons. Similar relationships were discovered for chemicals which, in very small quantities, are of decisive influence in the growth and sexual development of man and animals. The availability of the new knowledge of bile substances made it possible to determine the chemistry of sex hormones within a relatively short time (see p. 166).

1 9 2 8
ADOLF WINDAUS
(1876-1959)

*"For his studies on the constitution of the sterols and
their connection with the vitamins."*

BIOGRAPHICAL SKETCH

Adolf Windaus was born in Berlin and received his early
schooling there. He studied medicine at Freiburg and Berlin. Emil
Fischer's personality and work turned his interest, like that of so
many others, toward chemistry. After receiving his doctor's degree
at Freiburg, with chemistry as major and physics and zoology as
minors, he returned to Berlin for a year at Fischer's laboratory, then
went back to Freiburg in 1901. Here, Heinrich Kiliani (1855-
1945) studied the saponins in digitalis, identifying the sugars in
these glycosides and investigating the corresponding sapogenins.
Windaus carried out his thesis work in this field and obtained his
doctor's degree in 1899. His work on cholesterol and on digitalis
started soon thereafter.

Cholesterol received its name from the Greek words for bile
(*chole*) and solid (*stereos*). M. Chevreul had shown its presence
in fats, as that part of them which could not be converted into
soap by reaction with soda or potash. Similar unsaponifiable residues were found in many plant seeds and fruits, but they were
not identical with cholesterol. The work which Windaus performed in defining these substances as members of a whole group

of sterols can be compared with that of Wallach (see pp. 42-44) in the field of terpenes. Cholesterol itself, which can be easily prepared in crystallized form from gallstones, has 27 carbon atoms in one molecule. Eight of these carbon atoms are split off by a mild oxidation; they represent a side chain attached to the larger part of the molecule, which contains four rings of carbon atoms.

A connection between research on sterols and on digitalis was found in the ability of one of the substances from the digitalis leaves, digitonin, to form insoluble precipitates with certain sterols. Windaus used this reaction to distinguish between the products obtained by irradiating ergosterol. At that time, he was professor at the University of Göttingen, a post which he had held since 1915, after having occupied the chair of applied medical chemistry at Innsbruck for two years.

DESCRIPTION OF THE PRIZE-WINNING WORK*

"What is the biological role of cholesterol itself? Many experiments have been designed to answer this question. Several investigators emphasize the physical, especially the colloid-chemical, properties of cholesterol. They point to the ability of cholesterol to emulsify fats and to the importance for the permeability of the cell. These relationships are very much in need of further clarification.

"One fact in particular has aroused the interest of chemists and physiologists during recent years, the connection between sterols and the anti-rachitic vitamin. This vitamin is relatively abundant in the unsaponifiable part of cod-liver oil, which is a good remedy for rachitis. The German doctor Huldschinski was the first, to my knowledge, who found that, besides cod-liver oil, irradiation by ultra-violet light is a remedy for rachitis. Two American scientists, Hess and Steenbock, later found independently of each other that it is not at all necessary to irradiate the sick organism, but that it is sufficient to irradiate the food which he gets. The same scientists and, at about the same time, the Englishmen Rosenheim and Webster, in London, found later on that the reactive substance is

---

* Translated from Les Prix Nobel en 1928.

present in the unsaponifiable part of the foodstuffs and that it is identical with the sterols.

"It was at first believed that all sterols, from animals, plants, and fungi, could be activated by ultra-violet light. Physical measurements and biological experiments showed later that cholesterol and sitosterol contain an admixture in trace quantities which is responsible for the formation of the active compound. Cholesterol can be freed of this impurity quite easily. This admixture has been proved to be identical with the ergosterol of fungi, or, to express it more cautiously, it has exactly the same absorption spectrum and exactly the same physiological behavior as ergosterol.

"The conversion of ergosterol into the anti-rachitic vitamin takes place in ultra-violet light of wave length between 253 and 302 $m\mu$; light of longer wave length than 313 $m\mu$ or shorter than 248 $m\mu$ does not have a reliable effect.

"The activation succeeds even at —183° C. About 700 to 1000 ergs are required to produce a quantity which is just biologically active (about 1/50,000 mg). By irradiation for too long a period, vitamin D is destroyed.

"When a mixture of ergosterol and eosin is irradiated with visible light, a stoichiometrical reaction between the two occurs, eosin is hydrogenated and ergosterol is dehydrogenated to a pinacone $C_{54}H_{82}O_2$. When all the eosin is hydrogenated, the reaction stops.

"In the presence of oxygen, eosin acts as a catalyst in the visible light, and a crystallized ergosterol-peroxide is formed. But both ergosterol products are inactive as antirachitics, a vitamin-formation in visible light has not been achieved.

"In order to obtain reproducible results of irradiation, it is necessary not only to exclude oxygen completely—which is very difficult —but also to irradiate all parts of the solution as uniformly as possible. We tried the activation at first by pumping a 0.25 percent alcoholic solution of ergosterol under nitrogen pressure through a quartz spiral wound around a mercury lamp.

"Later on we heated the ethereal solution of ergosterol, through which purified nitrogen was percolating in a double-walled quartz vessel, while inside the quartz vessel electric sparks were produced between magnesium poles."

CONSEQUENCES IN THEORY
AND PRACTICE

Although Windaus's work on cholesterol helped to provide the foundation for the chemistry of sex hormones (see p. 166), and although his research on digitalis similarly influenced the technical preparation of cardiac tonics and sedatives, his investigation of methods for producing vitamin D had the widest applications. In these investigations, Windaus combined physical and biological procedures with those of organic chemistry. Absorption spectra and feeding tests were correlated with purely chemical reactions. The advantages which can be obtained from group work were spectacularly demonstrated. This meticulous research showed that irradiations can be beneficial, but that they have to be closely controlled, because overdoses may be detrimental. The energy required for the conversion of ergosterol into the vitamin is small; the combustion of one gram of petroleum furnishes the energy-equivalent necessary for the conversion of 10 grams of ergosterol. The specific form in which this amount of energy is applied is decisive for the effect. Bourdillon called this vitamin calciferol; Windaus later designated it as vitamin D_2, to distinguish it from the mixture originally called vitamin D. One ounce of the pure vitamin would be sufficient to provide the vitamin D requirements of three thousand children for one year! In continued research, safe and efficient methods for enhancing the vitamin D content of foods, particularly milk, have been developed, using the principles which Windaus stated. Milk in continuous, regulated flow streams through stainless steel tubes which have a rod-shaped ultra-violet lamp in the center, and air is carefully excluded.

Who could calculate in precise figures the value of the work from which this development grew, and to which a great number of scientific and technical studies contributed?

ARTHUR HARDEN
(1865–1940)

HANS VON EULER-CHELPIN
(1873–)

"For their investigations on the fermentation of sugar and of fermentative enzymes."

BIOGRAPHICAL SKETCH

HARDEN

ARTHUR HARDEN WAS BORN IN MANCHESTER, ENGLAND. HE received his doctor's degree in chemistry from the University of Erlangen, Germany, in 1888. As lecturer and demonstrator in chemistry at Owens College, Manchester (1888-1897) he was mostly interested in teaching. He collaborated with Henry Roscoe (1833-1915) on his great textbook and wrote a *Practical Organic Chemistry* together with F. C. Garett. After joining the Jenner Institute of Preventive Medicine (later Lister Institute) in 1897, he began to study fermentations as a means for differentiating among varieties of bacteria. He included work with yeast juices. When yeast is kept in a warm place, its enzymes liquefy the cell substance. The self-digested, or autolyzed, yeast juice still contains the fermentation enzyme-complex called zymase. Heating autolyzed yeast juice to boiling should destroy all enzyme activity. Yet, as Harden

111

found, the addition of boiled autolyzed yeast increases the rate of fermentation considerably. The active agent, which Harden called co-zymase, contains phosphoric acid or its salts. Are they responsible for the activity? He added potassium phosphate to a mixture of sugar and Buchner-juice (see p. 30) and observed a great increase in carbon dioxide. More detailed measurements showed relationships between CO_2 and phosphate (PO_4). Later on, a compound of sugar (hexose) and phosphate was discovered. Obviously, it had to be assumed that a special enzyme was here involved. Since it appeared to act upon phosphates, its name was to be phosphatase. Further research led to the finding that several compounds are formed in which sugar acts like an alcohol, so that these sugar-phosphates are comparable to other compounds of an alcohol with an acid, which are usually called esters.

Harden retired as head of the biochemical division of the Lister Institute in 1930.

In personal contact, he was uncommonly reserved, but to the scientific public he gave much of his efforts, as an author of books and as editor of the *Biochemical Journal.*

EULER-CHELPIN

HANS VON EULER-CHELPIN WAS BORN IN AUGSBURG, BAVARIA. At first he intended to become an artist and studied painting in particular; then his interest in colors made him change to physics and chemistry. After graduation from the Univeristy of Berlin, in 1895, he continued physico-chemical work in Nernst's laboratory, became physics assistant to Arrhenius in 1897, and spent two summers (1899 and 1900) with van't Hoff. By 1900 he was already docent for physical chemistry at Stockholm, where he became professor of general and organic chemistry in 1906.

With physical chemistry as a foundation he turned to biochemistry, as Arrhenius had done. New prospects were seen to open up when the general laws of the course of chemical change, and the physical concepts and equipment used to measure characteristic single properties, were applied to the complexities and mysteries of chemical change occurring in organisms and caused by them. Fermentation and enzyme chemistry in general could thus be brought into systematic connection with the rest of chemistry. Euler presented such a system in his book *Chemie der Enzyme* (The Chemistry of Enzymes), which was published in 1910 and saw several later editions.

The familiar chemical relationships illuminated the darkness of enzyme reactions when Euler and his collaborators showed that a chemical bond between an enzyme and the substance upon which it acts, its substrate, is in effect a bond between an acidic (carboxyl) group and an alkaline (amido) group. His particular interest was directed toward the subsidiary agents which co-act with the enzymes, the co-enzymes. Harden had found a heat-stable, or at least boil-proof, co-enzyme of zymase. Euler purified it and dissected it chemically. The result was that this co-enzyme has the nature of a special ester of sugar and phosphoric acid which is chemically combined with a purine and is related to compounds found in muscle. He characterized the purity of co-zymase (abbr. Co) by its activity A per unit weight of "Co."

This co-action, the fact that a bio-active substance needs a helper, had its analogies in immunology. Euler also found its counterpart in certain "poisoning" effects on enzyme actions, where the inhibiting force of one substance is disproportionately increased by the addition of a second inhibitor. On the other hand, substances of high biological effect usually have counteracting substances. Vitamins have anti-vitamins, and, in general, if the active agents are designated as ergones, we may discover their specific anti-ergones.

With such thoughts, always substantiated by extensive experiments, Euler came from enzymology to questions of medicine and of heredity. In the foreword to the first edition of his book on the chemistry of enzymes, he had expressed the thought that in this field, as in others, theory will be of practical value to the physician and the technician. His assistance in showing the practical value of theory found a particular recognition in 1929, when a new institute, the biochemical institute of the University of Stockholm, was dedicated to his work. It has been directed by Euler since then.

DESCRIPTION OF THE PRIZE-WINNING WORK

HARDEN *

"A striking feature of fermentation by yeast preparations is that it proceeds much less rapidly than fermentation by a corresponding amount of living yeast. Thus Buchner's yeast-juice ferments at only about 1/20-1/40 of the rate of the yeast from which it is derived.

"The fact that the rate of fermentation of such a juice can be raised under favourable circumstances some 10-20 times simply by increasing the supply of phosphate seems to me to indicate clearly that a large fraction, at least half, of the fermenting complex of the yeast has escaped injury in the preparation and has passed into the juice, but that the mechanism for the supply of inorganic phosphate has been to a large extent destroyed. Neither arsenate nor phosphate has an accelerating action on the rate of fermentation by living yeast. This may be due to the fact that the supply of inorganic phosphate in the interior of the yeast-cell is already optimal, but some doubt exists as to whether or not these salts freely penetrate the cell. If, however, as seems to me probable, it is true that in the preparation of yeast-juice etc. it is the phosphate-supplying mechanism that is thrown out of gear, it becomes an object of enquiry in what way this is brought about.

"The process least likely to inactivate an accelerating substance is probably that used by Buchner, but the possibility also exists that such a substance, if present, might be absorbed and thus be removed from the juice by the large quantity of kieselguhr employed.

"Experiments (not yet published) have recently been made in my laboratory by Miss Macfarlane to find out at what stage in the process the change occurs and whether a juice richer in phosphatase could be obtained by modifying the process of grinding and pressing out. It appears, however, that simple grinding with sand pro-

* From *Les Prix Nobel en 1929.*

duces a change of the same order as that observed in Buchner's yeast-juice.

"Minor differences were observed when different substances were substituted for the kieselguhr used by Buchner, the most active juice for example being obtained by the use of $CaCO_3$ whereas $BaCO_3$ yielded totally inactive material.

"When fermentation of sugar by yeast preparations is carried out under suitable conditions in the presence of added inorganic phosphate, a rapid production of CO_2 and alcohol occurs and a phosphoric ester of a sugar accumulates, the amount of phosphate found in this form being approximately proportional in the ratio (CO_2/PO_4) to the increased production of CO_2 and alcohol caused by the addition of the phosphate (Kluyver and Struyk, it is true, have found lower ratios than this, but there is no doubt that high ratios 0.8-1 are often observed).

"The phosphoric ester produced, however, may consist mainly of the hexosediphosphate originally described by Young and myself or of the hexosemonophosphate described by Robinson and myself and subsequently studied by Robinson or it may be a mixture of these in any proportions. In the case of fermentation by dried yeast (and possibly by other preparations) a further complication is afforded by the fact that a disaccharide-phosphoric ester (trehalosemonophosphate) may also be present."

EULER-CHELPIN *

"An enzyme acts by combining with its substrate according to a definite affinity. For example, when egg white is digested, it becomes a long chain of amino acids from which egg white more or less is composed, and by-products which contain two such amino acids, so-called dipeptides.

"Dipeptides have their special enzymes, dipeptidases. The question arises with which group contained in the dipeptide the combination with the enzyme occurs. It is a general fact that the split-product which results from an enzyme reaction has an impeding action; here, amino acids do it. Now we wanted to find experi-

---

* Translated from *Les Prix Nobel en 1929.*

mentally what kind of group a split-product had to contain to exert this impeding action, and from the work of Josephson with a special dipeptidase we found that it had to be an amino group.

"Studies of the circumstances under which the impeding effect takes place and those under which enzymes combine with dipeptides showed that it is a carboxyl group attached to the enzyme which combines with the substrate, and thereby the bond between enzyme and substrate was for the first time explained by definite atom groups.

"The reason for our devoting much time and work to the purification and chemical investigation of co-enzyme is that co-enzyme is one of the most widely spread and most important of activators in plants and animals. The difficulties of isolating co-zymase begin with the great dilution in which it occurs. Yeast is considered the most convenient raw material, although one kilogram of yeast gives only 20 milligrams at best.

"After a long sequence of purification procedures we obtained a substance with the maximum activity, expressed in rational units, of $A Co = 85,000$, while the starting material is characterized by $A Co = 200$. This substance could be converted into salts from which the co-zymase was regenerated in unchanged activity. The composition of the purest product corresponds to that of a nucleotide; it contains a sugar residue, a purine residue, and phosphoric acid and is thus closely related to adenylic acid."

CONSEQUENCES IN THEORY AND PRACTICE

Phosphates are important in the life processes of organisms. Plants need them and they have become an essential part of fertilizers. Proteins such as casein contain phosphates, and they occur in bones and in urine. It was known that they are present in yeast, so that it was quite natural to look for them in the boiled yeast juice which had such an unexpected influence on fermentations. Harden's discovery that sugar combined with phosphate as a first step in fermentation indicated something of the biochemistry of phosphate. It was clear, from the standpoint of enzymology, that the intermediate compound needed a splitting enzyme, phosphatase, but first another enzyme had to exert a combining, or phosphorylating, action. Phosphorylase was found in animal tissues, yeast, plants, and bacteria, although it was not of the same kind in all these cases. Adenylic acid was sometimes involved in its structure. Although it may appear strange that sugar had to be built up into the phosphoric acid ester in order to be degraded into the simpler products of fermentation, the paths of sugars in nutritional change to utilize its energy are still more complicated. Transfers of phosphoric acid between substrate and enzymes of several kinds take place before the muscle obtains the calories from sugars.

Sugar phosphates found a practical application for special nutritional needs. Calcium salts of hexosephosphate are very soluble in water and offer the possibility of supplying both calcium and phosphorus in easily assimilated form.

Cozymase was later recognized as being a complex of several enzymes. In cozymase I, a diphosphoric acid molecule is esterified by 2 ribose sugar molecules that are chemically combined with nicotine amide and adenine. The importance of such phosphate compounds in biologically active substances became clear in subsequent work; see Sir Alexander Todd, 1957.

| nicotinic acid amide | adenine | ribose | phosphoric acid |

That enzyme reactions proceed through the intermediary of a bond between enzyme and substrate is widely accepted. The nature of this bond, which Euler and Josephson were able to interpret so simply for their dipeptide, is far from clear in most other cases. Much more work will be required to explain the high specificity of enzyme response to chemical constitution.

1 9 3 0
HANS FISCHER
(1881–1945)

"For his researches into the constitution of hemin and chlorophyll, especially for his synthesis of hemin."

BIOGRAPHICAL SKETCH

HANS FISCHER, BORN IN HÖCHST, NEAR FRANKFORT ON THE Main, was equally interested in chemistry and in medicine. He received his doctor's degree in chemistry from Marburg University in 1904, and in medicine from Munich University in 1908. Medical work in Munich was followed by chemical research in Berlin at Emil Fischer's institute. Fischer succeeded Windaus at Innsbruck, in 1916, as professor of medical chemistry, and returned to Munich as professor of organic chemistry in 1921. He filled this office as a teacher, researcher, and editor of scientific journals to the end of his life.

When Fischer began his extensive study of the blood dyestuff, the chemical nature of the corresponding green pigment of plants had become much clearer. The red hemin and the green chlorophyll had a peculiar structure in common: magnesium in the center of a large molecule in chlorophyll, iron in a corresponding place in the molecule of hemin. In both cases, this center atom can be removed without hurting the rest of the structure. Hemin, thus gently deprived of its iron, proved to be identical with substances previously found as products of a mild degree of putrefaction of hemin and called porphyrin. There was, however, great uncertainty concern-

118

ing the relationships and identities of substances obtained by chemical change of hemin. A first important step toward deeper insight into the chemistry of hemin was made with Fischer's investigation of a natural degradation product of hemin from gall (bile). Among the gall pigments, one is bilirubin. As the name indicates—fortunately, among the great number of artificial names in this field, there are a few which have at least a partial relation to some general properties—bilirubin, although a degraded hemin, is still red. By splitting of the molecule in half on heating with acetic and hydro-iodic acid, a new acid was obtained in which a section of the hemin molecule was still intact. It was relatively easy to identify its structure and to relate it to pyrrole, the oily and smelly product which earlier chemists had obtained by heating animal substances to high temperature and condensing the oil out of the vapors.

From this basis, which was secured by W. Küster in 1912, Fischer began the approach to the chemistry of hemin itself. Bilirubin and its close relatives could be made by synthesis. A fundamental structure of four pyrrole molecules was recognized. The pyrrole, a simple ring of four carbon atoms closed by one nitrogen atom, is modified by methyl, ethyl, and propionic acid groups and an unsaturated ethyl group which has the name vinyl, now so familiar to users of plastics. The number of possible variations of these groups combined with the pyrrole ring, and the sequence in which the four modified pyrroles are arranged to form hemin, were gradually tested. The vinyl group caused particular difficulties, until it was saturated with hydrogen and thus reduced to ethyl. A porphyrin so altered was designated as mesoporphyrin.

After elimination of unlikely arrangements, the final test for the proposed structure of hemin was made by its synthesis from simpler organic materials of which the structure was known.

DESCRIPTION OF THE PRIZE-WINNING WORK*

"The blood pigment hemoglobin is a complex compound which can be split up into its components, dyestuff and protein, by several

---

* Translated from *Les Prix Nobel en 1930*.

methods. Teichmann observed this cleavage first in a microscopic preparation in which a mixture of glacial acetic acid and sodium chloride acted on blood. Schalfejeff, Nencki, Piloty, Willstätter, and others developed this method on a larger scale, so that the Teichmann crystals are now available by the kilograms. The Swedish scientist Mörner had also worked out a method of disaggregation by means of alcoholic sulfuric acid. By this method esters of hemin are formed.

"Hemin has the formula $C_{34}H_{32}O_4N_4FeCl$. Innumerable variations of this atomic combination are possible. The pyrrole-nature of hemin was proved by the methods of analytical degradation developed by Nencki, Küster, Piloty, Willstätter, H. Fischer, and their students. By these methods it was also possible to obtain a far-reaching insight into the constitution of hemin. When hemin is deprived of its iron, porphyrins are formed. These substances have [photochemical] sensibilizing effects, as Hausmann has shown.

"These porphyrins are widely distributed in nature. It was possible to start with the assumption of a relationship with the porphyrins of the blood pigment as a working hypothesis, and it was to be expected that the determination of the constitution of the natural porphyrins would also offer some clues for the constitution of hemin itself; just as the disaggregation products of bilirubin, which had been formed from blood pigment in a biological way, had given evidences for the determination of the constitution of the blood pigment itself. This was the reason why I attacked the investigation of the natural porphyrins in a systematic way, and similarly also the biological degradation of the blood pigment itself.

"In porphyrinuria, a light-disease, man secretes large quantities of porphyrins. It was formerly assumed that only hemato-porphyrin was involved, but this assumption could be refuted. At least two porphyrins are secreted, uroporphyrin and coproporphyrin, which both occur in the urine, although coproporphyrin occurs in greater amounts in the excrements. One of them, probably coproporphyrin, had been observed already by Hammersten. It is not always the same coproporphyrin which is present in the urine. Hijmans van den Bergh observed an isomeric coproporphyrin, but up to now only in one case of porphyrinuria. It may be of interest to note that uroporphyrin occurs also in the flight-feathers of African birds of the Turacus family, in which it is present as a complex copper salt.

"Closely related to uroporphyrin is conchoporphyrin, which is present in mussel shells, probably as a calcium salt. Natural copro-porphyrin is very widely distributed. Traces of it are contained in normal urine and also in yeast. It is possible to force yeast to pro-duce considerable quantities of coproporphyrin by inadequate culture conditions. Yeast is thus brought into a state which is com-parable to human porphyrinuria.

"A porphyrin (ooporphyrin) is also contained in the eggshells of birds breeding in the open. By putrefaction of the blood pig-ment a porphyrin is produced which is identical with this ooporphyrin and was called Kämmerer's porphyrin. By protracted putre-faction deuteroporphyrin is formed.

"Ooporphyrin is identical with protoporphyrin or Kämmerer's porphyrin. When iron is introduced into ooporphyrin by a complex bond, hemin is obtained. When ooporphyrin ester is reduced with hydrogen iodide, mesoporphyrin is formed. In a similar manner it is possible to transform the ooporphyrin ester into tetramethyl-hematoporphyrin and hematoporphyrin. The following diagram may illustrate these transformations, some of which are reversible:

Mesoporphyrin

↑

Tetramethyl- ⇄ Ooporphyrin ester ⇄ Hematoporphyrin
hematoporphyrin   ↑   ↓

Hemin ester"

CONSEQUENCES IN THEORY AND PRACTICE

There is a close relationship between hemin and chlorophyll. Fischer, who showed details of this relationship, proceeded from the synthesis of hemin to that of chlorophyll; the latter work was nearly completed at the time of his death. The way in which the organism synthesizes these substances is still obscure, although

Fischer himself obtained pyrroles from acetic acid and ammonia. The degradation of hemin into bile pigments, into urobilin and coproporphyrin, is better understood in its chemical results since the structure of hemin is known. A recent survey of this research comes to the conclusion that "we have undoubtedly made only a beginning in these studies."

Even the synthesis of the dyestuff in blood, the crowning event of long research, is only a beginning of more intimate studies of the natural compound formed by hemin and the protein-substance globin, itself containing about 136 amino acid residues. In the red blood cell, hemoglobin is again associated with other substances— sugars, fats, cholesterin. The chemical unit hemin is only a small part of the biological unit, hemoglobin.

The knowledge of hemine and bile acid structures was essential in the efforts to elucidate the chemistry of vitamin B_{12}.

1931
CARL BOSCH
(1874–1940)

FRIEDRICH BERGIUS
(1884–1949)

"In recognition of their contributions to the invention and development of chemical high-pressure methods."

BIOGRAPHICAL SKETCH

BOSCH

FROM EARLY YOUTH, CARL BOSCH, A NATIVE OF COLOGNE, GERmany, was interested in things one can do, in materials one can shape by hand. At school he was in advance of his class in mathematics, physics, and chemistry, but he disliked language studies. In preparation for a planned chemical career he spent a year in machine shops and took up mechanical engineering at the Technische Hochschule in Charlottenburg. He was graduated from Leipzig in 1898 under Johannes Wislicenus with a thesis in pure organic chemistry. In 1899 he started on the synthesis of ammonia at the Badische Anilin und-Soda Fabrik. Experienced as a carpenter, mechanic, engineer, and laboratory chemist, he was well equipped to attack the problem of manufacturing an inorganic chemical substance. Studies in the behavior of metals and alloys as materials of construction, in equipment for automatic indication and control of temperatures and pressures, and in the development of safety devices made it possible for Bosch to take Fritz Haber's invention (see p. 73) out of the laboratory into production.

A solid scientific foundation was to Bosch the first requirement for industrial success. He criticized the conditions under which engineering was taught at Charlottenburg and most technological institutes where rule of thumb prevailed and science was neglected. For him the way from pure science to practice did not include speculation or philosophy but steady, systematic search for fundamental facts. His systematic investigation of catalysts included practically all available chemical elements and combinations of them. For this and for research on raw materials, purifications, and utilizations, he organized the Ammonia Laboratory in Oppau, which at times employed 180 academically trained people and more than one thousand helpers. For research on the cooperation of soil, fertilizer, and plant he created a large experiment station (Versuchsanstalt), in 1915, and in addition a "biolaboratory" to explore the function of nitrogen in life.

Germany's advantage, "the only advantage we still have," Bosch stated in 1925, was that its scientists had a broad foundation and that they did not specialize immediately, at the beginning of their education. He took a prominent part in the efforts to help students and to provide fellowships for scientists. When he succeeded Max Planck as director of the Kaiser Wilhelm Gesellschaft his efforts led to the organization of an Institute for Biophysics.

One of Bosch's hobbies was the collection of butterflies. As a leading figure in the German I. G. Farben concern, he was one of the most prominent men in industry; yet he stated (in an interview in 1936) that in the scientific occupation with nature man "feels the great heart-beat of the world, and only here man moves to his own modest place as a minimal part of the cosmos."

BERGIUS

FRIEDRICH BERGIUS WAS BORN IN GOLDSCHMIEDEN (NEAR BRESlau), Germany, where his father had a chemical factory. He received the doctor's degree in 1907 for an investigation of concentrated sulfuric acid as a solvent, carried out at the University of Leipzig. In order to continue work in the field which connects physics and chemistry, he went to Nernst in Berlin. Here and during his short period in Haber's laboratory at Karlsruhe he was impressed with the growing importance of high pressure in chemical reactions. He decided to enter this relatively new field. In Hanover he began, in 1909, to work on the production of calcium superoxide by reacting lime with oxygen under high pressure; at first he worked at the Technische Hochschule, then in his private laboratory. Technical problems of constructing vessels and valves had to be solved. High pressure became for Bergius the method by which to produce commercial chemicals. His interest was not so much in new compounds as in known substances with a potential future. It was the visionary part of his endeavors to foresee this future and to help in bringing it into industrial being.

A method for obtaining hydrogen by reacting water with coal seemed promising. When Bergius' attention was drawn to the future importance of converting heavy oils into motor fuel, he conceived the idea that this should be accomplished by adding hydrogen under pressure. The old method of cracking, in which heavy oils were split into smaller molecules by heat, had the serious disadvantage that methane gas on the one hand and solid coke on the other were formed, with the desired light oil as only a small part in between. The addition of hydrogen remedied this. In 1913 Bergius was ready for a first basic patent application. When the war started, in 1914, he joined the Goldschmidt organization in Essen for the purpose of developing hydrogenation on an industrial scale. Soon the problem of converting wood into sugar to relieve the food situation was added to the program, and in 1916 Willstätter's method of treating cellulose with highly concentrated hydrochloric acid became the basis for a new development.

Work on both processes was far from being completed when the war ended. It was continued in laboratory and pilot plant. The hydrogenation patents were sold to the I. G. Farben interests in 1927. The production of sugar from wood and its further conversions into alcohol, yeast, and dextrose remained Bergius' main project. This work furnished a sizable amount of carbohydrate and food materials in Germany during the last war.

The production of ethylene glycol from ethylene gas and phenol from chlorinated benzene, for which he invented methods, later developed into large-scale operations with which Bergius was no longer directly connected.

Although he remained deeply interested in the chemical and industrial progress of his work, Bergius' foremost activity gradually became the financing of these developments. Motor fuel, alcohol, and foodstuffs have wide economic implications. Bergius saw his great task in securing the right place for the new industrial products against much shortsightedness and selfishness.

At the end of the Second World War Bergius moved to Austria; later, upon invitation by the governments, he went to Spain and then to Argentina. He died in Buenos Aires.

DESCRIPTION OF THE PRIZE-WINNING WORK

BOSCH *

"We started from the apparatus which Haber had used for his experiments. . . . Since this apparatus had several disadvantages, it was completely remodeled; in its new form it has been in use in 24 units uninterruptedly, days and nights, for years. Thus we could carry out the numerous investigations necessary to find the catalysts and to develop highest efficiency. The number of experiments has gradually reached the figure 20,000.

"We constructed an apparatus which comprised circulation pump, ammonia separator, and, the most important and interesting part, a contact tube (of about 30 mm wall thickness).

"The two contact tubes, made by Mannesmann, had an operating life of 80 hours; then they burst. If we had filled them with osmium instead of the new catalyst, the entire world store of this precious metal, which we had by now bought, would have disappeared.

---

* Translated from *Les Prix Nobel en 1931*.

"Chemical investigation showed no trace of nitrogen in the embrittled metal. The explanation came through metallographic research, a method of approach which was, at that time, almost unknown in chemical engineering, but with which I happened to be familiar because I had started my career as a metallurgist.

"Our starting point was that the diffusion of hydrogen into the iron, the decarbonization of the perlite, and the formation of brittle iron-hydrogen were unavoidable. They had to be rendered harmless by a change of construction. The contact-tube wall has two tasks: to withstand the pressure of the highly compressed gas and to form a gas-tight enclosure. How would it be if the two functions were separated and assigned to different elements of construction? This could soon be carried out. The first experimental oven built upon this principle showed that the idea was correct.

"The long sought solution consisted in providing a pressure-bearing steel mantle with a thinner inner lining made from soft iron, so that hydrogen, which alone diffuses through the thinner lining, finds an opportunity to escape without pressure, before it can attack the outer steel mantle at the prevailing high temperature.

"In the beginning we had great trouble with the high-pressure compressors. Up to that time, larger compressors were known only for the compression of air. These high-pressure compressors had been built in only moderate size. Little attention had been paid to the stuffing boxes. With air, leakages were not critical, and short periods of idle time were accepted as unavoidable. The situation was quite different with hydrogen and the delicate contact process. . . . In long years of work we succeeded, starting with experiences with small compressors which ran no more than half a day without disturbances, to build the mighty 3000-horsepower aggregates which run reliably for six months without interruption.

"It is not exaggerated when I say that profitable technical operation depends entirely upon even and undisturbed procedure. A great help in achieving this were the control instruments. We paid great attention to them from the beginning, since the processes in the ovens could be followed only by continuous registration. To-day all this has become commonplace, and most of this equipment

Dimensions of Synthesis Ovens and Steel Weights
for Equal Production:

Year	1913	1914	1915	1924	1927
Oven:					
diameter	300	500	800	800	800 mm
length	8	8	12	12	12 m
Relative weight	27	11	6	3.6	1.8

is commercially available. We had to construct and test it our-selves."

BERGIUS [*]

"As early as 1910 Ludwig Landsberg had suggested to me that I take over the problem of splitting heavy oils and oil residues into gasoline. Experts could conjecture that the progress of automobilism would lead to a substantial increase in the consumption of gasoline, although nobody at that time had as yet developed a real concept of the extent of this development. The then known cracking processes were extremely unaccomplished.

"We tried to incorporate the highly compressed hydrogen in the molecular structure of the high-boiling petroleum fractions loosened by high temperature. Experiments carried out at first in vertical autoclaves showed distinctly an increase in hydrogen in the cracked oils, with no coke formation and a less unsaturated character of the newly formed lighter oils.

"It soon became evident that the range of temperatures within which hydrogen reacted favorably was quite narrow.

"Conditions of temperature and pressure for the hydrogenation of heavy oils are practically the same as for coal, and since in both reactions good contact of the hydrogen with the liquid or suspension to be hydrogenated was necessary, it could well be assumed that an apparatus which was suitable for oil hydrogenation would,

---

[*] Translated from *Les Prix Nobel en 1931.*

with some additional equipment, also be applicable to coal liquefaction. In both processes it was required that solid materials be
introduced into the reaction chambers—in oil hydrogenation a
relatively small quantity of iron oxide for desulfuring, in coal
hydrogenation the entire raw material. It was clear from the beginning that this introduction of solids into a high-pressure vessel and
the removal of solid residues would cause special difficulties. The
work of several years was necessary before a satisfactory solution
for this technical task was found.

"Heating was carried out inside the pressure vessel by installing
in the pressure-carrying tube a second, relatively thin-walled tube.
The heating medium under the pressure of the reaction zone was
pumped through the narrow space between the two tubes.

"The splitting reaction is the better the more rapidly the newly
formed products are removed from the system. Hydrogen was
therefore used in excess. It had to be kept in circulation. Hydrogen
left the reaction vessel with the gaseous and liquid products. It
separated upon cooling from the condensed oils and from the
greater part of the oil-soluble methane and was then returned to
the reaction by a circulating pump.

"Hydrogen consumption was, on an average, 5 percent of the
weight of coal. There was no difficulty in bringing much more
hydrogen to react with the primary products and thus increasing
the yield of low-boiling products at the expense of the high-boiling
oils. Economic considerations will decide about how far to increase
the hydrogen consumption in hydrogenating coal and its liquefied
products.

"From the gaseous products, methane and ethane, hydrogen and
carbon dioxide can be produced in a high-temperature reaction with
water vapor. We have carried out this reaction successfully for
some time. . . . It is sufficient to convert a part of the methane-
ethane mixture in this manner in order to obtain the amount of
hydrogen required for the process. The carbon dioxide admixed
with the hydrogen can be separated easily by water under pressure
after compressing the gases. This principle of hydrogen production is now, as far as I know, used in America for oil hydrogenation.

"The separation of the heavy oils from inorganic substances has presented considerable difficulties. . . . The separation was the less difficult the more completely the product had been subjected to hydrogenation.

"From the heavy fractions of the coal oil it was possible to obtain oils of good lubricating qualities."

CONSEQUENCES IN THEORY AND PRACTICE

The technical development described in the excerpts from Dr. Bosch's Nobel Prize lecture started from the production of ammonia and soon extended to several other chemicals produced in high-pressure reactions. The continued effort resulted in special metal alloys and a new principle of reactor construction, catalysts of specific activities, improvements in gas compressors, a new science of instrumentation for indicators and regulators of important process factors. The progress achieved through continuous research can be characterized by comparative figures for the weight of steel required for a given production of synthetic ammonia. In 1913, this figure was 27; in the two following years it dropped to 11, then 6; in 1924 it was only 3.6, and in 1927 just about half of this value.

On this foundation grew the production of methanol by synthesis from carbon monoxide and hydrogen. Until 1923, wood distillation had been the only source of this alcohol. When the I. G. Farben concern began to manufacture the synthetic alcohol and to export it to the United States, it seemed as though the wood distillation industry were doomed. It survived, but its production in 1946 was just about 3 percent of the synthetic product of the United States. In 1931, Bosch proudly pointed to a German annual production of 40,000 tons; in 1946, the United States produced about 250,000 tons of synthetic methanol by this process.

Of still greater importance is the synthesis of urea from ammonia and carbon dioxide under high pressure. Urea is a convenient form of fertilizer with high nitrogen value, and it is a basic raw material for a synthetic resin which has found extensive application for molding and as a glue.

The work on hydrogenation of oil and coal was carried out in the Bergius organization in the years 1910 to 1925. When the I. G. Farben concern took it over, it expanded particularly the investigation of catalytic effects. A great store of experience from the methanol-synthesis developments was available. The hydrogenation of heavy oils could be speeded up and directed toward special products by the use of selected catalysts. The problem of avoiding the poisoning influence of sulfur, which is always present in mineral oils, was solved. Catalytic hydrogenation became an important method for increasing the efficiency of motor fuels up to the highest "octane numbers."

In a first approximation, Bergius had declared that the dividing line between coals which are easily hydrogenated and those which do not respond readily was characterized by a carbon content of 85 percent in the coal. It has been found since then that carbon content is not a sufficient means for distinguishing between coals; the proportions of hydrogen to oxygen and the age, rank, and type of coal influence its chemical behavior toward hydrogen very greatly.

Hydrogenation methods furnished a considerable part of the motor fuels produced in England and in Germany during the last war. Recently, large-scale experiments have begun in which the pressure and temperature conditions for coal hydrogenation are sought in a considerably higher range than before.

1 9 3 2
IRVING LANGMUIR
(1881-1957)

"For his discoveries and investigations in surface chemistry."

BIOGRAPHICAL SKETCH*

"IRVING LANGMUIR WAS BORN IN BROOKLYN, NEW YORK, January 31, 1881. His early education was obtained in the public schools of Brooklyn which he attended until 1892 when he went with his parents to Paris. There he studied in French schools for three years. Returning to the United States in the fall of 1895, he entered Chestnut Hill Academy at Philadelphia. The following year he returned to Brooklyn for study at Pratt Institute High School. Upon completion of his course at this institute, he entered the School of Mines at Columbia University from which he was graduated in 1903 with the degree of metallurgical engineer. He took up post graduate work at the university of Göttingen under Professor Nernst, being awarded the degree of M.A. and Ph.D. in 1906, his major subject having been physical chemistry.

"Returning to America, Dr. Langmuir became instructor in chemistry at Stevens Institute of Technology, Hoboken, New Jersey, where he taught until July 1909, when he entered the Research Laboratory of the General Electric Company at Schenectady where he is at present associate director.

"Dr. Langmuir's researches have been conducted in the fields of chemistry, physics and engineering, and have largely been the out-

---

* From Autobiography in *Les Prix Nobel en 1932.*

growth of studies of vacuum phenomena. In attempting to derive the atomic and molecular mechanisms of these chemical and physical phenomena, he has been led to make fundamental investigations of the properties of adsorbed films and surfaces and of the nature of electric discharges in high vacuum and in gases at low pressures.

"Dr. Langmuir has published about 150 papers in scientific journals. A list of his contributions in the field of low pressure, chemical reactions and adsorption phenomena is given at the end of his Nobel lecture. Some of his publications in other fields concern: Heat Flow, Tungsten Filaments and Lamps, Rates of Evaporation and Vapor Pressures of Metals, Electric Discharges in High Vacuum, Electric Discharges in Gases, High Vacuum Pumps, Atomic Structure and Valence and some General Matters."

DESCRIPTION OF THE PRIZE-WINNING WORK*

"*Thorium on Tungsten.* When a tungsten filament which is made from tungstic oxide containing about 1 percent of ThO_2 is heated to temperatures of 2,800° or more, a minute fraction of the thoria is reduced to metallic thorium. The thoria exists in the filament in the form of minute spherical particles distributed throughout the tungsten crystals and not at the boundaries of the crystals. If the filament is then heated for a period of a few minutes at 1,900 to 2,000° K, the metallic thorium which has been produced at the higher temperatures diffuses slowly through the crystal grains to the crystal boundaries, then diffuses rapidly along these boundaries to the surface of the filament and then spreads over the surface of the filament by surface migration and forms a monatomic film of adsorbed thorium atoms on the surface of the filament. At 2,000° the rate of evaporation of thorium from the filament is so small that sufficient thorium soon accumulates on the filament to form a nearly complete monatomic film. If the temperature is raised to 2,200 or 2,400°, the rate of evaporation of the thorium from the surface increases so much more rapidly than the rate of arrival

* From *Les Prix Nobel en 1932.*

from the interior by diffusion, that the actual surface concentration decreases greatly.

"These changes in the thorium content of the adsorbed film can be studied by measurements of the electron emission from the filament at a standard low temperature, called the testing temperature, which is chosen so low that neither diffusion to the surface, nor evaporation from the surface, causes appreciable changes in the adsorbed film. A convenient testing temperature is $1,500°$. At this temperature the presence of adsorbed thorium on the surface may increase the electron emission as much as 10^5 fold over that from a pure tungsten surface.

"*Oil Films on Water.* When a pure saturated liquid hydrocarbon is placed upon the water, it remains on the surface as a drop or lens which has no effect on the surface tension of the surrounding water. If, however, an insoluble fatty or oily substance, such as the common vegetable and animal oils, is placed upon clean water, it spreads out almost instantly as a thin film over the surface. If the motions of the surface are made visible by dusting the surface with powdered talc, it may be seen that, with a limited amount of oil, the film only spreads out sufficiently to cover a definite area, or at least if the area exceeds a rather definite value, the oil has no effect on the surface tension of the water. A comparison of various insoluble organic substances has proved that the spreading tendency depends upon the presence of certain active groups or radicals in the organic molecule, these being the groups which tend to increase the solubility of organic substances in water. For example, pentane, C_5H_{12}, is practically insoluble in water but amyl alcohol, $C_5H_{11}OH$, is relatively soluble. Thus the OH groups in organic molecules exert strong attractive forces on the OH groups in the water molecules and these manifest themselves by an increase in solubility. Similarly the carboxyl group COOH tends to make the lower fatty acids much more soluble in water than the corresponding hydrocarbons.

"Hydrocarbons with high molecular weight such as $C_{18}H_{38}$ are extremely insoluble in water. If the carboxyl group replaces the CH_3 group at the end of the chain $C_{18}H_{38}$, one end of the molecule only tends to dissolve in water, whereas the rest of the molecule still retains the insolubility of the hydrocarbons. By spreading over the surface of the water, molecules of this kind can bring their carboxyl group in contact with the water without separating from one another.

"An oil film formed in this way must consist of a single layer of molecules packed closely on the surface layer of the water. If there is a surplus of the fatty acid, as compared with the limited area over which it can spread, the endeavor of the carboxyl groups to come in contact with water causes the molecules to become so crowded at the surface that they stand nearly erect, side by side on the surface. The area occupied by each molecule is thus determined by the cross section of the hydrocarbon chain or by that of the head in contact with water, if this happens to be larger than the cross section of the chain. The thickness of the film is then determined by the length of the hydrocarbon chain.

"*Catalytic Action of Surfaces.* A monatomic film of oxygen on tungsten at 1,500° acts as a catalytic poison for nearly all the reactions which would otherwise occur in contact with the tungsten surface. Thus the dissociation of hydrogen into atoms at 1,500° K is stopped by a trace of oxygen, as is also the decomposition of ammonia, methane or cyanogen. The effect of the oxygen is to cover the surface so that the other gas cannot make contact with the tungsten surface.

"Similarly hydrogen and carbon monoxide act as catalytic poisons on platinum surfaces. The rate at which carbon monoxide and oxygen combine in contact with platinum is proportional to the pressure of oxygen and inversely proportional to the pressure of the monoxide. The reaction velocity depends on that fraction of the platinum surface which is not covered by adsorbed molecules of carbon monoxide. The oxygen molecules that can become adsorbed in these vacant spots and so be adsorbed on the platinum surface can thus react with adjacent adsorbed molecules of carbon monoxide."

CONSEQUENCES IN THEORY AND PRACTICE

The surfaces of water, glass, and metals are the seats of peculiar forces. It is as though a substance could not end abruptly and completely with its surface, but had to communicate with the surroundings. Although the forces residing in surfaces are delicate, they are very important. Interactions through surfaces govern our physiological life processes. Actions on surfaces are the bases of great industrial operations. Most of the motor fuels we use are made by chemical conversions which are governed by apparently inert substances with specific surface actions.

Langmuir's research on such actions started with metal wires in electrical lamps. As a result of his work, incandescent lamps last longer and convert more of the electrical energy into light.

Langmuir's investigation of the spreading of water-insoluble substances on water has led to applications for reducing the amount of light reflected from glass surfaces and thus reducing glare.

Recently Langmuir has applied surface research to the formation of water droplets from clouds. By "seeding" clouds with centers of aggregation—dry ice or finely dispersed silver iodide—he has sought artificial induction of rain. The method has been widely, and in part adversely, discussed. Whatever its real possibilities of causing rainfall, we may share with Langmuir the hope that it may develop into a means for modifying and diverting hurricanes.

1 9 3 3

No Award

1934
HAROLD CLAYTON UREY
(1893–   )

"For his discovery of heavy hydrogen."

BIOGRAPHICAL SKETCH

HAROLD C. UREY WAS BORN IN WALKERTON, IND. AFTER graduation from the high school in Waterloo, Ind., he taught three terms in country schools, then entered the University of Montana and received the Bachelor of Science degree in zoology there in 1917. His experience during the war years is best described in his own words from the autobiographical note submitted to the Nobel Prize Committee: "When the United States entered the World War he went to Philadelphia to help in the manufacture of war materials. He regards this experience as most fortunate, for it convinced him that industrial chemistry was not to be his major interest, and definitely directed him toward academic work." He returned to the University of Montana as instructor in chemistry, and then went to the University of California. His interests in physical and mathematical chemistry developed there under the stimulating influence of Gilbert N. Lewis. He found further inspiration for them during the year 1923-1924 with Niels Bohr at the Institute for Theoretical Physics in Copenhagen. Then followed a few years as associate in chemistry at Johns Hopkins, and his appointment as associate professor of chemistry at Columbia University in 1929. He became a full professor at Columbia in 1934.

From Aston's research on isotopes, combined with quantum

theory and thermodynamics, Urey calculated that it should be possible to separate the hydrogen isotope of atomic weight 2 by physical operations. This isotope, which he named deuterium, had twice the weight of the ordinary element, while all the other isotopes differed from their common element only by fractions of their atomic weights. Experiments verified the theoretical predictions. Later Urey extended this work to the separation of a nitrogen isotope of atomic weight 15; common nitrogen has an atomic weight of 14.

Urey had a prominent part in the development of the scientific work underlying the production of the atom bomb during the Second World War. He has since then made fundamental contributions to the use of isotope research in problems of geology, astrophysics and paleontology.

His book "The Planets, Their Origin and Development" was published by the Yale University Press in 1952.

DESCRIPTION OF THE PRIZE-WINNING WORK*

"The determination of the exact atomic weight of H^1 relative to O^{16}, taken as the standard of atomic weights equal to 16 units, and the determination of the chemical atomic weight of the natural mixture of the oxygen isotopes showed, as was first pointed out by Birge and Menzel, that a hydrogen isotope of mass 2 might be present to the extent of 1 part in 4,500 of the light variety. This was the maximum abundance that could be expected, since the presence of any heavier isotope of hydrogen would have meant that all additional isotopes must be less abundant than one part in 4,500. This estimate is based upon a difference of 2 in the fourth decimal place in atomic weights when reduced to the same standard; this is only slightly greater than a reasonable estimate of the probable error of the chemical determinations. More recent determinations of the abundance of O^{18} necessitate a revision of this estimate to 1 : 3,700 instead of 1 : 4,500.

---

* From *Les Prix Nobel en 1934*.

"In order to demonstrate the existence of such a rare isotope, it seemed to be necessary to concentrate it in some way, for no isotope so rare as this had been found by any of the methods known at that time. This was subsequently shown not to be true because of the adoption of a very sensitive method for the detection of this isotope, namely the use of atomic spectra, which can be used in this case because of the relatively large atomic isotope effect to be expected from the theory of Bohr. However, the isotope of hydrogen of atomic weight 2, or deuterium, was concentrated by the distillation of hydrogen in order to facilitate its detection.

"The use of this simple theory gives for the ratios of vapor pressures of hydrogen to hydrogen deuteride and of hydrogen to hydrogen tritide, the values 2.23 and 3.35 respectively. Using these values for the ratios of vapor pressures, simple calculations showed that very effective concentration of deuterium should be secured by the simple distillation of solid hydrogen at the triple point. Of course, it was impossible to be certain that these differences would apply to the liquid state, but it was a reasonable postulate that at least some of the effect would persist into the liquid state.

"Dr. F. G. Brickwedde, of the United States Bureau of Standards, very kindly prepared samples of hydrogen evaporated in accordance with the conditions indicated by the theory outlined above. The best sample was obtained from 4,000 cc. of liquid hydrogen which was evaporated near the triple point until a residue of approximately 1 cc. remained. My research assistant, Dr. G. M. Murphy, and I, in the fall of 1931, investigated the atomic spectrum of this sample and other samples of fractionated hydrogen as well as natural hydrogen, using a 21-ft. concave grating having 15,000 lines to the inch. We found three members of the Balmer series of deuterium even when commercial electrolytic hydrogen was used. The light of these wave-lengths was increased by a factor of four or five times in the samples prepared by Dr. Brickwedde.

"Though the deuterium line is easily dectectable in the natural hydrogen, it would have been very difficult to have definitely established its existence if the more concentrated samples prepared by distillation had not been used, for irregular "ghosts" of a ruled grating might conceivably have accounted for the observed additional lines. Thus, the method of concentration devised for and used in these original researches, was important in proving the existence of this isotope.

"Rittenberg and I have used this theory to show that easily detectable differences in the equilibrium constants of reactions involving hydrogen and deuterium should exist, and subsequent experimental work confirmed these calculations in the case of hydrogen and deuterium with iodine to give hydrogen iodide and deuterium iodide. This confirmation was confidently to be expected, but this seems to have been the first time that an equilibrium constant of a chemical reaction had been calculated before one of the elements involved had been prepared in sufficient quantities to confirm the theory.

"The extensive researches which have been carried out with the use of deuterium in the last two years were made possible in a large part by the discovery by Washburn of the electrolytic method for the separation of hydrogen and deuterium. Other methods could be used at the present time for the separation of these isotopes. The exchange reaction between water and hydrogen could probably be adapted to counter-current scrubbing methods, and could be used effectively for the separation of the hydrogen isotopes as suggested by Farkas."

CONSEQUENCES IN THEORY
AND PRACTICE

Urey announced the discovery of hydrogen having the atomic weight 2 in December 1931. Almost immediately after this confirmation of a theoretical prediction, the industrial production of heavy hydrogen was contemplated. The method to be used was not the fractional distillation near the triple point where hydrogen exists in all three states, solid, liquid, and gas, but followed the late E. W. Washburn's way, electrolysis. When hydrogen gas is made from water by electrolytic decomposition, the gas is rich in the light isotope and the residual water contains a higher proportion of deuterium. The Norwegian hydroelectric plant at Rjukan started to manufacture deuterium and its oxide, "heavy water." The use of heavy water as a means for slowing down neutrons in atomic piles was so important that a daring, and successful, raid was made on the occupied Norwegian plant during the Second World War to remove the store of heavy water from German hands.

New methods for separating deuterium from hydrogen, especially as heavy water, comprise improved heat exchange in fractional distillation, or interchange between water and gaseous hydrogen compounds, e.g. H_2S.

1935
IRÈNE JOLIOT-CURIE
(1897-1956)

FRÉDÉRIC JOLIOT
(1900-1958)

"For their synthesis of new radioactive elements."

BIOGRAPHICAL SKETCH

IRÈNE CURIE, THE DAUGHTER OF PIERRE AND MARIE CURIE, WAS born in Paris on September 12, 1897. As a student of mathematics and physics, she helped in radiologic hospital work during the First World War. She became an assistant to her mother and graduated in 1925 from the Curie Laboratory of the Radium Institute in Paris with a thesis on alpha rays of polonium. In 1936, Irène served for a short time as undersecretary of state for scientific research. From 1947 on she was professor and director of the radium laboratory at the Sorbonne.

FRÉDÉRIC JOLIOT WAS BORN IN PARIS ON MARCH 19, 1900. After receiving his engineer's diploma from the School of Physics and Chemistry of Paris in 1923, he joined the staff of the Radium Institute. They married in 1926. In their collaboration, Irène Joliot-Curie was more concerned with the physical aspects, while Frédéric Joliot was particularly interested in the chemical identification of the radioactive substances. They extended the investigation of artificially radioactive substances to the products of atomic fission and

142

were greatly concerned with the use of atomic forces for peace. Frédéric Joliot combined radiological with biochemical research in the synthesis of hormones and thyroid substances containing radio-actively labeled elements.

Husband and wife held important positions in the French atomic energy commission from 1946 to 1950 and 1951 respectively. To-gether with R. Grégoire, the Joliots published a book on nuclear physics in 1948.

Irène died of leukemia contracted through exposure to radio-active materials during her research work.

DESCRIPTION OF THE PRIZE-WINNING WORK

IRÈNE JOLIOT-CURIE *

In addition to the electro-negative electron which constitutes β-radiation, and the positively charged helium-particles of α-radiation, Rutherford's hypothesis contained a positive hydrogen-particle called proton. James Chadwick discovered a neutral particle of the mass of the hydrogen atom, the neutron. A proton can lose its posi-tive charge by giving off a positive electron and thereby changing into a neutron. (See: Nobel Prize Winners in Physics, year 1935.)

"In studying the transmutations occurring with the emission of neutrons from light elements upon irradiation by alpha particles, we encountered certain difficulties in interpreting the emission of neutrons by fluor, sodium, and aluminum. Aluminum can be trans-formed into a stable atom of silicon by capture of an alpha particle and emission of a proton. If, however, a neutron is emitted, the product of the reaction is not a known atom.

"We then observed that when aluminum or boron is irradiated by alpha rays, not only protons and neutrons but also positive elec-trons are emitted. We thereupon assumed that the neutron and the positive electron were simultaneously emitted instead of a proton; the resulting atom should be the same in both cases.

---

* Translated from *Les Prix Nobel en 1935*.

"It was in the beginning of 1934 that we noticed a fundamental difference between this transformation and all those which had been produced up to that time; all reactions of artificial nuclear chemistry were instantaneous, even explosive. On the contrary, the positive electrons produced by aluminum under the action of a source of alpha rays continue to be emitted for some time after the source is removed. The number of emitted electrons decreases by one half in three minutes.

"This is, therefore, a real radioactivity, indicated by the emission of positive electrons.

"We have shown that a radioactivity can also be communicated to boron or magnesium through bombardment with alpha rays and with emission of positive or negative electrons. These artificial radio-elements behave entirely like natural radio-elements."

FRÉDÉRIC JOLIOT *

"There is no doubt that radium (atomic weight = 226, atomic number = 88) is spontaneously transformed into a radioactive gas, radon, while emitting alpha particles or helions. We can write the corresponding reaction formula with certainty:

$$_{88}^{226}\text{Ra} \longrightarrow \, _{86}^{222}\text{Rn} + \, _{2}^{4}\text{He},$$

because the quantity of the several elements in this reaction can be so great that their chemical and spectroscopical identification can be undertaken successfully.

"When the nucleus of aluminum captures a helion, it should be transformed into silicium in case there is an emission of a proton:

$$_{13}^{27}\text{Al} + \, _{2}^{4}\text{He} \longrightarrow \, _{14}^{30}\text{Si} + \, _{1}^{1}\text{H}.$$

---

* Translated from Les Prix Nobel en 1935.

"The new atom formed is probably silicium, but with the infinitesimal quantity of this element, it cannot be chemically identified. However, when the newly formed atom is radioactive, it can be identified by radiochemical methods. For example, when aluminum, irradiated by alpha rays, sends out neutrons, the transmutation reaction according to the general rules would be:

$$^{27}_{13}Al + {}^{4}_{2}He \longrightarrow {}^{30}_{15}P + {}^{1}_{0}n.$$

"A thin film of aluminum which has been irradiated with alpha rays is attacked and dissolved in a solution of hydrochloric acid. The chemical reaction produces hydrogen which entrains the radioactive element into a thin-walled tube which is inverted over water. This separation shows that a chemical element, different from aluminum, was formed during the irradiation. It furnished an indisputable proof of the achieved transformation; traces of phosphorus would have separated from the aluminum under the same conditions.

"The activated aluminum can also be dissolved in an acidic oxidizing solution. A small quantity of a sodium phosphate and of a zirconium salt is added to this solution; the phosphate of zirconium which precipitates carries the radioactive element with it. In the case of aluminum, these experiments are delicate, since they have to be carried out in about 6 minutes, because the half-life of the newly formed radioactive atoms is less than 5 minutes. Chemical tests of this kind have shown that the radio-element formed in boron under the influence of alpha rays is an isotope of nitrogen.

"We have proposed to name these new radio-elements (isotopes of known elements, but not found naturally) radio-nitrogen, radio-phosphorus, radio-aluminum (in the case of alpha-irradiated magnesium), and to designate them by the symbols RN^{13}, RP^{30}, RAl^{28}.

"Soon after these first findings we suggested that the same phenomenon could occur for kinds of transformations which are produced by the impact of particles other than those of alpha rays, for example, protons, deutrons, neutrons."

CONSEQUENCES IN THEORY
AND PRACTICE

All the usual means we have for influencing the properties of substances—heat, pressure, chemical reaction—do not change radioactivity, which thus seemed to be as immutable as the elements themselves. Now a method was found by which radioactivity could be imparted to an ordinary element. This element becomes radioactive and is converted into the isotope of its neighbor in the system of elements. Since this discovery, over four hundred new isotopes have been described. The method which the Joliots discovered for imparting artificial radioactivity did not remain the only one; cyclotron and nuclear reactor pile furnished radioactive materials in great variety and increased quantities. Originally, the new elements were known only as radiations. Then, sizable quantities of the pure radioactive elements were produced. Since they follow their normal isotope in all its chemical reactions, they could be used as indicators which reveal their presence, even in smallest quantities, by the specific radiation. Radioactive carbon of atomic weight 14, a long-lived radiating substance, oxidized to carbon dioxide, thus served to show the ways in which green leaves convert carbon compounds in assimilation. Radioactive iodine is quickly absorbed in the thyroid. This absorption can be used for medical purposes or for studies of comparative anatomy. Radioactive phosphorus fed to animals in the form of sodium phosphate permits one to follow the chemical metabolism of this substance and its conversion into body substance, or even serves as a means for identifying individual animals by a radioactive mark. Radioactive elements were built into synthetic medicaments and much information about their fate and action in the organism were thus obtained.

These artificially radioactive elements are isotopes of previously known elements. Most recently, such artificial production has been extended to a complete synthesis of elements with higher atomic weights than any known before.(see 1951, pp. 219-231.)

1 9 3 6
PETER J. W. DEBYE
(1884–   )

"For his contributions to the study of molecular structure through his investigations on dipole moments and on the diffraction of X rays and electrons in gases."

BIOGRAPHICAL SKETCH

PETER DEBYE WAS BORN IN MAASTRICHT, HOLLAND. HE AT-tended the high school in his home town and then went across the border, to Aachen, to become an electrical engineer. From there, he traveled to centers of research in theoretical physics, particularly Munich, where he received his doctor's degree in 1910. After one year as professor of theoretical physics in Zurich (1911-1912) he returned to Holland (Utrecht) for two years. Göttingen, with its prominent school of mathematics and theoretical physics, held him for five years. Then followed Zurich (1919-1927), Leipzig, and Berlin, where he was director of the Kaiser Wilhelm Institut for Theoretical Physics from 1935 to 1940. Since 1940 he has been at Cornell University.

In his many important contributions to physics and chemistry Debye seeks to probe the state of atoms and molecules by their response to vibrations. These vibrations may be the large waves of heat or the very short waves of light. An example from the early part of his work is his theory of specific heat. The number of calories needed to raise the unit weight of a substance by one degree

147

in temperature changes with the temperature. Since heat waves are large in comparison with the distance of atoms from each other, he assumes that for this particular property a solid substance can be considered as continuous instead of molecular. This permits him to develop a relationship of specific heat to temperature which becomes particularly simple at very low temperatures, where heat waves are relatively long and atomic heats are proportional to the third power of the absolute temperature.

At the same time, 1912, Debye also investigated substances by electromagnetic waves. These waves reveal molecular structures, and particularly the degree to which positive and negative electrical charges coincide. Where the resultant centers of gravity of these charges are at a distance from each other, the molecule is polar. This is shown by their alignment when they are subjected to a magnetic field. Such a structure can be found in gases, and even in solutions. The atoms in such molecules are restricted in their rotatory movements around each other.

For the state of molecules in solution Arrhenius had given a theory (see p. 12) which was limited to high dilutions. Debye extended the concept of ionization to the solid, crystallized state of matter. For concentrated solutions, the influence of the solvent could now be measured and defined. The closest that ions can approach each other, the mean ionic diameter, is much greater than the distance found in crystallographic measurements. The diameter of ions appears to be enlarged by the association with molecules of the solvent (Debye-Hückel theory, 1923).

The type of information obtainable through irradiation of matter depends upon the size of structural detail in relation to the wave length. Gamma, or Röntgen, rays show the atomic structure of crystals. In Göttingen, Debye and P. Scherrer discovered that it is not necessary to use well-developed crystals to obtain the interferences of gamma rays which indicate the spatial arrangement of the molecules, but that a fine powder can serve as well. In most recent years, Debye derived a method for investigating solutions containing large molecules by means of optical waves. The light is scattered by the molecules, particularly those of high polymers or soap. The degree of light scattering is easily measured and correlated with size, shape, and concentration of the dissolved substances. With the aid of mathematical developments which make use of earlier (1910) theories of Einstein, optical methods can thus serve to measure osmotic pressures or molecular weights.

His book Polare Molekeln (Leipzig, 1928) also appeared in an English translation as "Dipole Moments and Chemical Structure." His "Collected Papers" were published in 1954 (Interscience, New York).

DESCRIPTION OF THE PRIZE-WINNING WORK*

"The atoms of the noble gases are non-polar, in correspondence with the central-symmetrical structure of their electron cloud. Diatomic molecules which consist of equal atoms (N_2, O_2) have, in the same way, been proved to be non-polar. However, as soon as the two atoms are different, a polarity of the molecule appears at once. This polarity is small if the two atoms are close to each other in the periodic table (CO), and becomes great only in molecules such as HCl. The magnitude of the dipole moment, however, does not come near the value which would be proper to a structure consisting of an H-ion and a Cl-ion in the given nuclear distance. In fact the moment is only about $1/6$ of that value, since μ ** was found to be $1.04 \cdot 10^{-18}$. Considering the HCl molecule as formed from two ions which are brought close together, the hydrogen nucleus penetrates the electron sphere of the Cl-ion, whereby $5/6$ of the originally existing moment becomes compensated. A real quantum-theoretical calculation of moments seems rather difficult. In any case up to now the calculation of Kirkwood for the molecules HF, HCl, HBr, and HI is the only one which has led to a result.

"Molecules which consist of three atoms can be divided into two groups: CO_2 and CS_2 are non-polar, but the molecules H_2O, H_2S, SO_2 have a permanent moment. The explanation is that in the first case the arrangement of the atoms in the molecule is linear, whereas in the second case the atoms are situated at the corners of

---

* Translated from Les Prix Nobel en 1936.
** μ is the symbol for the relationship between electric charge, mass and length called "magnetic moment."

a triangle. The moments of inertia, which follow from the analysis of the band spectra, furnish an independent proof of those structures. In a similar manner the observed polarity of the molecules NH_3, PH_3, AsH_3 leads to a structure in which N, P, or As is placed at the point of a three-sided pyramid and the three H-atoms at the corners of its basis.

"From the measurements by R. Sänger (1929) on CH_4, CH_3Cl, CH_2Cl_2, $CHCl_3$, CCl_4 it follows that of the members of this series the first and the last are non-polar, those in between are all polar. This is in nicest accord with the views on carbon valences introduced into organic chemistry by van't Hoff.

"The conviction of the chemists that the structural formula is in fact a representation of the spatial arrangement of the atoms in the molecule which corresponds to nature is apparently completely confirmed by the previous enumeration. Sometimes only one thing is missing, that the representation be according to a scale. We shall, therefore, look for a method to perform measurements of the distances within the molecule. We know since Laue's discovery of crystal-interferences that the wave lengths of X rays are small enough to be adapted to this purpose. If, however, we want to examine free molecules, the difficulty arises that we have to operate with particles which cannot be fixed in a definite orientation in space, like a crystal. Fortunately, however, I was able to demonstrate that every atomic structure that is irradiated with X rays must produce recognizable interferences in its dispersed radiation, even when it changes its orientation in space permanently and uncontrollably. I was led by this consideration when, together with Scherrer, the interferences of crystalline powders and of liquids were discovered. These experiments were the preliminary steps for the first attempt, carried out in 1928, together with Bewilogua and Ehrhardt, to produce interferences by dispersion on CCl_4—vapor.

"It can be proved for the benzene molecule, and most beautifully for hexa-chloro-benzene, that the six-membered ring is planar and that it corresponds to the carbon-ring of graphite and not to that of diamond. This is indicated also by the C-C distance itself, which has the value 1.54 Å in aliphatic compounds, but 1.41 Å in aromatic substances. This distance becomes still smaller in double or even triple bonds."

CONSEQUENCES IN THEORY AND PRACTICE

The concept of electrical polarity in molecules and the measurement of its magnitude gave added accuracy to the pictures which chemists had drawn. Now the actual distances between the atoms in a molecule could be determined. Where doubts existed concerning the relative positions of the atoms, as in cases of complicated isomerisms, the new method often made it possible to reach decisions. Polarity was of practical importance when materials of construction had to have certain electrical properties, particularly when they had to be good insulators. The knowledge of polar moments in synthetic resins and their plasticizers serves to direct selection of existing materials and construction of new materials for use in sonar or radar equipment.

Debye's pioneering work in this field was recognized by the designation of the unit of polar moment (which is of the order of 10^{-18}) as "one Debye."

1937
WALTER NORMAN HAWORTH
(1883–1949)

"For his researches into the constitution of carbo-
hydrates and vitamin C."
(*The award for 1937 was shared with Paul Karrer; see*
below, pp. 161-164)

BIOGRAPHICAL SKETCH

WALTER HAWORTH WAS BORN IN CHORLEY, LANCASHIRE, ENG-
land. He studied at the universities of Manchester and Göttingen,
where Otto Wallach and W. H. Perkin were his teachers. Since
both were prominent in research on essential oils, it is not surprising that Haworth, with a doctor's degree from Göttingen (1910)
and a D.Sc. from Manchester (1911), worked on the chemical
substances found in fir needle oil and pine root oils as a professor
at the University of St. Andrews, Scotland, from 1912 on. He
undertook research in sugar chemistry a few years later and continued it at Armstrong College, Newcastle, in 1920, and at the
University of Birmingham from 1925 on.

The two fields of research were, at least in part, connected by
the common starting material, wood. Organic solvents extract

essential oils, aqueous alkaline solutions extract a complex sugar which had been given the name xylan (from the Greek word for wood) at the time when this was the only sugarlike substance obtained from wood. When boiled with slightly acidified water, xylan is split (hydrolyzed) into xylose, a sugar with five carbons in its molecule, and a small proportion of an isomer, arabinose. Emil Fischer's method of reacting sugars with methanol to attach the methyl group to the aldehyde group or to replace hydrogen by methyl groups was extended by Haworth and his co-workers. Methylated sugar derivatives can be used to characterize the constitution of sugars. One of the results was to demonstrate that the carbon atoms in sugars are linked by oxygen into the form of rings. They contain either five carbons and one oxygen, in which case they are called pyranose, or four carbons and one oxygen, which is a furanose structure, because it underlies the structure of furfural. A perspective representation of these structures, proposed by Haworth, found general acceptance.

The fundamental molecule of xylan contains five carbon atoms; that of starch and cellulose contains six. A relative of these plant-carbohydrates is glycogen, a polymeric carbohydrate occurring in liver. Glucose is the building unit in glycogen, as it is in starch and cellulose. With the experience gained in work on the constitution of these carbohydrates, Haworth and his collaborators approached the problem of vitamin C, or ascorbic acid. This vitamin had been shown by F. Micheel to be related to carbohydrates as a special product of oxidation. It can be derived from a sugar which is similar to fructose, sorbitose. The acids obtained upon its oxidation split off water within their molecule, in a manner first observed with lactic acid and therefore called lactone-formation. In 1934, Haworth and his colleagues found a way to synthesize ascorbic acid. This gave the final proof of its chemical constitution and indicated directions in which technical methods for artificial production of this important vitamin could be found.

During the Second World War, Sir Norman took an active part in chemical problems related to the application of atomic energy.

In 1929, he published a book "The Constitution of Sugars" (Arnold & Co., London).

DESCRIPTION OF THE PRIZE-WINNING
WORK*

"The model of glucose which I introduced in 1925 is represented in skeleton form as being built up of a ring of six atoms, five of these being carbon and one oxygen, together with an additional side-chain carbon atom. This I described as the pyranose form. When this model is clothed with its constituent oxygen and

Skeleton Model of Glucose.   Model of β-Glucose.

hydrogen atoms it then appears as represented in the second picture above where the model of β-glucose is portrayed. If we depart from this atomic representation and sketch a formula for α- and β-glucose it will be best to have this model in mind and represent it by perspective formulæ.

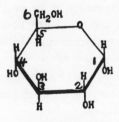

α-Glucopyranose   β-Glucopyranose

---

* From *Les Prix Nobel en 1937*.

"Other normal hexoses have been shown to conform similarly
to this same structural plan. Thus the normal varieties of β-man-
nose, β-galactose, and β-fructose are illustrated below, all of them
being pyranose forms i.e. forms which are based upon the ring
structure present in pyran. Similarly the normal pentoses have
been shown to be pyranose in structure and their formulations are
here given.

"Much less stable forms of pentose and hexose are those which
I have described as the furanose forms. Only the derivatives of
these have been isolated as homogeneous crystalline substances,
e.g. the ethyl- and methylglucosides which are hydrolysed with
something of the order of 100 times the velocity of the normal
methylglucosides. Yet it is in this form that certain sugars occur
in a state of combination in nature, particularly the pentose ara-

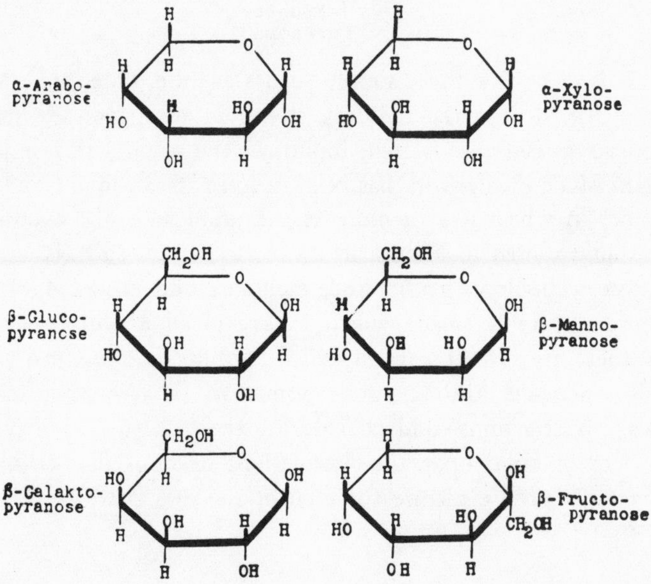

binose and the hexose known as fructose or lævulose. When these
sugars are isolated they revert to the normal or pyranose forms
which have six atom-rings.

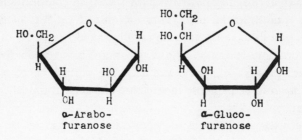

α-Arabo-
furanose

α-Gluco-
furanose

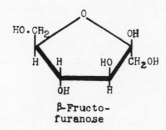

β-Fructo-
furanose

"It is clear that these simple sugars acquire wider significance when regarded as the building stones in such complex natural products as cellulose, starch, inulin, or the wood gum known as xylan. Much of my work has been devoted to an inquiry into the manner in which two or more sugars unite with one another or are found united in Nature in the disaccharides such as sucrose, maltose, cellobiose, gentiobiose, melibiose and others. From the picture of simple sugars which I have given it will be evident that there are several ways in which two glucose units may unite, by loss of water, through the intermediary of a common oxygen atom. Investigations conducted during the past 15 years have enabled us to build upon the speculations of Emil Fischer and to arrive at a precise picture for each of the disaccharides. The expression

$$C_6H_{12}O_6 + C_6H_{12}O_6 = C_{12}H_{22}O_{11} + H_2O$$

merely indicates the union of two hexose residues with loss of water to give a biose. Any of the five hydroxyl positions present in a hexose such as glucose are available as a means of attachment

to a similar glucose residue. Actually those bioses found in Nature
do not exhaust all the possibilities which are available as a means
of assembly of pairs of sugar units.

"If we utilise a method of numbering the carbon atoms of a
pyranose, beginning with the reducing group or potential aldehyde
group in an aldose as No. 1, this will facilitate our reference to
the various structures which apply to the known disaccharides. It
must be remarked that the hydroxyl group attached to No. 1 position is located below the plane of the ring in the α-form and
above the plane of the ring in the β-form and these two formulae

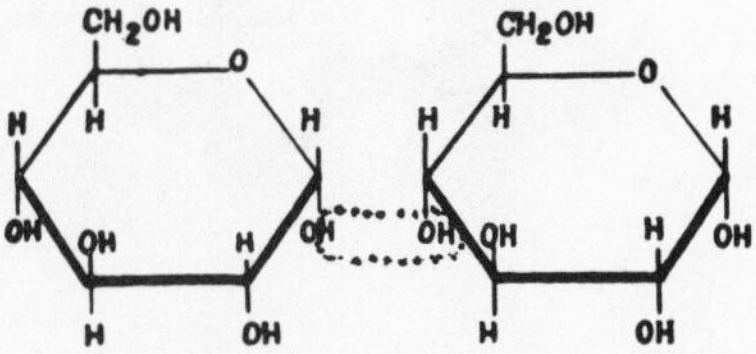

Union of two α-Gluco-
pyranose molecules

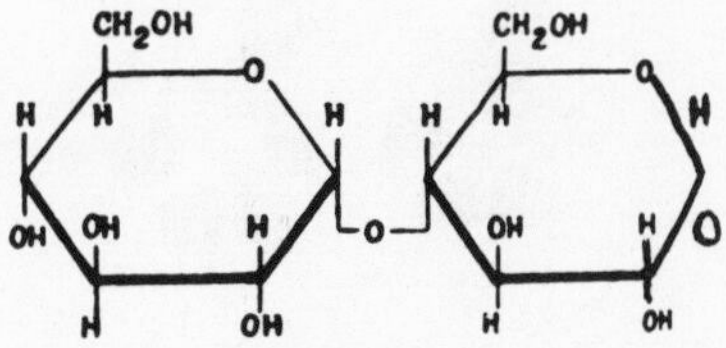

α-Maltose

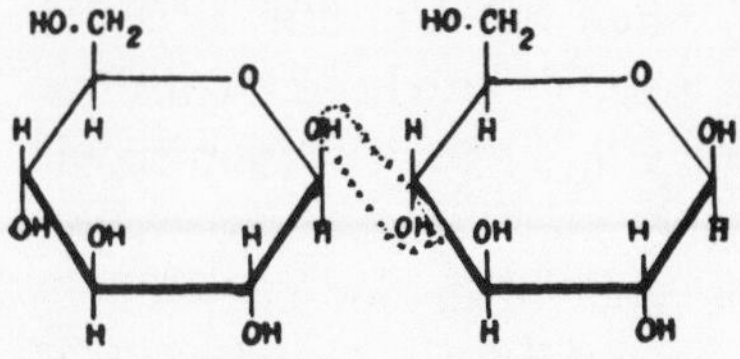

Union of two β-Gluco-
pyranose molecules

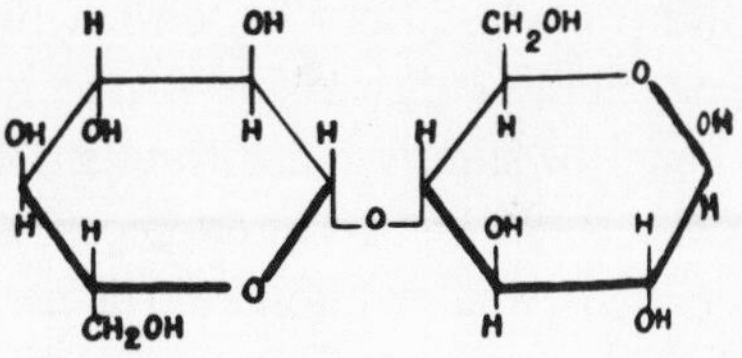

β-Cellobiose

are illustrated above. When we come to consider the mode of
assembly of the pairs of glucose residues which occur in the representative bioses such as maltose and cellobiose, it is found that
a unit of α-glucopyranose is linked with the hydroxyl at the 4th
position of another glucose residue to give maltose, but on the
other hand cellobiose is found to be derived from β-glucopyranose
which is linked to a similar unit at the same 4th position. This is
illustrated in the formulae shown above. In the case of cellobiose
it is seen that the active group at No. 1 position of one glucose
unit is above the plane, and is united to a hydroxyl group below

the plane of the ring in the second residue at position 4. To bring the rings into alignment in the final cellobiose formula shown on the right, one of these rings is now inverted or turned through 180°. Although the units participating in the union of maltose are structurally identical with those assembled in cellobiose yet these products are widely different in kind.

"The difference lies entirely in the spatial arrangement of the left-hand formula indicating the α- or β-form of glucopyranose. This simple distinction furnishes the reason for the different en-

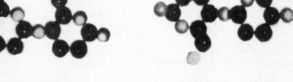

Maltose skeleton.   Cellobiose skeleton.

tities of maltose and cellobiose. This difference is fundamental and provides also a reason for the difference in identity of starch and cellulose. It is found that starch is based entirely on the maltose model inasmuch as maltose is obtained in high yield from starch. On the other hand cellobiose is the representative disaccharide derived from cellulose and it is the mode of linking obtaining in cellobiose which is repeated throughout the whole molecule of cellulose. These constitutional forms are seen more clearly in the atom models which I represent as the skeletons of maltose and cellobiose.

"*The Structure of Carbohydrates and of Vitamin C.*   A question of particular moment is concerned with the length of the chain of repeating units in starch, cellulose and glycogen. For it may now be said that glycogen has the same internal constitution as starch. On the other hand xylan or wood gum is constituted on a similar plan to cellulose except that it is built up of xylose units, largely, in place of glucose. Wisdom dictates that in a problem of this complexity all the available polysaccharides should be studied together as a group. Information which may not be readily available from the study of one polysaccharide may be revealed by the study of another, and it is probable that a conclusion will be reached which is common to all of them. It is a reasonable supposition that Nature in building up polysaccharides follows a common plan. For this reason I have developed what is now known as the end-group assay of methylated polysaccharides as a preliminary to the study of the chain length. Unless these chains are constituted as continuous loops then there must be a terminal group which carries one more non-reducing hydroxyl than any of the intermediate units in the chain, or than the remaining end-group which will terminate with a reducing unit. Our study of xylan has been important from this point of view. In xylan some 17 or 18 β-xylopyranose units are assembled in a chain which is terminated by one unit of arabofuranose. This latter can be easily removed by hydrolysis and there remains only a chain of xylose residues. In 1934 I pointed out that this picture of xylan was probably typical of other polysaccharides in that these chains of limited length aggregated to form a larger entity and the nature of the bonds effecting the union of adjacent chains was discussed. It was suggested that these might be either united by principal valency links or by some other type of bond such as that which is responsible for co-ordination. Whatever this kind of agency or link may be, I prefer to describe it as the polymeric bond and as such it may differ from ordinary valency bonds and may find currency in the whole field of polymeric substances.

"In starch, for example, the individual chains terminate after 26 or 30 α-glucopyranose units and the chains are assembled by the same aggregative force as that just mentioned. It has been found possible to effect the reverse change of disaggregation in the case of starch. This was effected by mild acid treatment of the starch grains followed by acetylation and methylation. Very recently this observation has been confirmed by my former colleague E. L. Hirst who has isolated the methylated form of a single chain of 26 α-glucopyranose units. In the case of glycogen the chains differ from starch in being shorter in length and we have examined specimens of glycogen which contain continuous chains of both 12 and 18 α-glucose units. These chains again are interlinked by the polymeric bond to form a very large molecular complex showing a molecular weight of 1,000,000 or more.

"The same experimental methods have been applied in order to gain an insight into the molecular size of cellulose.

"*Constitution of Ascorbic Acid.*   Ascorbic acid is a monobasic acid, giving well defined salts of the type $C_6H_7O_6M$. It is a powerful reducing agent and its oxidation can be effected in stages, the first of which requires the equivalent of one atomic proportion of oxygen for each molecule of ascorbic acid. When oxidation is arrested at this stage the product can be reduced quantitatively to ascorbic acid by reducing agents such as hydriodic acid or hydrogen sulfide. Ascorbic acid is specially sensitive to oxidation by gaseous oxygen in the presence of minute traces of copper as catalyst, but in these circumstances the reaction proceeds beyond the reversible stage and involves destruction of the molecule.

"An important observation was that, when newly formed, the primary reversible oxidation product from ascorbic acid does not possess acidic properties but behaves in all respects as a lactone, which develops acidity when kept in aqueous solution. It followed that the acidic character of ascorbic acid is due to an enolic hydroxyl group and not to a free carboxyl group and, in order to determine the structure of ascorbic acid, it remained only to discover the nature of the lactone ring in the primary oxidation product. The main features of the constitution of ascorbic acid were now established and its formulation as a lactone of 2-keto-l-gulonic acid, capable of reacting in various tautomeric modifications, was first announced from the University of Birmingham early in 1933.

"A still simpler method for the synthesis of l-ascorbic acid consists, as I have shown by my experiments, in the direct oxidation of l-sorbose, which like d-fructose, is specially sensitive to oxidation at the primary alcoholic group at C_1."

PAUL KARRER
(1889–   )

*"For his researches into the constitution of caroti-
noids, flavins, and vitamins A and B."*

BIOGRAPHICAL SKETCH

PAUL KARRER WAS BORN IN MOSCOW. HIS PARENTS WERE SWISS
and in 1892 moved to Switzerland, where he went to school and
received his doctor's degree in 1911 from the University of Zurich.
He remained there as lecture-assistant to Alfred Werner and began
work on organic arsenic compounds. Paul Ehrlich became interested
in this work and invited Karrer to join him at the Georg Speyer-
Haus in Frankfort. Combining his experience with complex metal
salts as Werner's student with the new research on therapeutic
arsenicals, Karrer developed a silver-salvarsan complex. After six
years in Frankfort, he returned to Zurich and succeeded Werner in
1919. Medicinal chemistry was now replaced by biochemical research on high-molecular carbohydrates, including starch, cellulose,
and lichenin from lichen. Soon tannin, lecithin, and amino acids
from proteins were added to the program.

In 1926, Karrer began to investigate plant pigments, particularly
the yellow ones which are related to the pigment in carrots and are,
therefore, called carotinoids. Carotene itself was separated into
several components of the same chemical composition, but with
different arrangement of the double bonds between carbon atoms
at the end of the long molecules. In the central chain of carbon
atoms of the carotenes, single bonds alternate with double bonds.
Since the presence of double bonds between carbon atoms in a
molecule is indicated by adding the syllable -ene to the name,

carotenes are called polyenes. They are converted into vitamin A in the human body, through a process which Karrer found to consist in a chemical hydration in the middle of the symmetrical molecule. The yellow substance present in milk or yeast, lactoflavin, is chemically different from carotenes and related to vitamin B and to important enzymes.

In 1927, Karrer published his textbook on organic chemistry, which has gone through many editions in several languages. His book on Carotenoids (with Ernst Jucker, 1950) is the standard work in this field.

DESCRIPTION OF THE PRIZE-WINNING WORK*

"The blue and red pigments of blossoms and berries, the anthocyans, were formerly thought to be uniform and characteristic for the several plants. Newer investigations have shown these anthocyans to be mixtures of many closely related substances. There is perhaps not one flower, not one berry, which owes its coloration to one single anthocyan. Similar conditions prevail in another group of natural pigments, the carotenoids. In the well known book of L. S. Palmer on carotenoids which had been published in 1922, only six carotenoids are described which had been crystallized and analyzed (carotene, lycopene, xanthophyll, lutein, fucoxanthin, and rhodoxanthin). In addition also bixin was known at that time. Until four years ago the number of these pigments which can be found in nature had risen to 15; today we know already 40 natural pigments of this group. Their purification was made possible only by the new methods of separation.

"The carotenoids have found attention in recent work not only for their unique structure, but also for their close relation to the vitamins. Some carotenoids are provitamins of vitamin A and are transformed into vitamin A by the animal organism. The investigation of the structural constitution of the vitamins started from carotene. When it was possible, in 1930, to establish the correct

---

* From *Les Prix Nobel en 1937* (translation).

constitutional formula for β-carotene, the structural formula for no other vitamin or provitamin was known as yet. Shortly after that (1931), however, it was also possible to clear up the constitution of vitamin A itself. Thus, insight into the structure of a vitamin was obtained for the first time. We may perhaps remember, that not ten years have passed since the time when some scientists questioned the material specificity of the vitamins, and thought that a special state of matter, a special colloidal nature was the cause for the peculiar vitamin effects which had been observed.

"The vitamin A action is, therefore, extraordinarily specific, it depends upon a very definite structure. Today it is possible to show the atomic arrangements in a poly-ene which are characteristic of vitamin A much more reliably by biological assay with animals, than by any chemical reaction of degradation or measurements by spectral analysis. This high specificity is the more surprising as it is hardly possible to speak of a specificity of constitution with regard to most hormones, e.g. the female sexual hormones and the plant-growth hormones. In the animal organism similar physiological effects are caused by not only closely related chemical substances, but it often occurs that compounds of entirely different constitutions have the same effects as the natural products.

"This strongly pronounced specificity of the constitution of vitamins may be connected with the results of some recent investigations, which revealed that many vitamins are functional groups of ferments; the highly specific properties of ferments have been known for a long time. It was possible to prove this close relationship between ferments and vitamins first for vitamin B_2 or lactoflavin. According to investigations of Warburg and Theorell the phosphoric acid ester of vitamin B_2 is the functional group of the yellow oxidation ferment. Today lactoflavin and any number of other flavins can be synthesized, and thus it was possible for us to investigate to what extent the vitamin-effect is connected with a certain constitution."

CONSEQUENCES IN THEORY
AND PRACTICE

Haworth and Karrer came to vitamin research with a background of work on polymeric carbohydrates. The new information concerning the structure of starch and cellulose was of great help in the technical preparation of modifications and derivatives for use as plastics, fibers, and glues.

It had long been known that citrus fruits and green vegetables prevent and cure scurvy. The factor in these natural products which is anti-scorbutic, an "ascorbic" acid, was now shown to be a definite chemical compound. It could be made in the laboratory, and soon also in the manufacturing plant. When the chemical constitution of indigo had been disclosed, the chemical synthesis of this dyestuff was quickly followed by the production and application of a host of chemically modified indigoes; for vitamins, the biological action is so specific that no changes or modifications of the molecular structure are permitted. This is true of vitamin C, and particularly of vitamin A. The importance of vitamin C in fruits and vegetables caused a great amount of investigation into the stability of this valuable constituent during storage and cooking. Milk and butter won increased attention as sources of vitamin A; its extraction from fish-liver oils developed into a carefully controlled chemical industry.

The sensitivity of vitamin C to oxidation suggested its role in processes of food assimilation. The influence of vitamin A on the functioning of the eye was further elucidated when its relationships to pigments in the retina were found (by G. Wald).

1938
RICHARD KUHN
(1900–   )

"For his work on carotinoids and vitamins."

BIOGRAPHICAL SKETCH

WHEN RICHARD KUHN WAS AWARDED THE NOBEL PRIZE, ITS acceptance was forbidden by the German government. After the war he received the gold medal and diploma of the Prize.

Kuhn was born in Vienna and was one of the youngest graduates of Willstätter's laboratory in Munich. His doctor's thesis (1922) continued Willstätter's work on enzymes. In 1926 he became professor at the Swiss technical high school in Zurich. Three years later he moved to Heidelberg as professor at the University and director of the chemical division of the Kaiser Wilhelm Institut for Medical Research.

Kuhn's textbook on the chemistry, physico-chemistry, and biology of enzymes (1927) was distinguished by the combination of skill in experimental detail with systematic coordination of the new experiences. He followed Willstätter's example in combining studies of enzymes with investigations of plant pigments. A deep connection between color and enzymic activity had been discovered by Otto Warburg (see "Nobel Prize Winners in Physiology and Medicine," 1931), and Kuhn tried to penetrate into its chemical and biological meaning. The way began with systematic organic chemistry. For a long time, chemists were fascinated by the six-carbon ring structure of benzene. Willstätter diverted this fascination by showing that a derivative of the alkaloid pelletierine (from pomegranates) had as its basis a ring formed from eight carbon atoms. The bond between these carbon atoms was alternately single and double, a sequence of conjugated bonds. Kuhn constructed substances with an open chain of such conjugated carbon atoms, called polyenes. He and his associates synthesized members of the group of diphenyl-polyenes

$$C_6H_5(CH = CH)_nC_6H_5$$

up to $n = 15$. They were interesting for the system of organic chemistry, and much more so because long chains of conjugated carbons occur in many plant pigments—in carotenes from carrots, in lycopene from tomatoes, in crocetins from crocus. Kuhn and Karrer (see pp. 161-164) were lively competitors in elucidating the intimate chemical structure of these pigments which have pronounced biological activity and, in part, are related to vitamins. The chemical constitution of lactoflavin, also called riboflavin and vitamin B_2, was confirmed by synthesis along different ways in the laboratories of Kuhn and Karrer in the same year, 1935. Alloxan, this close relative of barbituric acid, known from Adolf von Baeyer's work, was used in this synthesis.

For crocetin in particular, Kuhn showed highly specific influences on the sexual ripening of spores (gametes) of certain lower plants. With fine technique and clear reasoning, complex chemical structures were determined on milligrams of substance. Nature uses many different kinds of chemical structures for specific biological actions. Sea urchins, for example, secrete a sex hormone which is a naphthalene derivative (hydroxylated naphtho-quinone). Yeast contains enzymes and vitamins. One of the vitamins, ascribed to the vitamin B group, acts against a skin disease; it was therefore called adermin. It has other names too: vitamin B_6 and pyridoxin. This latter name indicates its chemical composition; it is an oxygen-containing derivative of pyridine. In the year of the Nobel Prize award, Kuhn gave the complete chemical formula of this vitamin, of which one-hundredth of a milligram in the daily diet of a rat is able to heal its dermatitis.

In their natural habitat, enzymes, pigments, and vitamins are combined with sugars, fats, and particularly with proteins. Willstätter called such loose chemical combinations symplexes, because they are comparable to symbioses of several different kinds of organisms living together. Kuhn found a practical method for dissolving symplexes from plants in the use of invert-soaps, so called because the role of organic acid with inorganic base of ordinary soap is inverted to inorganic acid with organic base. Some of these invert-soaps are old, but they have only recently found applications in the medical field.

One of these invert soaps, derived from tetrazol

is strongly bactericidal, even in concentrations of only 1 to 600,000.

The synthesis of adermin (vitamin B_6) was achieved in 1939.

1 9 3 9
ADOLF BUTENANDT
(1903–   )

"For his work on sex hormones."
(*The award for 1939 was shared with Leopold Ruzicka;
see above, pp. 171-174*)

BIOGRAPHICAL SKETCH

ADOLF BUTENANDT WAS BORN IN WESERMÜNDE, GERMANY. HE
studied chemistry in Göttingen, under Windaus, and was graduated in 1927; he became director of the organic and biochemical
laboratory three years later. His meteoric career resembles that of
Richard Kuhn, with whom he shared the fate of not being permitted to accept the Nobel Prize.

The year 1929 is remarkable in the history of biochemistry, because the hormone which determines the sexual development of
females was obtained in pure and crystallized form by Doisy in
this country and, independently, by Butenandt in Germany. This
substance, first called folliculin to indicate its source, the follicle,
or estrone, the substance preparing the organism for the pregnancy
cycles, can be distilled at high vacuum. It has a definite melting
point of 256° C, and 0.025 millionth of a gram is sufficient to
produce uterus developments in the castrated mouse.

This hormone was found in the urine of pregnant women. It
was logical to search for male sex hormones in the urine of males.
C. Funk in London showed the presence of such a hormone and
initiated methods for its isolation. When this material is fed to

capons, the comb begins to grow. A unit of hormonal activity can be defined by the rate of growth per weight of substance used. In a purified, neutral oil from male urine, the hormone is enriched to the extent that about 20 milligrams provide one hormonal unit. Butenandt removed more of the accompanying material by extractions with acids and alkalies, by transferring it from one selective solvent to the other. The activity of 20 mg was thus obtained in only 0.3 mg. This product must still be quite impure, compared with the activity found for the pure female hormone. Methods of adsorption or extraction failed to remove any of the suspected impurities; but when hydroxyl-amine was added, this common reagent which combines with ketone ($C=O$) groups, a small fraction of the material crystallized out. The carefully separated crystals gave a threefold increase in activity. When the amine group was split off again and the residue subjected to sublimation in a vacuum, a crystallized substance was obtained, of which one millionth of a gram, applied in ten portions over five days, had a definite hormone effect. In 1931, Butenandt reported that 15 milligrams of this substance had been prepared; they represented the active substance contained in about 7000 gallons of urine.

Butenandt continued this work in Danzig, in 1933, and as director of the Kaiser Wilhelm Institut for Biochemistry in Berlin-Dahlem, from 1936 on. He found the relationship to the basic carbon skeleton of cholic acid and cholesterol simultaneously with Merrian (London, 1930), and discovered a number of different derivatives having specific activities in animals and plant seeds. In one of these hormones, a ketone group is situated at carbon number 3, and a hydroxyl group at carbon number 17. If in this compound carbons 4 and 5 are connected by a double bond, it acts as a strong male hormone; if the double bond is translocated to extend between carbons 1 and 2, the hormone has strong estrogenic effects. This was one of the most surprising and important results of this work.

This interesting discovery contains the implicit warning that great care must be exercised in the medical use of hormone concentrates. At the same time, the relationships in chemical structure of sex hormones and cancer-producing substances is not only of scientific interest. In an extended test in which about 3000 mice were used, Butenandt searched for possible carcinogenic properties of hormones obtained from follicles; for these particular hormones at least, he found no indications of such effects.

Since 1945, Butenandt has combined the direction of the institute (now the Max Planck Institut) in Tübingen with a professorship of physiological chemistry at the University there.

Now at the Max Planck Institut für Biochemie, München, his work is concentrated in the chemical actions in genetics. Thus, he has delineated the path genes direct the chemical reactions, which lead from typtophan to the ommatins, the pigments of insect eyes.

CONSEQUENCES IN THEORY AND PRACTICE

When we draw general conclusions from experimental results we have to be alert for exceptions and limitations; they lead, often enough, to new and surprising general rules. The chemistry of the higher terpenes offers many such examples. Older generalizations concerning the way in which carbon atoms form ring structures had to yield to new rules when Ruzicka found that as many as 17 carbon atoms could be involved. On the other hand, we have to use our generalizations to their largest extent so as to make them more definite by finding their limitations. The "isoprene rule" will remain a valuable guide even when its field is restricted by other rules.

Generalizations are particularly difficult in the field of biologically and medically active chemicals. An apparently slight change in the composition or in the relative position of the atoms in the molecule of such a substance may cause a decided change in its actions on organisms. Such relatively small changes in the molecular structure cause cholesterol to influence the development of organs which are connected with sexual ripening of the organism. With knowledge of the intimate chemical structure of sex hormones it has become possible to manufacture synthetic products of great therapeutic value. A close relative of these hormones proved to cure arthritis. The synthetic production of this substance, cortisone, reduced its price from $200 to about $35 per gram and proved necessary in order to supply the increased demands.

1939
LEOPOLD RUZICKA
(1887–   )

"For his work on polymethylenes and higher terpenes."
(*The award for 1939 was shared with Adolf Butenandt; see below, pp. 168-170*)

BIOGRAPHICAL SKETCH

LEOPOLD RUZICKA WAS BORN IN VUKOVAR, YUGOSLAVIA. HE started his academic career in Zurich, in 1918. In 1926 he became professor at the University of Utrecht, Holland, and three years later returned to the Technische Hochschule in Zurich. His research on essential oils led him to recognize the presence of a group of "higher" terpenes. Otto Wallach (see pp. 41-44) had found that terpenes are related to a substance which was obtained on distilling natural rubber. Its chemical formula is C_5H_8; its molecule is formed from four carbon atoms connected by alternating (conjugated) double bonds, with a methyl group attached to the second of these carbon atoms. Terpenes have the general formula $C_{10}H_{16}$, and Wallach considered the C_5H_8 substance, called isoprene, as a half- or hemi-terpene. More than two isoprene units combine to form the higher terpenes. Ruzicka detected the isoprene unit in many non-terpene natural substances, and he derived therefrom his isoprene rule. This is a great help in understanding the molecular structure of carotinoids.

Nature does not use isoprenes to build fatty acids, which have a long chain of carbon atoms without any side chains. The structure of some natural oils of strongly pronounced scent appeared as a ring-closing of fatty acid chains, in which the acidic carboxyl group

171

COOH of the fatty acid was converted into a $C = O$ group, the ketone group.

Civet is an important material in perfumery. Ruzicka found an exceptionally large ring of 17 carbon atoms in one of the basic substances of this material. Later on he investigated ambergris, a pathological product from the digestive tract of the sperm whale, and established its relationship with the substance which gives violets their delicate odor.

The 6-carbon rings in terpenes contain more hydrogen than the comparable ring in benzene. One of the methods which Ruzicka used in his research on terpenes consisted in eliminating sufficient hydrogen, by dehydrogenation, to convert the hydro-aromatic substances into benzenelike, aromatic products which were then more readily connected with known substances.

Ruzicka is continuing this work in several directions at the Technische Hochschule in Zurich.

DESCRIPTION OF THE PRIZE-WINNING WORK*

"The fundamental experiments were carried out with civetone. I had to struggle less with the intricacies of this substance than with the general and personally shared prejudice against the possible existence of a 17-membered ring.

"After it had been found that the hydrogenation product dihydro-civetone, as well as the hydrocarbon obtained from civetone in the Wolff-Kirschner reaction, form the same dicarboxylic acid $C_{17}H_{32}O_4$, the completely symmetric formula for civetone had to be considered. The formulation of the dicarboxylic acid $C_{17}H_{32}O_4$ as hepta-decane-di-acid could be definitely proved by a comparison with the synthetic acid.

"Civetone and muscone seemed to contradict, as compounds of nature and in the system of organic chemistry, the old experience 'nature does not jump' ('Natura non fecit saltus'). Deliberations about the probable mechanism of the biochemical origin of the two

---

* Translated from *Les Prix Nobel en 1939*.

ketones lead to a plausible explanation of their peculiar structure.

$$HC{=}CH$$
$$(CH_2)_7 \quad (CH_2)_7$$
$$CO$$

Civetone

Civetone might be formed by an ω-oxidation of oleinic acid and subsequent cyclization of the unsaturated dicarboxylic acid in the organism of the civet cat. Muscone might similarly be a product of fat metabolism.

$$CH{-}(CH_2)_7{-}CH_3 \qquad\qquad CH{-}(CH_2)_7{-}COOH$$
$$CH{-}(CH_2)_7{-}COOH \qquad\qquad CH{-}(CH_2)_7{-}COOH$$

Oleic acid Unsaturated dicarboxylic acid

"The ring-homologous series of the cyclic ketones is a characteristic example of the relationship between physiological properties and details of molecular structure. While 5- to 8-membered ring ketones have the well-known odor of mixed bitter almond, caraway, and peppermint, the 10- to 12-membered ring ketones show typical camphor odor. The ketones with 14- to 18-membered rings represent musk odor.

"Since 1920 we have investigated, on a broad basis, sesquiterpenes, diterpenes, and later on also triterpenes, compounds which can be grouped together as "higher terpenes" or "polyterpenes." The persistent application of a simple working hypothesis and of an expedient working method revealed aspects of the structure of the carbon skeleton which soon led to a system of the higher terpene compounds. The working hypothesis of that time, which is now known as the isoprene rule, was founded on the assumption that the carbon skeleton of the higher terpenes is erected out of isoprene parts.

"The great number of higher terpene compounds in nature and their usually very complicated structure indicated that the usual methods of systematic structural analysis would not afford a general evaluation of the isoprene rule in a desirably short period of time. It appeared to us that the method of dehydrogenation should give results more rapidly.

"In summary, it may be emphasized that the selected method proved to be fruitful and that the results obtained by it corresponded to expectations.

Phytol   Vitamin A

"These are the formulae for two important natural compounds: phytol, which is the alcoholic constituent of chlorophyll, and vitamin A. It would have been extremely difficult to explain the constitution of these compounds, of which only small quantities were available, if the way had not been shown by the isoprene rule. In both cases, it was necessary only to control and confirm the formula derived according to the isoprene rule by synthesis either of the natural product itself (for phytol) or of its perhydro-derivative (for vitamin A).

"The over-all formula of androsterone had not been established definitely by analysis, but if our assumption concerning the connection of the sex hormones with cholesterol were correct, androsterone should have the formula $C_{19}H_{30}O_2$. There were four different stereometrically isomeric saturated sterines which might be used for the artificial production of androsterone. On oxidizing the acetates of the four isomers, we were able, in 1933/4, actually to obtain the acetates of the expected four isomeric oxy-ketones $C_{19}H_{32}O_2$, of which the one obtained from epi-dihydrocholesterol was identical with androsterone.

"This was not only the first artificial production but also the first complete proof of the constitution of a sex hormone, and it also was the first stringent demonstration of the connection of a sex hormone with a sterol which includes the finest steric details."

1 9 4 0 – 1 9 4 1 – 1 9 4 2

No Award

1943
GEORGE DE HEVESY
(1885–   )

"For his work on the use of isotopes as tracer elements in researches on chemical processes."

BIOGRAPHICAL SKETCH

HEVESY WENT TO SCHOOL IN HIS NATIVE BUDAPEST AND CONtinued his studies in Germany and England. From Freiburg im Breisgau, where he received his doctor's degree in 1908, he went to Haber in Karlsruhe and then to Rutherford in Manchester. Rutherford gave him the problem of separating radioactive radium D from the inactive radium G and lead. The attempt to solve this problem became decisive for Hevesy's life work. After he had shown that the separation by all available chemical means was impossible, he turned the failure into success by using just this property of radium D as a means for indicating the presence of lead and measuring its amount through the radioactivity imparted to the ordinary lead by the radioactive isotope. He developed the method in cooperation with F. Paneth at the Vienna Institute of Radium Research, in 1913.

Hevesy returned to Budapest and became professor there in 1918, but he did not stay long. Upon invitation by Niels Bohr, he spent a few years at the Institute of Theoretical Physics in Copenhagen. The investigation of zirconium minerals by Röntgen rays led Hevesy and Coster to the discovery of a new element, called hafnium, in 1922. At this time, he also attempted to separate isotopes by a physical method. It was based on the premise that the vapor phase over a mixed element should contain more of the lighter isotope, provided it is rapidly removed from the equilibrium with the mixed element. In delicate experiments with mercury and chlorine (in the form of hydrochloric acid) the more volatile fraction really showed an atomic weight which was smaller by less than 0.1 percent than the atomic weight of the residue.

Once more in Freiburg, in 1926, Hevesy studied the relative abundance of the chemical elements on the earth and in the cosmos. The calculations were based on chemical analysis by means of X-ray fluorescent radiation.

In 1934, the production of a radio-phosphorus of atomic weight 32, instead of the normal 31, gave Hevesy a powerful tool for unlocking the secrets of chemical reactions which have importance for life processes. From inorganic chemistry, through physics, Hevesy thus turned to organic chemistry.

Since 1943, Hevesy has been professor at the Institute of Organic Chemistry at the University of Stockholm.

Hevesy described the new techniques and experiences in "Radioactive Indicators, Their Application in Biochemistry, Animal Physiology, and Pathology," (Interscience, New York, 1948). In 1959, he received the Atoms for Peace Award.

DESCRIPTION OF THE PRIZE-WINNING WORK*

"Suppose that we dissolve 1 g. of lead in the form of nitrate in water, add radium D of negligible weight showing a radioactivity of one million relative units (an electroscope being used to measure the activity) and proceed to carry out the most intricate operations with this 'labelled' lead. If we then ascertain the presence of one radioactive unit in a fraction obtained in the course of these operations, we must conclude that 1/1000th mg. of the lead atoms present in the lead nitrate we started from are now present in the fraction.

---

* From *Les Prix Nobel en 1940-1944.*

"The first application of labelled lead was the determination of the solubility of some very slightly soluble lead compounds such as lead chromate. In these experiments, not radium D but another isotope of lead, thorium B, was applied as an indicator. Labelled lead chromate was obtained by adding a solution of 100,000 relative units of thorium B to lead nitrate containing 10 mg. of lead and converting the nitrate thus labelled into chromate. After the saturated solution of this compound had been held at the desired temperature in a thermostat for a sufficient time, its composition was ascertained by evaporating a few cubic centimeters to dryness and measuring the activity of the almost invisible residue in the electroscope. From the number of units of thorium B found, the amount of lead was calculated, one unit corresponding to 10^{-6} grams of lead; finally, the solubility of the lead chromate in moles per liter (2.10^{-7}) was computed.

"We prepared the radioactive phosphorus isotope by neutron bombardment of carbon disulphide and used this isotope in collaboration with Chiewitz in the study of phosphorus metabolism. In these experiments, 10 liters of carbon disulphide were used to absorb most of the neutrons emitted by a mixture of radium and beryllium kindly put at our disposal by professor Niels Bohr. The ^{32}P formed was extracted by treatment with dilute nitric acid or with water, the carbon disulphide being immediately available after the extraction for further neutron bombardment.

"The path taken by organically bound phosphate radicals in glycolytic processes was investigated by using labelled compounds prepared under the action of enzymes present in muscle juice or yeast. When labelled adenyl phosphate was added to fresh muscle pulp in which glycolysis occurred, no formation of active inorganic phosphate was found to take place, but active phosphate was detected in the Harden-Young ester formed during alcoholic fermentation.

"In a study of the interaction of labelled adenosine triphosphoric acid with non-labelled hexose monophosphoric acid ester, which leads to the formation of fructose-1,6-diphosphoric acid ester, the labelled phosphate given off by the adenosine triphosphoric acid was found to be exclusively present in the fructose-1,6-diphosphoric ester. . . . the free phosphate originated exclusively from the hexose-6-monophosphoric ester: adenosine triphosphoric acid + hexose-6-monophosphoric ester + H_2O → fructose-1,6-diphosphoric ester + adenylic acid + (free) phosphate.

"The most remarkable result obtained in the study of the application of isotopic indicators is perhaps the discovery of the dynamic state of the body constituents. The molecules building up the plant or animal organism are incessantly renewed. In the course of this renewal, not only the atoms and molecules taken up with the food participate, but atoms and molecules located in one organ or in one type of molecule will soon be found in another organ or in another type of molecule present in the same or in another organ. A phosphate radical taken up with the food may first participate in the phosphorylation of glucose in the intestinal mucose, soon afterwards pass into the circulation as free phosphate, enter a red corpuscle, become incorporated with an adenosine triphosphoric acid molecule, participate in a glycolytic process going on in the corpuscle, return to circulation, penetrate into the liver cells, participate in the formation of a phosphatide molecule, after a short interval enter the circulation in this form, penetrate into the spleen, and leave this organ after some time as a constituent of a lymphocyte. We may meet the phosphate radical again as a constituent of the plasma, from which it may find its way into the skeleton. Being incorporated in the uppermost molecular layer of the skeleton, it will have a good chance of being replaced by other phosphate radicals of the plasma or the lymph, but it may also have the good fortune to find a more or less lasting abode in the skeleton. This will be the case when it becomes embedded in a newly formed apatite-like bone crystallite."

CONSEQUENCES IN THEORY AND PRACTICE

By attaching a radioactive label to an element, we actually fasten onto that element a new physical property and one which can easily be measured. This makes it possible to determine quantities of the order of a millionth of a gram without preparing them in pure, isolated form. That the determination of such small quantities may have practical meaning can be realized when we consider that one billionth (10^{-9}) of a gram represents 600,000 billion atoms of an element such as chlorine. It has been found that some elements exert important biological actions on plant growth and ripening, or on the health of animals, when they are present in small traces.

Hevesy's method has served to give a direct proof of the theory which Arrhenius developed for the ionic state of substances in solution (cf. p. 12). It has advanced our knowledge of the assimilation of carbon dioxide and water by green plants. The fixation of iodine by the thyroid has been accurately measured by using radioactive iodine. The fate of foods, medicines, and poisons has become clearer through radioactive tracer techniques. When thin sections of tissue from glands, muscle, or bone are placed on photographic film, the development of two million β-particles per square centimeter of film can be detected.

When A. Butenandt and R. Beckmann studied the biological formation of eye pigments (ommachromes) from typtophan, they injected about 0.1 mg. of this substance marked with the radioactive ^{14}C isotope into the butterfly Vanessa; the pigment contained the radioactivity.

Information obtained by means of radioactive phosphorus has considerably helped in developing improved methods for applying phosphate fertilizers.

Since isotopes of carbon, phosphorus, iodine, and other elements are now available in convenient quantities produced by cyclotrons or uranium piles, the medical use of these substances grows in importance. "Cobalt 60" is the most recent addition to these isotopes of high medical activity and radiation.

According to a report of July, 1961, the shipments of radioactive isotopes from the Oak Ridge National Laboratory since 1946 numbered 150,000.

1944
OTTO HAHN
(1879–)

"For his discovery of the fission of heavy nuclei."

BIOGRAPHICAL SKETCH

OTTO HAHN WAS BORN IN FRANKFORT ON THE MAIN, GERmany. He studied chemistry in Munich and Marburg and in 1901 received the doctor's degree for a thesis in organic chemistry. After a few years of assistantship at Marburg, he spent a year in Sir William Ramsay's laboratory in London. His investigation of the radioactive decomposition of thorium resulted in the discovery of radio-thorium as one of the new elements of the thorium series, to which he later (1907) added a meso-thorium as a predecessor. The year before, he discovered radio-actinium during work in Rutherford's laboratory in Montreal. The mysteries of actinium, this radioactive element which is chemically similar to one of the rare-earth elements, lanthanum, attracted him again after he returned to scientific research from the war in 1918. Together with Lise Meitner, he found in a new element, prot-actinium, the mother-substance of the complex actinium series.

This research was carried out at the Kaiser Wilhelm Institut for Chemistry in Berlin-Dahlem, of which Hahn became a director in 1928. In all radioactive transformations, even in those which were artificially induced by bombardment with neutrons, the products were either isotopes or close neighbors of the originating elements. On January 6, 1939, there appeared Hahn's first publication of "experiments which contradict all previous results of nuclear physics." The nucleus of uranium was split into two parts, into two elements which were far removed, in the system of elements, from uranium. He soon found that this was not a clean break and that a host of debris in the form of other elements arose from the fission of the heavy nucleus.

Hahn was able to continue scientific work during the war years in Germany. In April 1946 he became president of the Kaiser Wilhelm Gesellschaft of the Western zones—the highest position in German science.

DESCRIPTION OF THE PRIZE-WINNING WORK*

"As the result of several years of work we (Hahn, Meitner and Strassmann) produced in 1935-1938 a considerable number of artificially radioactive kinds of atoms which seemed to originate directly or indirectly from the supposed short-lived artificial uranium isotopes by β-radiation and which would thus have to represent trans-uraniums—elements beyond uranium. . . .

"Curie and Savitch (1937 and 1938), independently from these trans-uranium investigations by Hahn, Meitner, and Strassmann, described a so-called 3.5-hour substance which they also had obtained by irradiating uranium with neutrons and of which the chemical properties were not easy to determine.

"Since this 3.5-hour substance was considered a trans-uranium I tried to reproduce it, in collaboration with Strassmann. Upon closer examination we arrived at remarkable results which we formulated about as follows: 'In addition to the trans-uraniums described by Hahn, Meitner, and Strassmann, there are produced, by two successive α-radiations, three artificially active β-radiating radium-isotopes of different half-lives which then go over into artificially active β-radiating actinium-isotopes.'

"However, the production of radium under the described irradiation conditions was very strange. Never had transformations with α-radiation been observed when neutrons of low energy had been

---

* Translated from *Les Prix Nobel en 1940-1944*.

used, whereas here again, as with the 'trans-uraniums,' several isotopes appeared at the same time!

"Experiments were carried out in different directions. Since the products radiated only weakly and the β-rays of the most stable of the new isotopes were strongly absorbed . . . , we tried to separate the artificial 'radium' as much as possible from the barium which had been added as a carrier.

"The attempts to separate our new artificial 'radium-isotopes' from barium failed completely.

"We mixed pure natural radium-isotopes with our artificial 'radium-isotopes' from which transformation products had been removed, and fractionated by the same method as before. The result was that the natural radium-isotopes could be separated from barium, but not the artificial ones.

"We checked these results in other directions. . . . Thus we again found that the alkaline-earth-isotope which we had mistaken for radium actually was an artificially active barium.

"The process, therefore, consists in a fission of the nucleus of uranium which has the nuclear charge 92, into two medium-heavy nuclei. If one of them is barium, which has the atomic number 56, then krypton, of the atomic number 36, must be generated at the same time. The two atomic numbers add up to 92. Both nuclei, as becomes obvious on comparing the mass of uranium with those of the natural stable isotopes of barium and krypton, have too great a mass—in other words, an excess of neutrons; they will therefore emit β-rays and form stable elements of higher atomic numbers.

"Mr. Strassmann and I also considered (in our communication of February 10, 1939) the possibility that neutrons might also be liberated in the fission process. F. Joliot was the first to find that this actually occurs.

"During the war we continued, at the Kaiser Wilhelm Institut für Chemie, the systematic search for chemical disentanglement of the rather complicated fission reactions, and new reactions were discovered. Japanese workers found that with rapid neutrons uranium splits more symmetrically than with neutrons which had been slowed down. And in early 1945 the Kaiser Wilhelm Institut für Chemie was able to tabulate 25 different chemical elements with atomic numbers 35 (bromine) to 59 (praseodymium) in the form of about 100 different active kinds of atoms as the immediate or indirect fractions of uranium fission. The active kinds of atoms which we had considered as trans-uraniums until 1939 were all active fission products and their active derivatives, but they were not elements beyond uranium!"

CONSEQUENCES IN THEORY AND PRACTICE

Natural radioactivity is a spontaneous reduction of the size of the atomic nucleus, a disintegration in which small particles are expelled at high speed. A reversed process could be produced artificially, with a slight increase of the atomic weight (see Joliot-Curie, p. 143). Hahn discovered that the disintegration can take place in such a manner that the heavy nucleus breaks apart approximately in the middle. Artificially radioactive elements emit β-particles, and Hahn's attention at first was concentrated on this kind of radiation, while the liberation of neutrons from the overloaded breakdown products appeared as a side reaction. Lise Meitner found, by calculating the new results on the basis of Bohr's theory of atom structure, that extremely high energies should be developed in this reaction. The great recoil-energy of the nuclear fission was measured experimentally by Frisch and somewhat later confirmed by Joliot.

A long development of theoretical considerations concerning the relationships of the elements to one another and of matter to energy had led to the conclusion that extremely high amounts of energy are stored in the heavier atoms. Aston had thought of what the consequences might be if we should learn to liberate this energy (see p. 87). Now the way was opened to the conversion of matter into energy, a way which may lead to destruction or to a wonderful future for mankind.

1 9 4 5
ARTTURI ILMARI VIRTANEN
(1895–)

"For his researches and inventions in agricultural and nutritive chemistry, especially for his method of fodder preservation."

BIOGRAPHICAL SKETCH

ARTTURI I. VIRTANEN WAS BORN IN HELSINKI, FINLAND. HE studied chemistry at the university there. His doctor's thesis, carried òut under the guidance of professor O. Aschan, contributed to the elucidation of the constitution of abietic acid, the main part of pine rosin. He did not consider his chemical education as completed with his graduation in 1919, but studied physical and biochemical methods during travels in Switzerland, Germany, and Sweden. He became docent at the University of Helsinki in 1924, professor of biochemistry at the Tekn. Högskolan (technical high school) of Finland in 1931 and at the University in 1939.

From about 1920 on, Virtanen investigated the processes which occur during storage of green fodder. Fermentations produce lactic acid, butyric acid, and breakdown products of the proteins which spoil the fodder, besides reducing its content in nutritive substances. By acidifying the pressed green fodder to a hydrogen-ion concentration below that corresponding to 10^{-4} (also expressed as pH $= 4$) the detrimental biological processes were arrested. How good was such an acidified fodder? Did it adversely influence health and milk? Extensive tests in 1928-1929 showed that the fodder was excellent, even when hydrochloric acid (with some sulfuric acid) was used for the conserving acidification. Not only calories and taste were satisfactory, but vitamins A and C remained undiminished.

Bacterial and enzymatic processes in the utilization of nitrogen, particularly by the nitrifying bacteria present in the root nodules of the leguminous plants, were the subject of extensive work spread over many years. Virtanen's hypothesis concerning the enzymatic reactions and affinities which are responsible for the utilization of nutritive materials has not yet found full recognition.

DESCRIPTION OF THE PRIZE-WINNING WORK *

"In 1925, when I, in connection with the investigations on legumes and legume bacteria, came to deal with the problem of preservation of fresh fodder, the situation was such that the rational exploitation of leguminous crops necessitated a complete reinvestigation of the silage problem in theory and practice.

"I had earlier studied the ability of different bacteria to decompose proteins and to form ammonia from amino acids. On the basis of these important observations it was held probable that harmful processes in silage could be prevented by an artificial acidification of the fresh forage to a pH below 4.

"Practical silage trials were needed to show whether the deteriorating processes: respiration, protein breakdown (and particularly ammonia formation) and harmful fermentations could actually be prevented by an acidification of the fresh crop to below pH 4. In this respect, the results of practical trials were in perfect accord with the theoretical postulations, in that the said harmful processes were indeed most effectively arrested.

"Another important practical question was the maintenance of the given pH value of 3-4 in the silage throughout the period of storing. If fresh grass is packed in a water tight container and acidified with mineral acids to, say, pH 3.5, the acidity of the mass will gradually decrease so that, after a few months, the pH value will

---

* The first selection is from *Cattle Fodder and Human Nutrition* (Cambridge, 1938); the second is from *Nature*, Vol. CLVIII (1946), p. 515.

have risen over the critical limit of pH 4. Once this occurs the detrimental breakdown process immediately sets in and the material gets spoilt. Even if this is not very serious, cattle generally dislike, and often refuse to eat, silage which has been soaking in the liquid. It appears, however, that the once-attained pH value of the fodder mass remained unchanged if the effluent was drained off.

"Nine years extensive practical use of the A.I.V. process in Finland has definitely proven the entire wholesomeness of the A.I.V. silage. It has been used up to 45 kg per cow per day without any harmful effects."

* * *

"In the light of our new experiments, especially the ones regarding the favourable competition of some amino-acids with nitrate and ammonia-nitrogen, it seems probable to us that in natural conditions plants use also organic nitrogen compounds for their nitrogen nutrition, at least in certain soils. As a rule, however, the uptake of organic nitrogen by cultivated plants is not great, since ammonium salts and nitrates are rapidly formed from organic nitrogen compounds in soil. Since however the uptake of organic nitrogen compounds even in small amounts may affect the plant markedly, the significance of these nitrogen compounds can be great. In the foregoing, alanine has been noted to cause pronounced changes in the shape of peas, and phenyl-ethylamine, the decarboxylation product of phenyl-alanine, which has been added to nitrate-containing nutrient solutions, has produced a branching of different type in pea. Effects of this kind can be expected to occur under certain conditions also in Nature."

CONSEQUENCES IN THEORY AND PRACTICE

Virtanen developed his method particularly for conditions in Finland, with its long winters. The acidification of green crops by addition of acids in a controlled measure makes a constant supply of palatable and nutritious fodder available at all times. The farmer has become independent of weather at harvest time. Extensive experiments showed that milk and butter of best grades are obtainable when cows are fed acid-preserved silage. The method has found wide application.

In his research on the nitrogen nutrition of higher plants, Virtanen found that the root nodules of legumes contain hemoglobin and methemoglobin. The equilibrium between the red and the brown pigment depends on the intensity of light and the development of the plant. Vigorously growing plants have red root nodules on days of sunshine, indicating high hemoglobin content. Brown color of the cut root nodules indicates lower activity. When neither hemoglobin nor methemoglobin is present, the color is green and nitrogen fixation has ceased.

Legumes are the only plants which can "fix" and use nitrogen from the air. Some of this nitrogen is secreted from the roots into the soil. The importance of organic nitrogen compounds, such as those amino acids which Virtanen found, still needs much further study before a clear picture can be obtained.

1 9 4 6
JAMES B. SUMNER
(1887-1955)

"For his discovery that enzymes can be crystallized."
(The award for 1946 was shared with John Howard North-
rop and Wendell Meredith Stanley; see below, pp. 192-197.)

BIOGRAPHICAL SKETCH

JAMES BATCHELLER SUMNER WAS BORN IN CANTON, MASS.
At school he was interested in physics and chemistry, but not in
any of the other subjects. He studied chemistry at Harvard College,
from 1906 to 1910. After a brief interlude of work in the cotton-
knitting factory which belonged to the family, and some chemistry
teaching, he returned to Harvard, this time to the Medical School
under Otto Folin, and became doctor of biochemistry in 1914.
Shortly afterward he accepted a position at the Cornell Medical
School, where he has been professor of biochemistry since 1929,
the year he went to Stockholm to investigate his crystallized enzyme
with Hans von Euler-Chelpin (see pp. 112-117) and The Svedberg
(see pp. 99-102).

Together with Karl Myrbäck he edited "The Enzymes, Chemistry and Mechanism of Action" (vol. 1, part 1, 1950; part 2, 1951;
vol. 2, part 1, 1951; part 2, 1952, Academic Press, New York).

DESCRIPTION OF THE PRIZE-WINNING WORK*

"The jack bean appeared to me to be extraordinarily rich in urease and I could see no reason why this enzyme could not be isolated in pure form and characterized chemically. Claude Bernard has said that success or failure may depend upon the lucky choice of some reagent or raw material. Willstätter was unfortunate in his choice of saccharase as an enzyme to isolate. I was fortunate in choosing urease.

"I started trying to isolate urease in the fall of 1917, having been occupied previously with analytical methods.

"At first we used to extract urease from jack bean meal with water. These aqueous extracts were viscous and therefore very difficult to filter. Glycerol extracts were even more bothersome. I learned that Folin used 30 per cent alcoholic extracts of jack bean meal as a source of urease for analytical purposes. It was found that extraction with 30 per cent alcohol was of distinct advantage, inasmuch as this solvent dissolved most of the urease but failed to dissolve a rather large quantity of the other proteins. Hence a considerable purification was achieved through the use of this solvent. The alcoholic extracts filtered very rapidly, leaving the undissolved material behind on the filter paper. The only disadvantage of 30 per cent alcohol lay in the slow inactivating action of this solvent upon the urease. However, if kept at low temperatures there was no inactivation of the enzyme.

"When kept at low temperatures 30 per cent alcoholic extracts of jack bean meal formed precipitates. These precipitates contained practically all of the urease, together with concanavalin A, concanavalin B and other proteins. At this time we had no ice chest in our laboratory and we used to place cylinders of 30 per cent alcohol extracts on our window ledges and pray for cold weather.

"It seemed to me of interest to employ dilute acetone instead of 30 per cent alcohol and to see whether this substitution would result in any improvement in the method of purification. Accord-

---

* From *Les Prix Nobel en 1946.*

ingly I diluted 316 cc. of pure acetone to 1000 cc. and used this as the means of extracting the urease. I routinely employed this dilution of acetone, since I had been preparing 30 per cent alcohol through diluting 95 per cent alcohol in this manner. The acetone extract was chilled in our newly acquired ice chest overnight. The next morning I examined the filtrate. It contained practically no precipitate, thus differing from alcoholic filtrates. However, upon observing a drop of the liquid under the microscope it was seen to contain many tiny crystals. These were of a shape that I had never observed previously. I centrifugated off some of the crystals and observed that they dissolved readily in water. I then tested this water solution. It gave tests for protein and possessed a very high urease activity. I then telephoned my wife, 'I have crystallized the first enzyme.' "

CONCLUSiON

"The enzymes pepsin, trypsin, chymotrypsin, carboxypeptidase, ribonuclease, and hexokinase have been isolated and crystallized. The precursors of pepsin, trypsin, chymotrypsin have also been isolated and crystallized. A nucleoprotein which appears to be bacteriophage has been isolated but not crystallized.

"The purity of the enzyme preparations, with the exception of carboxypeptidase, has been tested by means of solubility measurements, ultra-centrifuge analysis (pepsin, ribonuclease, hexokinase, and bacteriophage), and electrophoresis (pepsin, ribonuclease, hexokinase, chymotrypsinogen). They appear to be pure proteins by all these methods."

JOHN HOWARD NORTHROP
(1891–   )

WENDELL MEREDITH STANLEY
(1904–   )

"For their preparation of enzymes and virus proteins in a pure form."
(*The award for 1946 was shared with James B. Sumner, see above, p. 189*)

BIOGRAPHICAL SKETCH

NORTHROP

JOHN HOWARD NORTHROP WAS BORN IN YONKERS, N. Y., IN 1891. His father was a zoologist, his mother a botanist. He received his Ph.D. from Columbia University in 1915. During his connection with the Chemical Warfare Service, from 1917 to 1919, he "discovered and worked on a fermentation process for manufacturing acetone." He has been a member of the Rockefeller Institute at Princeton since 1924.

His book "Crystalline Enzymes" (with Moses Kunitz and Roger M. Herriot) came out, in a second edition, in 1948 (Columbia University Press, New York).

STANLEY

WENDELL MEREDITH STANLEY WAS BORN IN RIDGEVILLE, IND., in 1904. He was graduated from the University of Illinois in 1929

192

and worked for a year under Heinrich Wieland, in Munich, on sterols. Since 1931 he has been connected with the Rockefeller Institute for Medical Research. During the Second World War, he undertook extensive work on the separation of influenza virus and the preparation of a vaccine from it.

Together with F. M. Burnet, he edited "The Viruses," vol. 1, 1959 (Academic Press, New York), and wrote with Evans G. Valens "Viruses and the Nature of Life" (Dutton, New York, 1961).

DESCRIPTION OF THE PRIZE-WINNING WORK

NORTHROP *

"THE early workers were of the opinion that enzymes were probably proteins and in 1896 Pekelharing isolated a protein from gastric juice which he considered to be the enzyme pepsin. He was not able to crystallize the protein and his conclusion as to the identity of the enzyme and the protein was never accepted. I repeated these experiments about 1920 but was unable to carry them further at that time.

"Sumner's results encouraged me to take up the pepsin problem again and in 1930 I isolated a crystalline protein from a commercial pepsin preparation which appeared to be the enzyme pepsin. Since then five more enzymes, as well as some of their precursors, have been isolated in my laboratory. Trypsin, and its precursor trypsinogen, a polypeptide which inhibits trypsin, and a compound of this substance with trypsin, chymotrypsinogen, and three forms of chymotrypsin were isolated and crystallized by Kunitz and myself. Kunitz and McDonald isolated and crystallized ribonuclease and hexokinase. Anson crystallized carboxypeptidase, and Herriott isolated and crystallized pepsinogen. These experiments required a great deal of the most painstaking and difficult work and could not have been successfully carried out without my collaborators, Herriott, Anson, Desreux, McDonald, Holter, Krueger, Butler, and

* From *Les Prix Nobel en 1946.*

especially, Dr. Kunitz, who possesses a real genius for handling these unstable and elusive substances.

"As a result of these experiments, it appears probable that all enzymes and at least some viruses are proteins. The mere fact that the preparations are crystalline proteins is not, of course, sufficient to warrant this conclusion and we have spent a great deal of time in establishing the purity of our preparations and in testing by every method available the relation between the activity and the protein.

"Before discussing these results, I will describe briefly the experimental methods we have used in the isolation and crystallization of these active proteins. No one general method has been found which will lead to the isolation and crystallization of an enzyme, but certain general principles have been found to be of great assistance. In the first place large quantities of material are used, so that actual solid material is handled and not merely dilute solutions. The failure of so many early attempts to isolate enzymes was due, I believe, largely to the fact that nearly all of the work was carried out with dilute solutions. In the second place filtration by suction was used wherever possible since this method results in far better separation of the precipitate from the mother liquor than does the use of the centrifuge. Had Pekelharing filtered his pepsin preparation and then dissolved it in a very small amount of water, instead of centrifuging the precipitate and dissolving it in a large amount of water, I am quite sure he would have crystallized the enzyme nearly fifty years ago.

"In the third place fractionation was carried out largely by the use of concentrated neutral salts in the presence of which proteins are much more stable than in dilute salt solutions.

"Pepsin, for instance, decomposes at a rate of about 3 per cent a day in hydrochloric acid solution at pH 2.7 and 0° C. Even in nearly saturated magnesium sulfate solution at 0° C, the most stable condition known, the rate is 1 per cent a day.

"Trypsin at pH 8.0 and 30° C loses 90 per cent or more of its activity in a day. This reaction is exceptional since it is bimolecular so that in this case dilute solutions are more stable than concentrated ones."

STANLEY *

"ATTEMPTS to learn something about the nature of viruses through studies on their general properties began with Beijerinck's work in 1898 and were continued in different laboratories for over thirty years without too much success. Although Beijerinck and Allard made important contributions, perhaps the most significant work was that of Vinson and Petre during the years from 1927 to 1931 when they showed that tobacco mosaic virus could be subjected to several kinds of chemical manipulations without loss of virus activity. Nevertheless, when the work on viruses, which is recognized by the 1946 Nobel Prize for Chemistry, was started in 1932, the true nature of viruses was a complete mystery. It was not known whether they were inorganic, carbohydrate, hydrocarbon, lipid, protein or organismal in nature. It became necessary, therefore, to conduct experiments which would yield information of a definite nature. Tobacco mosaic virus was selected for these initial experiments because it appeared to provide several unusual advantages. Large amounts of highly infectious material were readily available and the virus was known to be unusually stable. Furthermore, it was possible to titrate or measure the amount of this virus in a preparation with ease and rapidity and with great accuracy.

"As a result of studies on the effects of over one hundred different chemicals on tobacco mosaic virus, it was found that the only chemicals which had a direct inactivating action could be classified as oxidizing agents, protein-precipitating agents and agents causing a hydrogen ion concentration known to inactivate the virus. It was concluded that, as a whole, the results are in harmony with the conception that the virus is a protein. As a result of these studies efforts were directed more definitely towards the development of procedures useful in the concentration and purification of proteins. The optimum hydrogen-ion concentration for carrying out the three principal steps in the lead acetate process for the purification of tobacco mosaic virus proposed by Vinson and Petre were determined. . . . Utilization of this process yielded colorless, partially purified solutions having a virus content equal to or somewhat

---

* From *Les Prix Nobel en 1946*.

greater than that of the starting material. Subsequently it was found that concentration and purification of the virus could be effected readily by means of a combination of isoelectric precipitation and salting out with ammonium sulfate.

"The protein in the filtrate is crystallized by adding slowly, with sufficient stirring, sufficient of a saturated solution of ammonium sulfate to cause a slight cloudiness, followed by a solution of 10 per cent glacial acetic acid in one half saturated ammonium sulfate sufficient to increase the hydrogen-ion concentration to about pH 5.

"Needless to say, for a time there was great scepticism that the crystalline material could be tobacco mosaic, due chiefly to the old idea that viruses were living organisms. A wide variety of experimental approaches has been used to test the proposal that the crystalline material represented tobacco mosaic virus. It was found that essentially all of the virus activity present in infectious juice could be isolated in the form of the crystalline material. The virus activity of this material was about 500 times that of the starting material. One ml of a solution containing but 10^{-9} grams of the material has usually proven infectious.

"Early determinations of viscosity and sedimentation yielded data which permitted the conclusion that the particles of tobacco mosaic virus consisted of rods, about 12 mμ in diameter and about 400 mμ in length, with a molecular weight of about 40 millions.

"An interesting and potentially very important property of the rods of tobacco mosaic virus is their ability to aggregate end-to-end. . . . The entire rod appears necessary for virus activity, for breakage of the rod into two halves is accompanied by loss of virus activity."

CONSEQUENCES IN THEORY AND PRACTICE

The word "enzyme," taken literally, means "in yeast." From yeast or malt sprouts, extracts were obtained which acted upon large quantities of organic substances, as in the conversion of starch to sugar and of sugar to alcohol. Willstätter (see pp. 65-69), who did much to introduce quantitative measurements into enzymology, had much opposition to his view that enzymes are chemicals. Real proof for this view was demonstrated when enzymes were purified to pure substances. It meant a triumph of the chemical technique and the chemical theory. The previously mysterious cause of activity was here shown to be enclosed within the unit which is the molecule of a pure substance. The activity is a molecular property, like the color of a dyestuff.

Crystallization was successfully carried out, for example, with potato-X-virus; with tomato bushy stunt virus, which forms rods, like tobacco mosaic virus; and also with strains of influenza virus, of which the pure particles have spherical form. The building stones of these viruses are amino acids, as in other proteins. Certain chemical changes can be carried out with the pure viruses so that the derivatives are still active and infectious. Structural changes produced by reaction with formaldehyde were accompanied with changes of activity; when the original chemical structure was restored, the activity also was restored.

These results closed a chapter of uncertainties in a biologically and medically very important investigation. And yet Dr. Stanley ended his Nobel lecture with the words: "The new field of virus research is really in its infancy and much remains to be accomplished." The same could be said of the new enzyme research. For dyestuffs, certain relationships between color and chemical constitution have been found. Corresponding relationships for enzymes and viruses are not yet in sight, but the problem can now perhaps be formulated with more confidence than ever before.

1947
ROBERT ROBINSON
(1886–   )

*"For research on certain vegetable products of great
biological importance, particularly alkaloids."*

BIOGRAPHICAL SKETCH

ROBERT ROBINSON WAS BORN IN BUFFORD, NEAR CHESTERFIELD,
Derbyshire, England, where his father manufactured cardboard
boxes and surgical materials on machines of his own invention.
He became Doctor of Science in Manchester, in 1910, and was
professor of organic chemistry at the University of Sidney, Australia, from 1912 to 1915. After his return to England he was
professor at several universities; since 1929 he has been at Mag-
dalen College of Oxford University.

Robinson's interest in the chemical constitution of plant dyestuffs soon extended to alkaloids. The red, blue, and violet pigments in flowers or roots, wood and bark, are highly complex
substances which are called anthocyanins. They can be split into a
sugar component and the basic colored compound, the anthocyani-
din. Robinson was at first particularly interested in the dyestuff
contained in certain kinds of wood which had long been used for
dyeing. The dyestuffs which can be extracted from them are
brazilin and hematoxylin. Robinson always attempted to supple-
ment analysis by synthesis. He found a method for synthesizing
tropinone, a relative of a substance which forms the characteristic
part of the molecule of atropine, an alkaloid which is used in

medicine, for example, to enlarge the pupil before eye examinations. He contributed greatly to the art of defining the arrangement of the atoms in the molecule structures of morphine and other alkaloids found in the sap of the seeds of poppies, which include papaverine and narcotine. Open chains of carbon atoms are closed into rings, and the orientation of attached atom groups in space relative to each other is determined.

Robinson said of himself: "Such contributions as I have been able to make are to the science itself and do not derive their interest from the economic or biological importance of the substances studied."

DESCRIPTION OF THE PRIZE-WINNING WORK*

"The study of brazilin and haematoxylin is by no means finished and in this connexion I would like to make a general observation. The synthesis of brazilin would have no industrial value; its biological importance is problematical, but it is worth while to attempt it for the sufficient reason that we have no idea how to accomplish the task. There is a close analogy between organic chemistry in its relation to biochemistry and pure mathematics in its relation to physics. In both disciplines it is in the course of attack of the most difficult problems, without consideration of eventual applications, that new fundamental knowledge is most certainly garnered.

"From the incidents of the brazilin investigation two fresh topics developed. In the first place the pyrrylium salt synthesis led to the much later extension to the synthesis of anthocyanidins and still later to that of the anthocyanins (see below). Secondly the facile ring closure of β-3:4-dimethoxyphenylpropionic acid to the ketone (II) suggested an application to the synthesis of papaverine.

"The structural or biogenetic relations of plant products as deduced from the recognisable architectural components of the molecules have been consistent guides in my investigations. An early instance was the change proposed in the constitution of berberine (1910). It seemed highly improbable that hydrastine and berber-

* From Les Prix Nobel en 1947.

ine, congeners in Hydrastis canadensis, could have totally differently oriented methoxyl groups. The change suggested was justified by the first synthesis of berberine by way of oxyberberine (with Perkin and Ray, 1925). Similar considerations underlay the revision of the structures of morphine and its relatives, made with J. M. Gulland in 1923-24.

"But the most fruitful thought along these lines was that which led to the establishment of an indole group of the alkaloids (with PERKIN and KERMACK).

"Here I remember very clearly the sequence of events and must admit that this was obscured in the publication. OTTO FISCHER had degraded harmine, $C_{12}H_9N_2 \cdot OCH_3$, to harman, $C_{12}H_{10}N_2$, and the first clue arose from writing down the possible or at least the most likely, structures for this substance. A great many of them would be methyl derivatives, $C_{11}H_7N_2 \cdot CH_3$, of $C_{11}H_8N_2$ which is the formula of a tricyclic aromatic substance containing benzene, pyrrole, and pyridine nuclei. Hence in 1912 we sought, and found, this methyl group, and also eliminated it. This was made easy by the fact that harmine, like quinaldine, forms a benzylidene derivative:

$$CH_3O \cdot C_{11}H_6N_2 \cdot CH_3 \ \rightarrow \ CH_3O \cdot C_{11}H_6N_2 \cdot CH = CHPh \rightarrow$$
$$CH_3O \cdot C_{11}H_6N_2 \cdot CO_2H \rightarrow CH_3O \cdot C_{11}H_6N_2 \ (\text{norharmine}).$$

"Later, norharman, $C_{11}H_8N_2$ was prepared by removing the methoxyl group from norharmine or the methyl group from harman.

"It seems incredible that the next step was not taken until some years had elapsed. One day, when in Liverpool, I happened to wish to refer to Richter's Lexikon for the melting point of a methylnaphthiminazole, $C_{12}H_{10}N_2$. It was interesting to see an old friend, harman, as No. 16 and a little further I noticed (19.) Verbindung (aus Typtophan) and a Zentral Blatt reference of 1903. The paucity of the information and the coincidence induced me to read the original (HOPKINS and COLE, 1902). The base from typtophan had m. p. 238° which was a few degrees higher than that attributed to harman but otherwise the properties of the two substances, especially the characteristic fluorescence in acid solution, were identical. Later the m. p. of harman was raised to 238° and direct comparison with a specimen of HOPKINS' base proved the identity. The mystery of the formation of a C_{12} base by oxidation of typtophan (C_{11} and loss of CO_2H occurs) with aqueous ferric chloride was easily resolved. The mixture had been extracted with ether and left for a few days; there is little doubt that alcohol in the ether was a source of acetaldehyde. It was in fact possible to synthesise harman by condensation of typtophan with acetaldehyde followed by oxidation, or by joint oxidation of typtophan and alanine.

harman, $C_{12}H_{10}N_2$

"The interlocking developments of the chemistry of strychnine and brucine cannot be usefully summarised and demands separate treatment. This is a most fascinating molecule and with its seven fused rings it is a kind of organic chemist's playground. For many years to come it will provide material for degradative studies. Nevertheless I believe that the problem of its constitution is finally solved in every detail. For a long time the formula (XXV) seemed satisfactory, but in 1945 Prelog and Szpilfogel gave good reasons for supposing that ring E is six-membered. Other evidence in the same direction has since accumulated. The chemistry of neostrychnine, an isomeride depending on a change in position of a double bond, created some temporary difficulties. These have been overcome by the recognition that neostrychnine contains $\diagdown N—CH=C\diagup$ with α, β labels.

which can be oxidized by perbenzoic acid to $\diagdown N—CHO \diagup CO,$

and changed by bromine to a bromo-hydrobromide which in warm

water becomes $\diagdown N—\overset{\beta}{C}—\overset{\alpha}{CHO}$, HBr (with R. N. Chakravarti,

1945-46). After careful and prolonged consideration I am satisfied that strychnine is (**XXVI**) (Experientia, 1946) and that no alternative can now be entertained."

(XXV)   (XXVI)

CONSEQUENCES IN THEORY AND PRACTICE

The synthesis of complicated organic substances such as alkaloids starts with the preparation of simpler compounds in a manner which is chemically transparent. It continues with the combination of such compounds into higher structures which we can then understand because we built them. The knowledge so gained is not limited to the particular alkaloid constructed; the substance is linked with others by similarities and analogies. Thus, the methods of synthesis and the insight into the structure of certain alkaloids had great consequences for the task of producing anti-malarial drugs. Sir Robert Robinson took a prominent part in this task during the last war.

The knowledge of natural alkaloids made it possible to set up specific objectives for the new effort and to formulate expected structures for which medical value could be reasonably predicted. The previously developed methods helped to pave the way to the new substances.

1 9 4 8
ARNE TISELIUS
(1902–   )

"For his researches on electrophoresis and adsorption analysis, especially for his discoveries concerning the complex nature of the serum proteins."

BIOGRAPHICAL SKETCH

ARNE WILHELM KAURIN TISELIUS WAS BORN IN STOCKHOLM. He went to school in Gothenburg and studied chemistry at Uppsala, where his grandfather had been professor of mathematics. From 1925 on, he was assistant to The Svedberg. His doctoral thesis, published in 1930, dealt with "The moving boundary method of studying the electrophoresis of proteins." The displacement of dissolved molecules under the influence of an electrical charge which is called electrophoresis is the result of many factors, such as concentration of the solution, size and form of the molecules, the medium in which they are dissolved, and the magnitude of the electrical charge. Many efforts had been made to use this displacement for the study of the sensitive, large molecules of proteins. It was necessary to select suitable conditions and optical systems with which the movement of the molecules could be followed. The front of this movement represents the "moving boundary."

Shortly after receiving his doctor's degree, Tiselius began the investigation of the second subject mentioned in the citation for the Nobel Prize, adsorption. He continued this work at Princeton, 1934-1935. Having returned to Uppsala, in 1937, he applied electrophoretic methods to the separation of proteins in the blood serum. A new professorship for the study of the chemistry and physics of life was created for him, and a new institute was built for this purpose.

Tiselius is greatly interested in general problems of scientific research. He has been president of Sweden's State Council for Research in Natural Sciences since its foundation, in 1946.

DESCRIPTION OF THE PRIZE-WINNING WORK*

"The advantages of the electrophoretic method are above all its gentleness and its marked specificity. During the entire course of a separation the substance remains in solution of approximately constant composition, thereby eliminating the risk of denaturation and other irreversible changes which so easily influence processes dependent on precipitation. This advantage is also characteristic of separation by ultracentrifugation. Frequently proteins, enzymes, and other substances which have been purified by precipitation or by repeated recrystallization are nevertheless found by electrophoretic analysis to be inhomogeneous. This is probably due to the fact that substances of such a nature show a great tendency to carry foreign substances with them on precipitation. The components are more likely to be free from one another in solution, and as the electrophoretic separation depends only on difference in mobilities it is of little importance if the impurities are present only in very small quantities. The separation proceeds just about as readily—in contrast to what is usually the case in most other separation methods.

"The method's great convenience has, however, certain limitations which should be indicated. In electrophoretic migration only those molecules or particles which are free from one another in the solution are separated. If complex groups or associations of some type exist, a separation can only be expected to the extent in which these complexes are dissociated. A component which under certain conditions in electrophoresis is observed to be homogeneous can also very well, under different conditions (with less gentle treatment or merely by a change of pH) show itself to be of com-

---

* From *Les Prix Nobel en 1948.*

plex nature. However, electrophoretic (as ultracentrifugal) observations are of considerable interest also in such a case from an entirely different point of view. The gentleness of the method should often make it possible to draw the conclusion that such demonstrated complexes may even be present in the original material, that is to say, when we deal with proteins, in the living organism itself. It is not necessary to be a vitalist in order to express the opinion, that what from a chemist's viewpoint may be taken as a strongly retained impurity (for example the lipid in a lipoprotein complex), from a biological viewpoint perhaps may possess a vital function. Throughout the course of biochemistry—quite naturally—principal interest has been directed to the chemical entities that have been isolated from biological materials, but there is little doubt that in the future much closer attention must be paid also to the existence of specific complexes in the living organism. It is the chain of events with linked reactions which is the key note of life's processes and its interrelationship or linkage can perhaps best be conceived as the result of an association of substances with different specific functions.

"In 1940 I began some experiments in order to make use of the chromatographic analysis in the separation of proteins and of their breakdown products. This was considered worth a trial on account of the remarkable specificity which this separation method shows for different organic substances, which had become evident in the course of numerous investigations during the years following the original work of Tswett in 1906. The particular difficulties which had been encountered (such as boundary anomalies) in the electrophoresis of peptides and similar breakdown products of proteins made it also desirable to find a method especially adaptable for the separation of these substances.

"Just as chromatographic methods in general, these methods are useful for the analysis of substances of the most varied sort. We have performed a very large number of model experiments on amino acids, peptides, sugars, fatty acids and fats, etc.

"For a quantitative estimation of these diagrams it is of utmost importance that as low a concentration as possible can be used. It is accordingly of great interest that Claesson has recently been suc-

cessful in constructing a new adsorption analysis interferometer with
approximately five times the sensitivity of the previous model. The
large separation of high polymers of the polymetacrylate and nitro-
cellulose types which Claesson has succeeded in accomplishing
indicates that adsorption analysis in this field will come to assume
great importance."

CONSEQUENCES IN THEORY
AND PRACTICE

The methods developed by Tiselius and in his institute offer very
gentle means for separating substances which differ only slightly
in their chemical constitution. This is of especial importance, for
such substances may differ widely in their effect on living organisms. In order to develop these methods, the chemist had to be a
good physicist and instrument designer.

Separations thus obtained are indicated by marked changes in the
refraction of light. Electrophoretic diagrams show several peaks
when the dissolved substance is not uniform. Thus, it is possible to
use the method as a fine analytical tool, as was done during the
work at Harvard on producing pure proteins by fractionating blood
plasma. The medical value of these fractions is highly specific and
greatly increased by the removal of biologically interfering substances. In some cases, the fractionating can even be carried out in
the electrophoresis apparatus.

The separation of related substances by adsorption is versatile,
because several influential factors can be selected and combined.
Such factors are the materials on which the substances are to be
held by adsorption and the solvents used first in anchoring the
substance on the materials and then in removing it from them.
This method has furnished valuable information about the presence
of polymeric substances in synthetic resins. Although the method
is usually described as the chromatographic method, it can now
be applied not only to the colored substances for which it was first
developed but also to colorless ones.

A particularly impressive use of the chromatographic method
was the recent separation of rare-earth element compounds which
have very similar chemical properties and play a role in research on
atom fission. (see 1952, pp. 232-241.)

1 9 4 9
WILLIAM FRANCIS GIAUQUE
(1895–)

*"For his work in the field of chemical thermody-
namics, particularly concerning the behavior of
substances at extremely low temperatures."*

BIOGRAPHICAL SKETCH

WILLIAM GIAUQUE WAS BORN IN NIAGARA FALLS, ONTARIO.
After graduation from high school and an interval of two years
at an industrial laboratory, he studied chemistry at the University
of California. There Gilbert N. Lewis directed his interests to the
beauties and problems of thermodynamics. A few years after obtaining the doctor's degree (1922), his study of the capacity which
substances have to hold internal energy at a specified temperature
led him to calculations of the influence of magnetism on this
capacity, usually called entropy. Several years elapsed before the
calculations were put to experimental test. In 1933, Giauque in
California and de Haas in Holland attained a temperature which
was only 0.5 degrees above the absolute zero of temperature.

From the viewpoints of entropy and thermodynamics all the
properties of matter are interrelated, and one of them can be used
to influence another or in interpreting another. Just as he combined magnetism with heat, Giauque concluded from spectroscopic measurements on oxygen that not all its atoms could have
the same weight. He predicted that, in addition to the well-known
species of oxygen atoms which have a weight of 16.00, atoms of

weight 17 and 18 should be present. This prediction of 1928 was soon proved correct.

As professor of chemistry at the University of California since 1934, Giauque has continued the development of low-temperature research with a great body of equipment. During the Second World War, his theoretical work found urgently needed applications in the construction of mobile units for the production of liquid oxygen.

DESCRIPTION OF THE PRIZE-WINNING WORK*

"The careful determination of entropy has often been accompanied by the discovery of unexpected physical properties. The discovery of the oxygen isotopes of atomic weights 17 and 18 was a case of this kind.

"An accurate measurement of the low temperature heat capacity of oxygen was undertaken with Dr. H. L. Johnston. . . . In this case, as had long been known, there are three crystal forms and the liquid before the gas state is reached and thus it was also necessary to measure the increase in entropy during each change of state.

"One of the principal lines of research which we had pursued in connection with the determination of entropy is the calculation of this, and other thermodynamic quantities, by means of quantum statistics and the entropy levels of gas molecules. These entropies can be obtained from band spectra. . . .

"This spectrum permits the determination of the energy levels of the oxygen molecule. When the entropy of oxygen gas was calculated from these strong lines [in the oxygen spectrum] it agreed exactly with the value obtained from our low temperature measurements.

"The spectrum also contains many weak lines, which were believed to be due to oxygen, but which were not understood. . . . It is rather interesting that these weak lines are themselves an unexpected by-product of a solar investigation by Babcock. When

---

* From *Les Prix Nobel en 1949*.

sunlight passes through the molecules in the earth's atmosphere, some of the light is absorbed selectively by them. The effect may be enhanced by photographing the sun when it is low on the horizon because the light then passes through a greater amount of air.

"An entropy calculation based on band spectra is not considered to be satisfactory unless the spectrum is completely explained. One way to explain weak lines is to assume that they are due to some higher energy state of the molecules, and are weak because not many molecules are in the higher energy state. Many of the weak lines in the oxygen spectrum are actually due to this effect, but they could not all be explained in this way.

"Months of thinking about this problem led to memorization of the essentials of the data and I literally awoke one morning with the realization that the lines must originate from an isotopic species. Detailed calculations by Dr. Johnston and myself confirmed this accurately and it was determined that isotopes of atomic weights 17 and 18 exist in the earth's atmosphere.

"The commonest question asked in the early days of this work [on very low temperatures] was 'How do you know it gets cold?' This was a fair question. Obviously, no one had ever made thermometers which were calibrated at temperatures that had never been produced. Since even helium gas has negligible pressure, at the low temperatures obtained, a gas thermometer is useless.

"Temperature can only be measured by some property of a substance which varies with temperature. In this case the magnetic susceptibility increases as temperature decreases.

"When an alternating electric current is passed through a measuring coil it becomes increasingly difficult for the current to pass as the magnetic susceptibility of the substance increases. This effect permits the quantitative determination of magnetic susceptibility.

"The resistance of the wire in measuring coils drops to such low values at the temperature of liquid helium that very large numbers of turns can be used. The sensitivity which is obtained with coils at these low temperatures is such that it is necessary to compensate for the small fluctuations in the Earth's magnetic field."

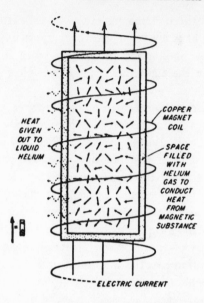

Fig. 16. Refrigeration by Means of Adiabatic Demagnetization. First step: Electric current is started through magnet. Heat is given out as paramagnetic substance is magnetized.

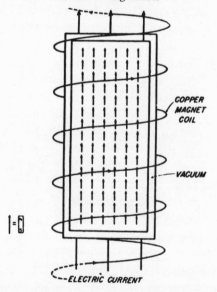

Fig. 17. Refrigeration by Means of Adiabatic Demagnetization. Second step: Full electric current through magnet. Magnetization is complete. The substance is now insulated against flow of heat by pumping a vacuum in the jacket.

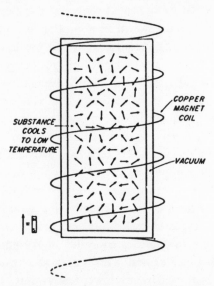

Fig. 18. Refrigeration by Means of Adiabatic Demagnetization. Third step: Electric current turned off. Substance is demagnetized. No heat can enter. Substance does magnetic work through space by inducing an electric current in copper coils of magnet. The work is done at expense of the molecular energy. Loss of energy cools substance. This is adiabatic demagnetization.

CONSEQUENCES IN THEORY AND PRACTICE

The relationships of all chemical and physical changes to temperature are the central theme of thermodynamics, and its central concept is entropy. Temperature is the result of the movements of the molecules, and it is measured on a scale derived from the expansion of gases upon heating. According to this scale and the concepts upon which it is erected, there is an absolute zero point of temperature. At this point, 273 degrees below the zero of the centigrade scale of Celsius, all molecular movement should come to a standstill. This absolute zero of temperature is a highly interesting state; Nernst derived some very practical applications from theories concerning the approach to this state. He could do this because we postulated this state from our experiences at normally accessible temperatures. The liquefaction of air and the production of liquid oxygen and nitrogen are very tangible results of thermodynamic calculation. When air is compressed, a part of the energy of molecular movement is converted into heat. This energy can be removed from the system by absorption in a cooling medium. When subsequently the cooled compressed gas is allowed to expand, internal energy is converted into greater movement of the molecules in the enlarged space at their disposal, so that the temperature drops. By repetition of the cycle of compressing, cooling, expanding, air is liquefied, and by the use of liquid air as the cooling medium, even helium could be converted into a liquid.

The effect of a magnetic field on a para-magnetic substance consists in bringing a higher degree of order into the movement of its electrons. This effect increases inversely with the temperature; it is 300 times as great at 1° as at room temperature (300° on the absolute scale). Imposing such a higher degree of order of internal movement upon a substance is equivalent to a compression; it results in a development of heat. This heat can be removed by a cooling medium which itself is at a lower temperature, such as helium at 1°. After such cooling, the removal of the magnetic field causes a further drop of temperature, because this corresponds to an expansion of the gas. Temperatures of only 0.003 above absolute zero were thus obtained.

The measuring of such extremely low temperatures is exceedingly difficult. The gas thermometer can be used only down to the boiling point of helium; from there on it has to be replaced by thermometers based on the electrical resistance of a pure metal. This method is complicated by the fact that there is a temperature that is characteristic for the specific metals, at which they suddenly become super-conductors of electricity with zero resistance. It is one of the objects of infra-low temperature research to obtain more information about this particular state of metals. Another aspect, of practical interest, is the relationship of para-magnetism with energy levels of electron movements around their own axis ("spin"). This kind of movement, associated with absorptions in the micro-wave range of the spectrum, must be better understood for the construction of improved radar equipment.

1950
OTTO DIELS
(1876-1954)

KURT ALDER
(1902-1958)

"For the development of the diene synthesis."

BIOGRAPHICAL SKETCH

DIELS

OTTO DIELS WAS BORN IN HAMBURG, GERMANY. HE STUDIED chemistry in Berlin and received his doctor's degree in 1899 for work carried out under Emil Fischer's inspiring direction. In the widely diversified field of organic chemistry the importance of many results of research remains confined to small areas. It was different in Diels's case. He made three main discoveries which aroused general interest.

The first of these discoveries was a substance, a gas which made its presence uncomfortably known by a penetrating odor and an irritating action on the eyes. He proved it to be a carbon oxide with the proportions of three carbon atoms for two of oxygen; the proportions in carbon monoxide are one to one and, in the most common of the carbon oxides, one to two. This discovery (1906) was remarkable not only for the properties of the highly reactive compound, but also because it concerned such widely known elements.

Discovery number two was a method of removing part of the hydrogen from the molecule of organic substances in a gentle and controllable way. The reagent used in this method is selenium, a metal which is a relative of sulfur, according to the periodic system of the elements. The selectivity of the action of this metal on hydrogen-rich compounds was of great help in recognizing the structure of such complex substances as sterols.

The third discovery again gave a generally useful method to organic chemistry. It is a method of synthesis which proceeds under mildest conditions and which, therefore, easily reveals the structure of the product. This synthesis is based on a peculiar property of compounds which contain two double-bonded groups of carbon atoms separated by a single bond. Since chemical nomenclature characterizes double bonds by the syllable -ene, these compounds are dienes. Butadiene $CH_2 = CH - CH = CH_2$ is a simple ex-

$$\underset{1}{} \quad \underset{2}{} \quad \underset{3}{} \quad \underset{4}{}$$

ample. Isoprene, the building block of natural rubber, is a butadiene with a methyl group (CH_3) attached to carbon number 2. An important diene with five carbons in a closed ring (cycle) is cyclo-penta-diene.

Diels, since 1916 professor at the University of Kiel, discovered and explored organic synthesis by means of dienes together with Kurt Alder.

ALDER

ALDER STUDIED CHEMISTRY IN BERLIN, THEN IN KIEL, AND received his doctor's degree at Kiel in 1926. The great variability of diene synthesis remained one of the primary subjects of research at the Kiel laboratory and spread from there to many places of research. Alder became professor at Kiel University in 1934. He applied results of his scientific work to technical problems of building large molecules for use in plastics and their ramifications while acting as a director of research for one of the plants of the I. G. Farben Industries. In 1940 he accepted the directorship of the chemical institute at the University of Cologne.

DESCRIPTION OF THE PRIZE-WINNING WORK*

"We have been successful in establishing that dienes, of which isoprene is a typical representative, are capable of an astonishingly great number of synthetic reactions which proceed under the mildest conditions. On the strength of our observations we do not doubt that they have an important role as a valuable principle of construction in all real organic syntheses, that is to say, in the organisms.

"The most essential step in developing diene synthesis, the transfer of experiments made with the azo-ester

$$RO_2C - N = N - CO_2R$$

to a suitable nitrogen-free system, was initiated by the study of an older publication by Albrecht, a pupil of Thiele's. He had observed that cyclo-pentadiene can combine with one or two moles of quinone, and he had suggested formulae for the two products of this reaction which we . . . proved to be wrong. The addition of cyclo-pentadiene to quinone occurs in the 1 — 4-position.

"According to this principle we succeeded in adding simple dienes such as butadiene itself or its alkylated derivatives, or even cyclic dienes, to alpha-naphtho-quinone and thus building many homologues of anthra-quinone. There is no visible limit to the number of syntheses possible according to this method. Since these reactions take place spontaneously, at any rate without involving other reagents, it seems generally logical to me that nature also uses this method in many cases to build up complicated derivatives of anthracene and other hydrocarbons.

"The incomparable fecundity of diene synthesis is the result of the fact that the two components of the reaction can be varied at will without changing their tendency to unite, and thus to form hydro-aromatic compounds."

---

* Translated from *Zeitschrift für Angewandte Chemie*, Vol. XLII (1929), pp. 911 ff.

* "The stereochemical rules mentioned before are so simple that they may appear almost plainly obvious or even selfunderstood. This is not true, however, for the problem is how the two partners are oriented in relation to each other. It was a long and difficult way to recognize and justify this stereochemical rule, the 'general scheme of orientation.'

"The starting point was the study of the thermic polymerization of cyclopentadiene. When this hydrocarbon is heated, it yields, according to some older experiences, a polymer-homologous chain for which the following sequence seemed to be true:

$$n = 1, 2, 3$$

"Our first contribution consisted in revising this intriguingly simple structural scheme. The principle, that four-membered rings were formed, had to be replaced by the schematism of the diene-synthesis. The new formulation is as follows:

"Here, for the first time, it became necessary to include stereochemical considerations in addition to the structural ones. The cause was the isolation of 2 trimeric cyclopentadienes (LXXIII). Chemical degradation led to the important conclusion that the 2 trimers are derived from 2 dimers (LXXII), i.e. that process a) already must occur in 2 sterical directions.

---

* Translated from *Les Prix Nobel en 1950*.

"These 2 directions, α and β (below) can be foreseen from the model. Since a β-dimer was isolated besides the long-known α-form and the configurations of each were found, the question seemed to be answered. However, this was not so, because of a special circumstance. The formulated transitions proceed at elevated temperature. The picture is much simplified when the changes of monomeric cyclopentadiene at room temperature are considered. In the course of only a few days, the liquid monomer is transformed into the camphor-like solid of the α-dimer. This process is structurally and sterically quite uniform.

"The sterical uniformity appears highly remarkable, since only one of the two possible ways, α and β, is followed at low temperatures.

LXXII, α   LXXII, β

"Experiments showed us soon that this phenomenon is not restricted to the dimerization of cyclopentadiene. Thus, the addition of cyclopentadiene with maleic anhydride proceeds sterically in only one direction, the same as found in the dimerization of cyclopentadiene."

CONSEQUENCES IN THEORY
AND PRACTICE

Diene synthesis shows a gentle way in which formidably complicated molecules are built by a reaction in which the parts are simply put together. The reaction does not require or produce temperatures outside of those at which organisms live. The formation of anthracene-structured dyestuffs or of cholesterol is thus brought closer to biochemical understanding. To a certain extent, we can imitate the production of these organismic substances. We establish the rules of these syntheses with the aid of simplified models. In the course of such work we can give proof by synthesis of the atomic arrangement in the molecules of, for example, higher terpenes. Phellandrene, a terpene obtainable from water fennel or eucalyptus plants, gave diene reactions which easily revealed its molecular structure. The diene synthesis of furane with maleic acid anhydride, two simple and readily available chemicals, furnished cantharidin, an old, medically used venom produced by the so-called Spanish fly and certain beetles.

Naphtho-quinone, one of the substances mentioned above (naphthalene containing two oxygen atoms at opposite ends of one of the rings in its molecule) forms derivatives which have vitamin K activity. They have been synthesized by adding butadiene to an appropriate partner. Similar reactions are being used and sought for the artificial production of other vitamins and of hormones.

Diene compounds can combine with one another to form polymers. The polymerization of butadiene, alone or in conjunction with styrene, leads to synthetic rubber. The experience with diene synthesis offers theoretical explanations for such polymerizations. With their guidance, the methods for manufacturing plastic and rubberlike materials have been improved.

1 9 5 1
GLENN T. SEABORG
(1912-   )

EDWIN M. McMILLAN
(1907-   )

*"For their discoveries in the chemistry of the
transuranium elements."*

BIOGRAPHICAL SKETCH

SEABORG

GLENN T. SEABORG WAS BORN IN ISHPEMING, MICHIGAN. HE
went to school in Los Angeles and received his doctor's degree in
1937 at the University of California in Berkeley for research on
neutrons. After McMillan (see next paragraph) had discovered
the new transuranium element neptunium, Seaborg found, in
1940, that the impact of neutrons on uranium also produces
plutonium. Uranium is number 92 in the series of chemical elements; neptunium is number 93, plutonium 94. Seaborg succeeded
in the following years to enlarge the series by four more trans-
uranites: americium, curium, berkelium, and californium. After
the war, he returned to Berkeley as professor of chemistry. In
1961, he was appointed Chairman of the Atomic Energy Commission.

MCMILLAN

EDWIN MCMILLAN WAS BORN IN REDONDO BEACH, CALIFORNIA. He studied at the California Institute of Technology, then continued at Princeton, where he received his Ph.D. in physics in 1932. He extended his research on high energy radiations at Berkeley. On the basis of these studies, the machines for producing particles of high energy were improved; from the pre-war cyclotrons emitting particles of one hundred thousand electron-volts the new construction of a bevatron has been designed to produce over six billion volts. Uranium, irradiated by neutrons, is partly converted into neptunium as McMillan discovered in 1940. He had to give up further work in this direction for research on radar and sonar equipment at the Massachusetts Institute of Technology, 1940-45. There, he laid the groundwork for the development of the synchrotron and synchro-cyclotron, by which the energy of artificially accelerated particles was extended into the regions of hundreds of million volts. Since 1946 he has been professor of physics at Berkeley.

DESCRIPTION OF THE PRIZE-WINNING WORK*

SEABORG

"A bombardment of uranium oxide with the 16 Mev deuterons from the 60-inch cyclotron was performed in December, 1940. Alpha radioactivity was found to grow into the chemically separated element 93 fraction, and this alpha activity was chemically separated from the neighboring elements, especially elements 90 to 93 inclusive, in experiments performed during the following months. These experiments, which constituted the positive identification of element 94, showed that this element has at least two oxidation states, distinguishable by their precipitation chemistry, and that it requires stronger oxidizing agents to oxidize element 94

---

* From *Les Prix Nobel en 1951*.

to the upper state than is the case for element 93. The particular isotope identified has been shown to be of mass number 238 and the reactions for its preparation are shown in the first slide (Figure 1).

$$_{92}U^{238} + {}_1H^2 \longrightarrow {}_{93}Np^{238} + 2n$$

$$_{93}Np^{238} \xrightarrow[2.1 \text{ days}]{\beta^-} {}_{94}Pu^{238} \text{ (90 years, } \alpha)$$

Figure 1.

"The chemical properties of elements 93 and 94 were studied by the tracer method at the University of California for the next year and a half. These first two transuranium elements were referred to by our group simply as 'element 93' and 'element 94' until the spring of 1942, at which time the first detailed reports concerning these elements were written. In order to write the report on the chemical properties, it became necessary to have chemical symbols for the two elements. It was remembered that McMillan had suggested the name 'neptunium' (symbol Np) for element 93 after Neptune, the planet immediately beyond Uranus, which gives its name to uranium, and, therefore, it was thought proper that element 94 should assume the name 'plutonium' (symbol Pu) after the next planet Pluto. These names and symbols have been adopted officially by the International Union of Chemistry and will be used here.

"The isotope of plutonium which is of major importance is the one with mass number 239. The search for this isotope, as a decay product of Np^{239}, was going on almost simultaneously, and these experiments were being carried on by the same group with the added collaboration of Dr. E. Segrè. The isotope Pu^{239} was identified and its possibilities as a nuclear energy source were established during the spring of 1941 using a sample prepared by the decay of cyclotron produced Np^{239} and later purified by taking advantage of the then known chemistry of plutonium.

"Once the value of the isotope Pu^{239} was thus established, the paramount problem was that of producing it on a large scale and isolating it after production. The production problem was solved through the development of the chain reacting units, or piles, utilizing the neutron induced fission reaction on U^{235} in natural uranium, in which the extra neutrons beyond those needed to perpetuate the chain reaction are absorbed by U^{238} to form the desired isotope Pu^{239}. These well-known reactions are summarized in the following slide (Figure 2).

$$U^{235} + n \longrightarrow \text{fission products} + \text{energy} + \text{neutrons}$$

$$U^{238} + n \longrightarrow {}_{92}U^{239} \xrightarrow[\text{23.5 minutes}]{\beta^-} {}_{93}Np^{239} \xrightarrow{\text{2.33 days}} {}_{94}Pu^{239}$$

Figure 2.

"The isolation of the plutonium was to be done by chemical means, and in the spring of 1942, I and a number of my colleagues moved to the Metallurgical Laboratory at the University of Chicago to work on this problem. Among the people who made outstanding contributions to this separation program, both at Chicago and at other sites, was Dr. I. Perlman, who, it is interesting to note, before this time had made an outstanding reputation in another field, the application of radioactive tracers to physiology and biochemistry. Investigations continued at the University of California under the direction of W. M. Latimer and A. C. Wahl, leading to further discoveries of importance to the program.

"During the first months at the Metallurgical Laboratory intensive effort was directed toward defining the process which was to be used in the production plants which were then being planned. Although it was felt that the separation process would depend on the use of the two oxidation states of plutonium which had been discovered during the early work at the University of California, the actual details, such as the best carrier compounds and best oxidizing and reducing agents, had not yet been discovered. Dr. S. G. Thompson is largely responsible for the conception and early development of the process which was finally chosen. I cannot, of course, give recognition individually to the large group of scientists who participated so successfully in the diverse phases of this overall problem. The first pure neptunium in the form of compounds of the isotope Np^{237} was isolated by L. B. Magnusson and T. J. La Chapelle at the wartime Metallurgical Laboratory in October, 1944. It is fortunately produced as a by-product in the chain reacting piles which has led to the isolation of gram amounts for research purposes. The chemical properties of neptunium in the macroscopic state have been studied with such material, and this had led to a thorough knowledge of the chemistry of this element.

"The identification of element 95 followed soon thereafter. This came in the very late fall of 1944 as a result of the bombardment of Pu^{239} with pile neutrons, the production reactions being as shown in Figure 8.

$$Pu^{239} + n \longrightarrow Pu^{240} + \gamma$$
$$Pu^{240} + n \longrightarrow Pu^{241} + \gamma$$

$$_{94}Pu^{241} \text{ (14 years)} \xrightarrow{\beta^-} {}_{95}Am^{241} \text{ (475 years, } \alpha\text{)}$$

Figure 8.

At the same time the isotope Cm^{242} is formed, and this is presently the best method for its production.

$$Am^{241} + n \xrightarrow{\beta^-} Am^{242} + \gamma$$

$$_{95}Am^{242} \quad \begin{array}{l} \text{(16 hours upper state)} \\ \text{(100 years lower state)} \end{array} \xrightarrow{\beta} {}_{96}Cm^{242} \text{ (162 days, } \alpha\text{)}$$

Figure 9.

"There are a couple of comments which should be made here concerning the rare earthlike properties of these two elements. Our hypothesis that they should have a stable (III) oxidation state and greatly resemble the rare earth elements in their chemical properties proved to be so true that for a time it appeared to be most unfortunate. The better part of a year was spent in trying to separate chemically the two elements from each other and from the rare earth elements but without success, and although we felt entirely confident, on the basis of their radioactive properties and the methods of production, that isotopes of elements 95 and 96 had been produced, the chemical proof remained to be demonstrated. The elements remained unnamed during this period of futile attempts at separation, although one of our group insisted in referring to them by the names 'pandemonium' and 'delirium' in recognition of our difficulties. However, they were finally separated and completely identified chemically, and, in fact, their present names were eventually proposed on the basis of their chemical properties but with a more serious basis. The name 'americium' (symbol Am) was suggested for element 95, thus naming it after the Americas by analogy with the naming of its rare earth homologue europium after Europe, and the name 'curium' (symbol Cm) was suggested for element 96 after Pierre and Marie Curie by analogy with the naming of its homologue gadolinium after Gadolin. These names and symbols will be used here and were used in the preceding slides.

"Americium was first isolated by Cunningham in the form of a pure compound in the fall of 1945 at the wartime Metallurgical Laboratory. It can be prepared in milligram amounts by the neutron bombardment of plutonium according to reactions shown on a foregoing slide (Figure 8), and thus it has been possible to investigate its chemical properties extensively through the use of macroscopic quantities.

"Curium was first isolated in the form of a pure compound of Cm^{242} by L. B. Werner and I. Perlman at the University of California during the fall of 1947. The isotope Cm^{242} is so highly radioactive, due to its short half-life, that chemical investigations with it in macroscopic concentrations are very difficult. Nevertheless a large number of such investigations have been carried on and much has been learned about its chemical properties.

"More recent work has led to the identification of a number of heavier isotopes of americium, curium, and plutonium which present interesting possibilities. It should be mentioned that the successful handling in a safe manner of the huge amounts of radioactivity in the target material was made possible through the use of the excellent protective equipment provided by Nelson Garden and the members of his Health Chemistry Group at our Laboratory.

"The name 'berkelium' (symbol Bk) was suggested for element

97 after the city where the work was done, in analogy with the naming of its chemical homologue terbium, which was named after the town of Ytterby here in Sweden where the rare earth minerals were first found. The name 'californium' (symbol Cf) was suggested for element 98 in honor of the University and State where the work was done; thus the name does not reflect its strong homology to dysprosium. These names are used in the present talk including the various slides.

"Soon following this work, it became possible on the basis of the interesting pioneer carbon ion bombardment experiments of Miller, Hamilton, Putnam, Haymond, and Rossi in the 60-inch cyclotron to produce isotopes of californium in better yield by this method. These experiments, in which uranium is bombarded with carbon ions, led to the production of californium isotopes according to the reactions given in Figure 15."

$$_{92}U^{238} + {}_6C^{12} \longrightarrow {}_{98}Cf^{244} \qquad\qquad + 6n$$

$$(45 \text{ minutes}, \alpha)$$

$$_{92}U^{238} + {}_6C^{12} \longrightarrow {}_{98}Cf^{246} \qquad\qquad + 4n$$

$$(36 \text{ hours}, \alpha)$$

Figure 15.

MCMILLAN

"In this talk I shall tell of the circumstances that led to the discovery of neptunium, the first element beyond uranium, and the partial identification of plutonium, the next one beyond that. The part of the story that lies before 1939 has already been recounted here in the Nobel lectures of Fermi and Hahn; I played no part in that and shall not repeat it now. Rather I shall start with the discovery of fission by Hahn and Strassmann. News of this momentous discovery reached Berkeley in 1939. The staff of the Radiation Laboratory was put into a state of great excitement and several experiments of a nature designed to check and extend the announced results were started, using ionization chambers and pulse amplifiers, cloud chambers, chemical methods, and so forth.

"I decided to do an experiment of a very simple kind. When a nucleus of uranium absorbs a neutron and fission takes place, the two resulting fragments fly apart with great violence, sufficient to propel them through air or other matter for some distance. This distance, called the "range," is a quantity of some interest, and I undertook to measure it by observing the depth of penetration of the fission fragments in a stack of thin aluminum foils. The fission fragments came from a thin layer of uranium oxide spread on a sheet of paper, and exposed to neutrons from a beryllium target bombarded by 8 MeV deuterons in the 37-inch cyclotron. The aluminum foils, each with a thickness of about half a milligram per square centimeter, were stacked like the pages of a book in immediate contact with the layer of uranium oxide. After exposure to the neutrons, the sheets of aluminum were separated and examined for radioactivity by means of an ionization chamber. The fission fragments of course are radioactive atoms, and their activity is found where they stop.

"The result of the experiment is shown in Fig. 1. The horizontal scale indicates the depth in the stack of foils, in terms of equivalent centimeters of air. The vertical scale indicates the activities of the foils, measured about two hours after the end of the neutron bombardment. The greatest depth of penetration and therefore

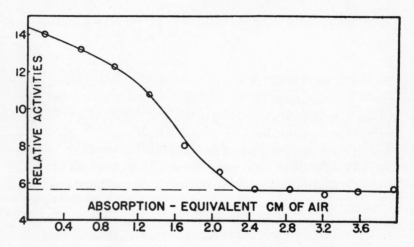

Fig. 1. Result of experiment to determine the range of fission fragments.

the maximum range of the fragments is seen to be a little over two centimeters; the activity beyond this depth is that produced by the action of the neutrons on the aluminum itself, and it is seen to be nearly as great as the fission product activity on the first foil. There were however some interesting details of the fission process whose observation would be rendered difficult by this large background of activity. The fission fragments have various masses and therefore various ranges; is there any difference in the rate of decay of the long-range and short-range fragments? To find this out, I did a second experiment in which the foils were made of paper, a material which would not itself become radioactive. Since ordinary paper contains mineral matter, the backing for the uranium oxide was filter paper, and the thin foils were cigarette paper that had been extracted with acid. These were neither as thin nor as uniform as the aluminum foils, but that did not matter in this experiment.

"Nothing very interesting about the fission fragments came out of this; the decay curves of the activities deposited on the various cigarette papers were about alike. However the filter paper, which held the uranium and at least half the fission products, showed something very interesting. Its decay curve was different; there was present a strong activity with a half-life of about 25 minutes, and another with a half-life of about two days. These lives could not be measured accurately because of the presence of part of the fission product activity in the same sample, but there was no doubt of their occurrence. The shorter period could with reasonable certainty be ascribed to the 23-minute uranium isotope U-239, discovered by Hahn, Meitner, and Strassmann in 1936. Since this is formed by simple neutron capture, it would not recoil out of the uranium oxide layer like the fission fragments. The two-day period could then be the product of the beta-decay of U-239, and therefore an isotope of element 93; in fact this was its most reasonable explanation. However some time was to elapse before the proof of this would be given.

"When it thus became possible to prepare a new active substance in reasonably good purity by simple physical means, the question of its chemistry could be investigated, and Segrè undertook to do this. The expected chemical properties of element 93, according to the periodic table, were those of rhenium. Segrè was very

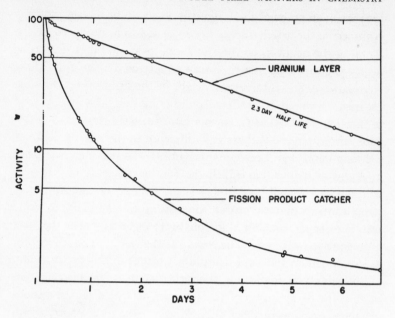

Fig. 2. Later part of decay curves of the activities found after neutron irradiation in a thin layer of $(NH_4)_2U_2O_7$, and in a sheet of cellophane ("fission product catcher") which was next to that layer during the irradiation.

familiar with the chemistry of this element, since he and his co-workers had discovered another of its homologs, now called technetium, in 1937; this was the first of the synthetic elements to be found. He showed that the 2.3 day material had none of the properties of rhenium, and indeed acted like a rare earth instead. Since rare earths are prominent among the fission products, this discovery seemed at the time to end the story. However as time went on and the fission process became better understood, I found it increasingly difficult to believe that one fission product should behave in a way so different from the rest, and early in 1940 I returned to the problem. By this time the 60-inch cyclotron was running and deuterons of 16 MeV were available. Two physical experiments were illuminating. In one, the effect of cadmium, which absorbs thermal neutrons, was investigated. It reduced the fission product activity compared to the two non-recoiling activities, without changing the ratio of the latter. In the second, the earlier recoil experiments were repeated with a fission product catcher made of very thin collodion, and it was found that the range of the 2.3 day substance was certainly not greater than 0.1 millimeter of air. These great differences in behavior from the fission products made the interpretation of the 2.3 day activity as a rare earth almost impossible.

"At this point I started to do some chemistry, and in spite of what the Nobel committee may think, I am not a chemist. However I did find that the 2.3 period did not always follow the rare-earth chemistry consistently. For instance, in a fluoride precipitation with rare-earth carrier, sometimes only a part of the activity would come down, part remaining in solution. The key to the situation was the state of oxidation of the material. When in a reduced state, it precipitates with rare earth fluorides; when in an oxidized state, it does not. In earlier work where the degree of oxidation was not controlled, erratic results are not surprising.

"After Abelson's rather industrious "vacation" was over I returned to the search for the alpha particles. The lanthanum fluoride precipitate bearing the products of the decay of the strong element 93 sample did show an alpha activity, which was at first suspected of being due to contamination with natural uranium. However a measurement of the range showed that it was too long for that and therefore might actually be from the long-sought element 94. I then tried bombarding uranium directly with the 16-MeV deuterons from the cyclotron, in the hope that this might produce a different isotope of element 94 with a shorter life, giving a greater rate of alpha-particle emission. This hope proved to be well founded, and a considerably stronger alpha-activity was found in the decay products of the element 93 separated from the deuteron-bombarded sample. The next slide (Fig. 6) shows the nuclear reactions involved in the formation of the two isotopes of element 94. At the time of which I am speaking, the half lives of the alpha emitters and the correct isotopic assignment of the one produced by deuterons were not known. However the names "Neptunium" and "Plutonium" had already been suggested so it seems appropriate that the corresponding chemical symbols are shown on the slide.

$$U^{238} + n \longrightarrow \gamma + U^{239} \text{ (instantaneous)}$$

$$U^{239} \longrightarrow \beta^- + Np^{239} \text{ (23 minutes)}$$

$$Np^{239} \longrightarrow \beta^- + Pu^{239} \text{ (23 days)}$$

$$Pu^{239} \longrightarrow \alpha + U^{235} \text{ (24,000 years)}$$

$$U^{238} + d \longrightarrow 2n + Np^{238} \text{ (instantaneous)}$$

$$Np^{238} \longrightarrow \beta^- + Pu^{238} \text{ (2.1 days)}$$

$$Pu^{238} \longrightarrow \alpha + U^{234} \text{ (92 years)}$$

Fig. 6. Nuclear reactions concerned in the production and decay of two plutonium isotopes. The times on the right are the half lives of the processes indicated.

CONSEQUENCES IN THEORY AND PRACTICE

The work for which the 1951 Nobel Prizes in physics and chemistry have been awarded has involved tremendous consequences for our life and science. The basis for this work was constructed through research for which twenty-five previous Nobel Prizes in physics and eleven in chemistry had been given. Some of the fundamental concepts, like that of the Periodic System of the elements, were the result of older efforts. In this system, there is a group of 15 elements, starting with lanthanum, which resemble each other very closely. Niels Bohr's theory (see p. 35) explained the resemblance by the arrangement of the electrons in the atom. From lanthanum (atomic number 57) through the lanthanides to lutetium (number 71), the number of electrons increases only in an inner shell; the electrons of the outer shell, which are those most active in chemical reaction, remain the same in this series. The actinides form an analogous series, beginning with the radioelement actinium (89). Fourteen members of this series (89-102) are now known, many of them through the discoveries of McMillan, Seaborg, and their associates.

The chemistry of the unweighable, of which Marie Curie (see p. 46) spoke, has become an ultra-micro chemistry dealing with much smaller quantities than F. Pregl (see p. 92) taught to handle. And these new elements, first obtained in microgram quantities as the result of an advance to new frontiers of physico-chemical operations, have been produced soon afterwards in large quantities with the use of giant plants in which the limits of engineering were extended beyond those of ten years ago.

While the advent of a new World War may have been averted up to now by the adaptability of some of the new elements for atomic weapons, their application as sources of energy is expanding in land-based power stations and sea-going ships.

The study of these new, synthetic elements continues. In 1961, the Atomic Energy Commission provided five European institutions with the following quantities:

Americium 243 mg., Curium 244 mg., Berkelium 249 micrograms, Californium 252 micrograms. A new high-flux isotope reactor is to be completed at the Oak Ridge Laboratory in 1964 and is expected to furnish greater quantities of synthetic elements.

1 9 5 2
Archer John Porter Martin
(1910-   )

Richard Laurence Millington Synge
(1914-   )

*"For their discovery of partition
chromatography."*

BIOGRAPHICAL SKETCH

MARTIN

ARCHER JOHN PORTER MARTIN WAS BORN IN LONDON IN 1910. At Cambridge University, his interest in engineering was diverted to biochemistry by J. B. S. Haldane. After graduating in 1932, he worked under L. J. Harris at the Dunn Nutritional Laboratory, mainly on vitamin E, until 1938, then at the Wool Industries Research Association at Leeds until 1946.

"From 1946-48 he was head of the Biochemistry Division of the Research Department of Boots Pure Drug Co., Nottingham. In 1948 he joined the staff of the Medical Research Council, first at the Lister Institute and later at the National Institute for Medical Research, where he is now head of the Division of Physical Chemistry. With Dr. A. T. James he has recently developed the method of gas liquid chromatography." *

---

* Quoted from the autobiographical note in *Les Prix Nobel en 1952*, p. 72.

SYNGE

RICHARD LAURENCE MILLINGTON SYNGE WAS BORN OCTOBER 28, 1914, in Liverpool. At Winchester School he first studied classics and then turned to science. He was a research student at the laboratory of F. G. Hopkins from 1936-39 and at the Wool Industries Research Association 1939-41. His doctor's thesis at Cambridge was on the amino acids of wool, 1941. In 1943 he went to the Lister Institute of Preventive Medicine, London.

"Since 1945 I have been mainly interested in analytical problems concerning the larger peptide molecules, as antibiotics and as intermediates in protein metabolism. From 1942 to 1948 I worked almost exclusively with the antibiotic peptides of the gramicidin group. I spent eight months (1946-47) studying under Arne Tiselius at Fysikaliskkemiska Institutionen, Uppsala, the application of his adsorption methods to these compounds. Since 1948 I have been head of the Department of Protein and Carbohydrate Chemistry at the Rowett Research Institute, Bucksburn, Aberdeenshire." *

DESCRIPTION OF THE PRIZE-WINNING WORK†

MARTIN

"Partition chromatography resulted from the marrying of two techniques, that of chromatography and that of countercurrent solvent extraction. All of the ideas are simple and had peoples' minds been directed that way the method would have flourished perhaps a century earlier. In fact the minds of laboratory workers seem to have been closed to countercurrent procedures, which were adopted in industry, e.g. in distillation and lixiviation, long before they were generally used in the laboratory. In industry the use of the countercurrent principle led to great economies in heat and

---

* Quoted from the autobiographical note in *Les Prix Nobel en 1952*, p. 73.

---

† From *Les Prix Nobel en 1952*.

solvents, and its value was obvious: in the laboratory such economies are of comparatively little importance and the more subtle
point that by its aid a vast improvement in certain difficult separations could be effected was not appreciated. Indeed it is only within
the last twenty years that high efficiency distillation apparatus has
been available in the laboratory and twenty-five years elapsed after
Tswett's classical work on chromatography before the latter method
was put to general use. Synge and I were fortunate to work at a
time when the need for new methods was apparent to many people,
so that our methods have gained general acceptance in ten years.

"I was already familiar with the use of filterpaper chromatograms as used by the dyestuff chemists and adopted at first their
technique. A ten-centimetre circular paper was cut to a semicircle
with a three-centimetre tail about one-centimetre wide at the centre.
On this tail near the centre was placed a drop of a solution of
valine and leucine. The tail was put in butanol saturated with water
contained in a Petri dish surrounded by water saturated with
butanol in a glass jar. The semicircle of paper rested on the edge
of the Petri dish. The top of the jar was covered with a glass plate.
When the butanol had reached the edge of the paper it was taken
out and dried and dipped in a solution of ninhydrin in ether. On
heating, two semi-circles of colour were observable, and it was
evident the method was a success. It was found quicker and more
convenient to hang strips of paper from troughs containing the
solvents, and this method was adopted as a routine. There followed
a period in which we tried all the solvents we could lay our hands
on, and logged the positions of the various amino acids in each of
these. Experiment showed that the theory we had put forward for
the silica columns applied equally well to paper chromatograms.
It was indeed surprising with what closeness the solvent power of
the water in the paper followed that of free water.

"No one solvent, however, was able to resolve a mixture of all
the common amino acids, and I tried to separate into acidic, neutral
and basic fractions by ionophoresis, prior to separation in a direction at right angles by chromatography. The method adopted was
rather clumsy. Each end of a square paper was treated with paraffin
wax so that a centimetre-wide strip of untreated paper was left,
nearer one end than the other. This strip was moistened with

acetate buffer and a drop of amino acid mixture put in the middle. Copper wires were applied to either end of the strip and a potential of two hundred volts applied. After a couple of hours the paper was dried, the paraffin wax removed with petroleum ether and the paper developed as a chromatogram with water-saturated butanol. A two dimensional separation of the amino acids was revealed on spraying with ninhydrin and heating. The separation however of the neutral group of amino acids was not satisfactory. Attention was therefore concentrated on chromatography successively in two directions at right angles.

"This two dimensional development of paper chromatograms, of the classical not the partition type, had already been done by Liesegang, but I was unaware of this until just lately.

The high sensitivity of the ninhydrin reaction made it possible to do a chromatographic analysis with a few micrograms of any amino acid. So little labour was involved that it was possible for hundreds of analyses to be done simultaneously. Even in the case of unknown substances, something could be inferred of their nature from their behaviour in different solvents.

"We were convinced that the method was by no means confined to amino acids. Partridge spent a day or two in our laboratory and a few days after his return to Cambridge, wrote to us that he had been able to separate reducing sugars, and detect them with silver nitrate. He found that practically the same solvent systems were satisfactory for sugars and amino acids. Later he worked out the methods for carbohydrates as completely as we had done for amino acids.

"Elsden and Synge showed that potato starch could be used to pack a column and gave essentially the same separations of amino acids as did paper sheets. Moore and Stein showed that with careful control, a complete quantitative analysis of a protein could be performed on starch columns using a ninhydrin colorimetric method. They also introduced the use of automatic fraction collectors which are now so widely used. Later the starch columns were superseded by ion exchange resins. Their methods now provide the best means of protein analysis.

"I will now return to the silica columns. For the acetyl amino acids we used water as the stationary phase. So also did Elsden, who adapted it for the lower fatty acids. Isherwood used sulphuric acid instead for the separation of hydroxy and dicarboxylic acids since it was desirable to suppress their ionisation. Levi used a buffer for penicillin separations, in this case to obtain a given proportion of the penicillin in the ionised form. These penicillin columns were widely used and kieselguhr rather than precipitated silica was found satisfactory in America. Its great advantage was that it was available commercially and was less variable than precipitated silica, and less likely to cause trouble due to adsorption. To get good columns, however, a new technique of packing the columns was required. This technique is not, however, difficult and I consider that for most purposes precipitated silica is now obsolete. Kieselguhr has an advantage in another respect. The pore size of precipitated silica is small enough to preclude its use for very large molecules, whereas that of the kieselguhr is relatively almost infinite. In fact, Porter and I have shown that it is possible to separate ribonuclease into two different fractions on a partition chromatogram using kieselguhr as support. Admittedly this is a small and atypical protein but Porter has extended its use to a few other proteins.

"The surface of silica is wetted preferentially by the more polar of a given pair of liquid phases in equilibrium. So that in the usual column the mobile phase has to be the less polar one, and only those substances whose partition coefficient is in favour of the less polar phase, can be satisfactorily separated. By treatment of the silica with a silicone or silane the surface becomes preferentially wetted by the less polar phase. A 'reversed phase' column thus becomes possible, suitable for the separation of substances which favour the less polar phase.

"The first 'reversed phase' chromatogram was a paper one loaded with rubber latex, and was due to Boldingh. He also used columns packed with powdered rubber, for the separation of the higher fatty acids. Paper alone or silane treated, will hold a liquid hydrocarbon and give satisfactory chromatograms, with say aqueous alcohols as the moving phase.

"Finally, I would like to mention gas-liquid chromatography. Synge and I suggested the possibility of this ten years ago in our first paper on the partition chromatogram. No one seems to have taken it up until James and I did so recently, to try and encourage ourselves after a very unsuccessful attempt to put fractional crystallisation on a column basis. These chromatograms differ from the usual ones only in that the mobile phase is a gas instead of the usual liquid. They are suitable of course only for volatile substances.

"Because gas is so mobile compared to liquid it is feasible to use much longer and thinner columns, and since diffusion is so much more rapid to move the gas rapidly without increasing the H.E.T.P. It is thus possible to use columns with a very high separating efficiency. So far our work has been confined to substances which can be titrated, acids and amines. A more general method of detecting vapours in the gas issuing from the chromatograms should, however, make this type of column available for use with all types of substances that can be distilled at a pressure of a few millimetres of mercury. Whereas, with distillation, apparatus has at most several hundred theoretical plates, gas chromatographic columns with one to ten thousand plates are readily possible, and the quantity of material required for analysis is milligrams instead of grams.

"It is very easy with the chromatographic apparatus to measure the free energy of solution of a given volatile substance in the stationary phase. I hope it will be possible to learn with its aid a great deal about the molecular forces involved in solution."

SYNGE

"About this time, in 1937, Dr. Hedley R. Marston (then, as now, director of the C. S. I. R. Nutrition Laboratory at Adelaide, South Australia) came to the Biochemical Laboratory in Cambridge for a year as a guest. He was given bench space in the room where Pirie and I were working. He brought with him apparatus much more complicated than most workers in that laboratory were accustomed to, including an "artificial rumen" for microbial digestion of cellulose and a long fractionating column for distilling the esters of the resulting fatty acids. This by no means occupied his whole time, and we were impressed by the large number of letters which he wrote and by the frequent recurrence of his birthdays, which he celebrated by inviting numerous colleagues to very lively scientific discussions in a nearby public house.

"After about six months I began better to understand Marston's extramural activities when he told me that he was advising an organisation called the International Wool Secretariat. This was given funds by the wool growers of Australia, New Zealand and South Africa for the purpose of publicity and research; they were worried both by the advent of various synthetic fibres which it was then thought might prove to be effective substitutes for wool. Marston's advice was to apply some of their money to fundamental studies of the nature of wool, and he suggested that part should be given to me as a Studentship to study in detail the amino-acid composition of wool, beginning by improving the methods of amino-acid analysis. 'If you work steadily at that for five years, you will revolutionize the whole of protein chemistry,' he said.

"The Studentship was on unusually generous financial terms, and as I also thought it would fit in with acquiring a more detailed knowledge of the protein side of the glycoprotein problem, I readily agreed. I began work in 1938 by studying the distribution of acetyl amino-acids between chloroform-water phases as a possible analytical procedure, directly suggested by Neuberger's experiments. The partition coefficients showed very encouraging differences, and I was advised from all sides to consult Dr. A. J. P. Martin as to how best to conduct the separations, since his bizarre-looking apparatus for purifying vitamin E at the Dunn Nutritional Laboratory had attracted wide-spread notice in Cambridge.

"I will discuss in most detail the application of partition chromatography to the study of proteins. Partly because the earliest work with the method was in this field, the results obtained with partition chromatography have been especially striking here, although the method has similar capabilities in other branches of biochemistry.

"First, the method has given the possibility of exhaustive analysis of complete hydrolysates of proteins.

"Partition chromatography has likewise been valuable for assessing the purity of amino-acids and simple peptides and for studying the actions of enzymes so far as such simpler molecules are concerned. Previously unsuspected "transpeptidations" and syntheses have been revealed by this means.

"The method has proved useful for the various procedures for allocating free functional groups within molecules of proteins or peptides; thus at present we have procedures for recognition of free amino groups by substitution with dinitrophenyl and other radicals, and of carboxyl groups by reduction to the corresponding alcohols or by enzymic hydrolysis of terminal amino-acids. These methods nearly always use partition chromatography as a final stage in the identification.

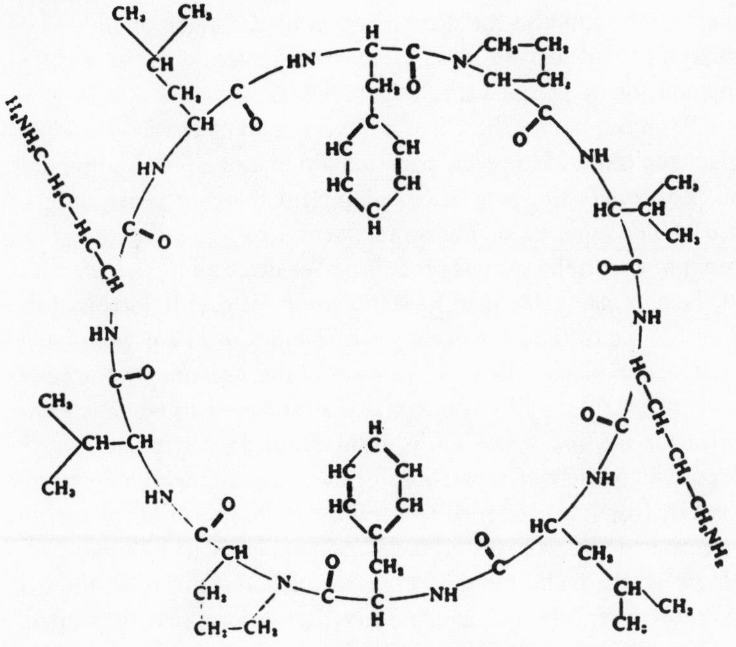

Fig. 3. Probable formula of gramicidin S.

"Finally, partition chromatography is of great importance for ascertaining the sequence of amino-acid residues in the peptide chains of proteins. Martin and I had this use particularly in mind throughout our work. If a peptide chain is partially degraded to dipeptide and tripeptide fragments etc., it should be possible, by identifying these, to recognize the original compound from which they are derived; thus in a simple case the peptide chain represented A-B-C-D-E will give rise to the fragments A-B, B-C, C-D, and D-E, permitting an unequivocal reconstruction. Martin and I, with

R. Consden and A. H. Gordon, were able in this way, mainly using partition-chromatographic methods, to determine the amino-acid sequence in gramicidin S, which is probably a cyclic decapeptide (Fig. 3).

"In the study of carbohydrates partition chromatography has played a very similar rôle. It can be used for determining ultimate hydrolysis products of polysaccharides qualitatively and quantitatively, it permits analysis of naturally occurring free sugars and their esters, and also the determination of the mode of linkage of the component parts of more complicated molecules by substitution methods or by partial hydrolysis methods.

"With the lipides there is not the problem of chemical study of giant molecules. However, partition chromatography is admirably adapted to effecting separations within homologous series, and the use of non-aqueous or multicomponent two-phase liquid systems combined with the various procedures for determining which phase in the chromatogram shall be stationary have greatly increased the scope of the method for dealing with lipides in recent years.

"Outside biochemistry, it is probably the technological applications of partition chromatography that are most important. However, the method, particularly using cellulose, has proved useful for a wide variety of separations of metals and inorganic ions, and the fact that it can be used to handle minute quantities of carrier-free radio-active isotopes gives it considerable scientific importance. However, the main importance of the method seems to be towards making easier, cheaper and quicker the various analytical operations used in industrial research and routine control of production. The applications in metallurgy are obviously considerable, and the method is useful for control of intermediates in organic-chemical industry generally, whether concerned with dyestuffs, drugs, explosives, plastic materials, or other products. The gas-liquid chromatogram, representing fractional distillation pushed to its logical conclusion, obviously has an important future role in industrial research and control wherever mixtures of volatile compounds have to be handled, as in the fermentation, tar-distilling and petroleum industries. Here the method seems likely to compete with mass spectrometry. Except possibly with the most expensive drugs, partition chromatography has had little use as a method for actual production, on account of the large bulk of apparatus, chromatographic materials and solvents in relation to the substances being separated."

CONSEQUENCES IN THEORY
AND PRACTICE

For chemical analysis, we use various means differing in the strength of their action on the substance to be investigated. The strongest actions are required for the determination of the elementary composition, finer gradations for recognizing the way in which the elements are combined in building complex molecules. The gentlest actions are required, when the task is to separate substances in chemically pure form out of a mixture and yet avoid interference with the composition of these substances. Analysis by chromatography is one of the means for analyzing in such gentle and yet efficient ways, with the additional great advantage that very small quantities of material can be used. Thus, the method has been successfully applied to the separation of the flavor substances in coffee and other fruits, the composition of tobacco smoke, tiny residues of insecticides on plant foods, or hormones added to animal feeds remaining in the meat. Another example is the separation and identification of about 125 substances in a sample of gasoline.

For these analyses, gas chromatography is used, with various kinds of surface-treated solid particles, with appropriate carrier gases, and with particular attention to the means by which the separated substances are measured. The most versatile of these is thermal conductivity. Process controls in laboratory and plant are thus carried out.

Chromatographic separations of solutions on paper or through absorption columns have also been greatly expanded. Analyses of complex mixtures of carbohydrates or proteins, of fats and vitamins are thus carried out quickly and delicately. The classical methods, which appear so much more cumbersome, have provided the foundations for these new advances. Some eighty related, but chemically different steroids have been found in urines by chromatographic techniques. Many advances in physiology and medicine continue to be made through these means.

1953
HERMANN STAUDINGER
(1881-   )

"For his discoveries in the chemistry of macro-molecular substances."

BIOGRAPHICAL SKETCH

HERMANN STAUDINGER WAS BORN ON MARCH 23, 1881, IN THE Rhine city of Worms. He studied at several German universities and obtained his doctor's degree at Halle in 1903. After a short semester as Privat-Dozent in Strassburg, 1907, he became associate professor in Karlsruhe, full professor at Zurich's Technische Hochschule in 1912 and at Freiburg/Breisgau in 1926. An Institute for macromolecular chemistry was founded for him at Freiburg in 1940. Since 1951 he has been professor emeritus there.

His first work was concerned with the highly unstable ketenes, obtained, for example, by internal dehydration of acetone. He described these compounds in his first book, "Die Ketene," 1912. Twenty years later, he presented his research on rubber and cellulose in his book: "Die hochmolekularen Verbindungen, Kautschuk und Cellulose." He enlarged his field of activities to "Makromolekulare Chemie und Biologie," summarized in his book of 1947. He edited the journal "Die makromolekulare Chemie" since 1947. He received honorary awards from many scientific organizations in many European countries.

DESCRIPTION OF THE PRIZE-WINNING WORK *

"The field of macromolecular chemistry has been intensively worked over in the last decades, scientifically as well as industrially. I myself have been active in macromolecular chemistry since 1920, first at the Eidgenössische Technische Hochschule in Zurich. Since moving to the chemical university laboratory in Freiburg, I have devoted myself completely to this field, and work continues there after my retirement.

"The preparation of macromolecular products uses several different ways. First, consider polymerization, which is a peculiar chain reaction unknown in the chemistry of low-molecular compounds.

Formulation:

Polymerization of Styrene:

$$CH = CH_2 \quad \xrightarrow{\text{Primary act}} \quad -CH-CH_2- \quad \xrightarrow{\text{Chain growth}}$$
$$\underset{C_6H_5}{|} \qquad\qquad\qquad\qquad \underset{C_6H_5}{|}$$

1. Styrene   2. Activated Styrene

$$-CH-CH_2-\left[\begin{array}{c}CH-CH_2\\ | \\ C_6H_5\end{array}\right]_n \;-CH-CH_2- \quad \xrightarrow{\text{Reaction stop}}$$
$$\underset{C_6H_5}{|} \qquad\qquad\qquad\qquad\qquad \underset{C_6H_5}{|}$$

3. Macro-radical

$$CH_2-CH_2- \left[\begin{array}{c}CH-CH_2\\ | \\ C_6H_5\end{array}\right]_n \;-C=CH_2$$
$$\underset{C_6H_5}{|} \qquad\qquad\qquad\qquad\qquad \underset{C_6H_5}{|}$$

4. Macro-molecule
$$n = 10 \text{ to } 10^4$$

---

* Translated parts from *Les Prix Nobel en 1953*.

"Next, macromolecular substances can be prepared by poly-condensation, a procedure long known in industry, which Leo H. Baekeland already used for obtaining the highly important pheno-plasts. This field was further elaborated by W. H. Carothers and led to technically valuable products, like Nylon.

"Another method of making macromolecular compounds is the polyaddition with diisocyanates, worked out by O. Bayer.

"It occurs that a polymeric compound can be converted into certain derivatives without any change in the degree of polymerization, exactly like small molecules. A polymeric compound can thus be transformed into polymer-analogue derivatives. Such transformation proves that all the fundamental molecules that are contained in the colloidal particle of these polymeric compounds are mutually held together by ordinary valences, in other words, this colloidal particle is a macromolecule. This method of proving the molecular state becomes particularly evident by the fact that in a polymer-homologous series several of its members can be transformed into polymer-analogous derivatives. This will be discussed with cellulose as the example.

"In a polymer-homologous series of degraded cellulose acetates of low molecular weights, the measurements of the molecular weight by means of terminal groups and by osmotic pressure give the same result, which proves that the molecules have the form of unbranched chains. The viscosity number Z, i.e. the increase in viscosity produced by adding one gram to one liter of solution of these compounds, is proportional to the degree of polymerization.

"With cellulose acetates of higher molecular weights, the measurement by terminal groups cannot be carried out. However, the relationships between osmotically measured degrees of polymerization and viscosity number Z are the same as for the lower polymers, which proves that these high-molecular cellulose acetates form macromolecules in solution and that their chains are unbranched.

"For other polysaccharides, e.g. starch, glycogen, mannan, and for several synthetic resins, it has been shown that the colloidal particles in their solutions are identical with the macromolecules. It is amazing that with these large and oftentimes complicated molecules the same kind of reactions can be performed as are known for molecules of low weight. Such polymer-analogous reactions thus show very impressively the stability of the macro-radicals, which are also important for the substances of the living cell.

"Among the deep-seated differences between macromolecular and low-molecular compounds is the influence, which the shape of the macromolecules exerts on the physical and chemical properties of the substances. For example, the normal nonnane with its long, extended molecules, and tetra-ethyl-methane with its spherical molecules, both hydrocarbons of the formula C_9H_{20}, are scarcely different in their properties. On the other hand, glycogen, in which 5,000 glucose residues are combined in spherical shape, is vastly different from a cellulose containing the same number of glucose residues arranged in the form of a long chain. This leads to a division of the macromolecular substances into two large groups, the sphero-molecular substances with spherical molecules, and the linear-molecular substances with thread-like molecules. Naturally, these two classes are connected by transitions. There is a large number of natural and synthetic products with many-branched macromolecules, e.g. starch.

"It is characteristic for the chemistry of macromolecular compounds that very small quantities of substances can produce great changes of the physical properties. For example, an addition of 0,0025% divinylbenzene to styrene is sufficient for connecting the chain of polystyrene by divinylbenzene bridges in polymerization. Thereby, the soluble polystyrene with its infinite ability to swell is transformed into the insoluble form, which absorbs solvent by solvatation and swells, but does not dissolve.

"The results of macromolecular chemistry show that a single macromolecule, no matter how big and complex, is not 'alive.' To become alive, it needs a definite quantity of substances composed of numerous macromolecules together with required small molecules in an exactly prescribed order, an 'atomos' of the living substance, which cannot be subdivided without losing its 'life.'

"To gain an impression of what quantities of macromolecules and lower molecules are required, at a minimum, for 'being alive,' the following estimate is offered:

"One bacterial spore with a diameter of 0.124 μ weighs 10^{-15}

grams (at spec. grav. $= 1$) and consists of 5×10^7 atoms, disregarding the water content of 50%."

"Number of molecules in one bacterial spore,
assuming it is composed of

30%	macromolecules	of 10^6 atoms	$=$	15	molecules
30%	"	of 10^5 "		150	"
10%	"	of 10^4 "		500	"
10%	molecules	of 10^3 "		5,000	"
10%	"	of 10^2 "		50,000	"
10%	"	of 10 "		500,000	" "

CONSEQUENCES IN THEORY
AND PRACTICE

Staudinger maintained the concept of the macromolecule against several efforts to prove that highly polymeric substances consisted of micelles and associations between the smaller units, represented by the basic formulas expressing the elementary composition. He showed, for the substances he investigated, that the usual molecule-forming forces provide sufficient explanation and that it was not necessary or warranted to introduce new kinds of forces of association. The problem recurs for the nucleoproteins, and Staudinger's thoughts and methods, e.g. measuring viscosities and relating them to molecular sizes, are being used in this field, as they were for cellulose.

A further extension comprises the calculation of bond-strengths within the molecule (Kurt H. Meyer, Hermann Mark, and others). These calculations appear highly theoretical, but they acquire very practical importance by being connected with the usual properties of macromolecular synthetic resins.

1 9 5 4
LINUS PAULING
(1901-   )

*"For his research into the nature of the chemical
bond and its application to the elucidation of
the structure of complex substances."*

BIOGRAPHICAL SKETCH

LINUS PAULING WAS BORN IN PORTLAND, OREGON. IN 1925, HE
received his doctor's degree from California Institute of Technology. At this institution, he became professor and director of
the Gates and Crellin Laboratories of chemistry.

From the study of crystals by means of X-rays, and of the
molecules in gases by electron-diffraction, he deduced values for
the lengths of chemical bonds. On this basis, he constructed
models for the structure of silicates. He collaborated with Maurice
L. Higgins on his table of atomic radii and expanded the concepts
of G. N. Lewis, together with those of Walter Heitler and Fritz
London, on explaining the chemical bond by electrons and
quantum mechanics. To the classical concept of chemical structure
he added that of resonance, i.e. a precisely defined vibration between two idealized states. From about 1936 on, he devoted most
of his research to biochemical problems, including the structure
of proteins, the physiological function of antibodies, the effects of
certain blood cell anomalies, and of anesthetics.

247

His book, "The Nature of the Chemical Bond" first appeared in 1939 and is now in its third edition.

He has received many honors, among them the Nichols Medal in 1941, the U.S. Medal of Merit for his contributions to research on medicine and on explosives during the second World War, the Willard Gibbs Medal in 1946 and the Royal Society's Davy Medal in 1947. His deep concern with human affairs found expression in his book "No More War," 1958.

DESCRIPTION OF THE PRIZE-WINNING WORK*

"The idea that the properties of many organic compounds— especially the aromatic compounds—cannot be simply correlated with a single valence-bond structure but require the assignment of a somewhat more complex electronic structure was developed during the period 1923 to 1926 by a number of chemists, including Lowry, Lapworth, Robinson and Ingold in England, Lucas in the United States, and Arndt and Eistert in Germany. It was recognized that the properties of aromatic and conjugated molecules can be described by the use of two or more valence-bond structures, as reflected in the names—the theory of mesomerism and the theory of intermediate states—that were proposed for the new chemical theory.

"In 1931 Slater, E. Hückel and others recognized that these theories can be given a quantum-mechanical interpretation: an approximate wave function for a molecule of this sort can be set up as the sum of wave functions representing the hypothetical structures that correspond to the individual valence-bond structures. The molecule can then be described as having a structure that is a hybrid of the individual valence-bond structures, or as resonating among these structures, and the theory itself is now usually called the resonance theory of chemical structure. Very many quantitative calculations—approximate solutions of the wave equation—for aromatic and conjugated molecules have been made, with results that are in general in good agreement with experiment. Perhaps

---

* From *Les Prix Nobel en 1954*.

more important than the quantitative calculations is the possibility
of prediction by simple chemical arguments. For example, the
amide group, an important structural feature of proteins, can be
described as resonating between two structures, one with the
double bond between the carbon atom and the oxygen atom, and
the other with the double bond between the carbon atom and the
nitrogen atom:

"The convenience and usefulness of the concept of resonance
in the discussion of chemical problems are so great as to make the
disadvantage of the element of arbitrariness of little significance.
Also, it must not be forgotten that the element of arbitrariness
occurs in essentially the same way in the simple structure theory
of organic chemistry as in the theory of resonance—there is the
same use of idealized, hypothetical structural elements. In the
resonance discussion of the benzene molecule the two Kekulé
structures have to be described as hypothetical: it is not possible
to synthesize molecules with one or the other of the two Kekulé
structures. In the same way, however, the concept of the carbon-
carbon single bond is an idealization. The benzene molecule has
its own structure, which cannot be exactly composed of structural
elements from other molecules. The propane molecule also has
its own structure, which cannot be composed of structural elements
from other molecules—it is not possible to isolate a portion of
the propane molecule, involving parts of two carbon atoms and
perhaps two electrons in between them, and say that this portion
of the propane molecule is the carbon-carbon single bond, identical
with a portion of the ethane molecule. The description of the propane molecule as involving carbon-carbon single bonds and carbon-
hydrogen single bonds is arbitrary; the concepts themselves are
idealizations, in the same way as the concepts of the Kekulé structures that are described as contributing to the normal state of the
benzene molecule. Chemists have found that the simple structure

theory of organic chemistry and also the resonance theory are valuable, despite their use of idealizations and their arbitrary character.

"Other extensions of the theory of the chemical bond made in recent years involve the concept of fractional bonds. Twenty-five years ago it was discovered that a simple theory of complex crystals with largely ionic structures, such as the silicate minerals, can be developed on the basis of the assumption that each cation or metal atom divides its charge or valence equally among the anions that are coordinated about it. For example, in a crystal of topaz, $Al_2SiO_4F_2$, each silicon atom is surrounded by a tetrahedron of four oxygen atoms, and each aluminum atom is surrounded by an octahedron of four oxygen atoms and two fluorine atoms. The valence of silicon, 4, is assumed to be divided among four bonds, which then have the bond number 1—they are single bonds. The valence of aluminum, 3, is divided among six bonds, each of which is a half bond. A stable structure results when the atoms are arranged in such a way that each anion, oxygen or fluorine, forms bonds equal to its valence. In topaz each oxygen atom forms one single bond with silicon and two half bonds with aluminum, whereas each fluorine atom forms only two half bonds with aluminum. The distribution of the valences hence then corresponds to the bivalence of oxygen and the univalence of fluorine. It was pointed out by W. L. Bragg that if the metal atoms are idealized as cations (Si^{++++} and Al^{+++}) and the oxygen and fluorine atoms as anions (O^{--} and F^{-}), this distribution corresponds to having the shortest possible lines of force between the cations and the anions—the lines of force need to reach only from a cation to an immediately adjacent anion, which forms part of its coordination polyhedron. Occasionally ionic crystals are found in which there are small deviations from this requirement, but only rarely are the deviations larger than one-quarter of a valence unit.

"The concept that the structure of metals and intermetallic compounds can be described in terms of valence bonds that resonate among alternative positions, aided by an extra orbital on most or all of the atoms (the metallic orbital), has been found to be of value in the discussion of the properties of these substances. The resonating-bond theory of metals is supported especially strongly by the consideration of interatomic distances in metals and intermetallic compounds.

"The valence theory of metals and intermetallic compounds is still in a rather unsatisfactory state. It is not yet possible to make predictions about the composition and properties of intermetallic compounds with even a small fraction of the assurance with which they can be made about organic compounds and ordinary inorganic compounds. We may, however, hope that there will be significant progress in the attack on this problem during the next few years.

"Let us now return to the subject of the structural chemistry of organic substances, especially the complex substances that occur in living organisms, such as proteins. Recent work in this field has shown the value of the use of structural arguments that go beyond those of the classical structure theory of organic chemistry. The interatomic distances and bond angles in the polypeptide chains of proteins are precisely known—the bond distances to within about 0.02 angstrom and the bond angles to within about 2 degrees. It is known that the amide groups must retain their planarity; the atoms are expected not to deviate from the planar configuration by more than perhaps 0.05 angstrom. There is rotational freedom about the single bonds connecting the alpha carbon atom with the adjacent amide carbon and nitrogen atoms, but there are restrictions on the configurations of the polypeptide chain that can be achieved by rotations about these bonds: atoms of different parts of the chain must not approach one another so closely as to introduce large steric repulsion, and in general the N—H and O atoms of different amide groups must be so located relative to one another as to permit the formation of hydrogen bonds, with N—H $\cdots$ O distance equal to 2.79 $\pm$ 0.10 angstrom and with the oxygen atom not far from the N—H axis. These requirements are stringent ones. Their application to a proposed hydrogen-bonded structure of a polypeptide chain cannot in general be made by the simple method of drawing a structural formula; instead, extensive numerical calculations must be carried out, or a model must be constructed."

CONSEQUENCES IN THEORY
AND PRACTICE

The symbolic representation of valences is a straight line between the connected atoms. Relationships between the numbers of atoms forming the molecule are thus correctly expressed, but beyond that, the straight valence-line is inadequate to represent the informations on the molecule, which are obtained from the spectra in various regions of wave lengths, from thermodynamic data and from other physical measurements. By explaining these in the electronic theory of the atom and with the concepts of quantum and wave mechanics, Pauling arrives at the conclusion that classical valences are simplified idealizations.

The pictorial representation of the benzene molecule by the two alternate Kekulé structures I and II does not signify that

I   II

in this substance some molecules "really" exist in structure I, others in the arrangement II. The electronic wave function for the normal benzene molecule can be composed of terms corresponding to the Kekulé structures I and II, plus some additional terms: hence, according to the fundamental ideas of quantum mechanics, if it were possible to carry out an experimental test of the electronic structure that would identify structure I or structure II, each structure would be found for the molecule to the extent determined by the wave function.

Previous attempts at developing more adequate pictures of the valence bonds introduced "partial" valences (Johannes Thiele) or valence fields (Alfred Werner) and other concepts for loosening the strict classical theory. Now, these attempts find their present completion in the theory of resonance and electronic vibrations.

Today, this theory has "only" theoretical consequences, enabling us to construct more meaningful pictures of the molecules, and to derive explanations of physico-chemical properties from the concept of hydrogen-bonds. The consequences in practice have not been developed yet. At the close of his book "The Nature of the Chemical Bond," Pauling wrote (3rd ed., p. 570): "The discoveries about the structure of polypeptide chains in proteins and polynucleotide chains in nucleic acids that have been made during the last decade have been largely based on considerations of resonance (planarity of the amide group, purines, pyrimidines) and hydrogen-bond formation. We may ask what the next step in the search for an understanding of the nature of life will be. I think that it will be the elucidation of the nature of the electro-magnetic phenomena involved in mental activity in relation to the molecular structure of brain tissue."

1 9 5 5
VINCENT DU VIGNEAUD
(1901-   )

"For his work on biologically important sulfur compounds and particularly for the first synthesis of a polypeptidic hormone."

BIOGRAPHICAL SKETCH

VINCENT DU VIGNEAUD WAS BORN IN CHICAGO, ILLINOIS, ON May 18, 1901. After studying at the University of Illinois, he was a biochemist at Philadelphia General Hospital and on the staff of the Graduate School of Medicine of the University of Pennsylvania. For work carried out at the Rochester School of Medicine, he received his doctor's degree in 1927. With grants from the National Research Council he worked at several medical research institutions here and abroad. In 1932, he became head of the Department of Biochemistry at George Washington University, School of Medicine, and in 1938 at Cornell University Medical College and Department of Biochemistry. In 1952, he gave a survey of his work in his book: "A Trail of Research in Sulfur Chemistry and Metabolism and Related Fields."

DESCRIPTION OF THE PRIZE-WINNING WORK *

"My interest in insulin was initiated through a lecture given by W. C. Rose, who succeeded Lewis as professor of biochemistry

---

* From *Les Prix Nobel en 1955.*

at Illinois. On his return from a meeting in Toronto in 1923, he gave an account of the exciting discovery of insulin by Banting and Best. I well recall the thrill of listening to Rose and my curiosity about the chemical nature of a compound that could bring about the miracles he described. Little did I know at that time that insulin would eventually turn out to be a sulfur compound.

"Some two years later, I received an invitation from J. R. Murlin at the University of Rochester Medical School to come and work on the chemistry of insulin in his department, a department that was devoted mainly to endocrinology and metabolism. The chance to work on the chemistry of insulin transcended all other interests for me, and I accepted Murlin's invitation.

"While I was at Rochester, I became intrigued with the fact that all of our preparations contained sulfur, and most of my efforts during the next two years were devoted to studying the sulfur of these insulin preparations. From these studies, I came to the conclusion that the sulfur was present in the form of the disulfide linkage and that insulin was most likely a derivative of the amino acid, cystine, and the suggestion was made that the cystine in insulin was linked to the rest of the molecule by peptide linkages.

"The following year, while working in Abel's laboratory at Johns Hopkins University, I took up the isolation of cystine from crystalline insulin, because the conclusive proof of the presence of cystine in insulin had to rest on the isolation of cystine in pure form. This isolation was eventually accomplished.

"In our earlier work on the preparation of cysteine, it had occurred to us that it might be possible to benzylate the sulfhydryl group of cysteine by adding benzyl chloride to the liquid ammonia solution of the sodium salt of cysteine produced by the reduction of cystine with metallic sodium. An excellent yield of S-benzylcysteine was obtained. Although the latter reaction was carried out in 1930 with Loring and Audrieth, it was not until sometime later that the possibility of cleaving a benzyl thio ether by this same means occurred to us in our work with Sifferd. S-Benzylcysteine was cleaved to cysteine in liquid ammonia with metallic sodium, cystine being isolated after oxidation.

"This same reductive procedure was also applied to the preparation of cystinylbisglycine from dicarbobenzoxycystinybisglycine and of cysteinylglycine from S-benzylcysteinylglycine.

GLUTATHIONE

"The effectiveness of these reactions impressed us with their potentialities as possible key reactions for a synthesis of glutathione, the structure of which was believed, through the work of Hopkins and of Kendall, Mason, and McKenzie to be γ-L-glutamyl-L-cysteinylglycine. If we could synthesize N-carbobenzoxy-γ-glutamyl-S-benzylcysteinylglycine, we felt that its reduction with sodium in liquid ammonia should yield glutathione.

"In work with Miller, we were able to obtain this desired intermediate by the coupling of suitable derivatives of the three amino acids involved. As is shown in Fig. 1, reduction of this intermediate with sodium in liquid ammonia gave glutathione, which, upon isolation in crystalline form, was shown to be identical with the natural product. Our synthesis followed shortly after the first synthesis of glutathione by Harington and Mead by a somewhat different approach.

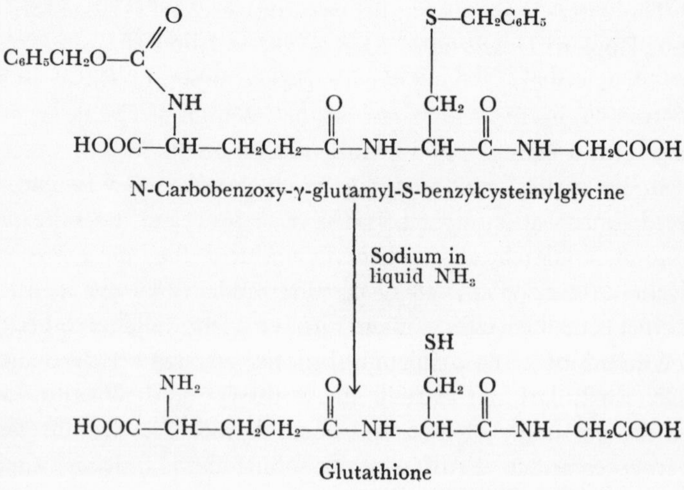

Fig. 1. A synthesis of glutathione.

POSTERIOR PITUITARY HORMONES

"The work on insulin aroused our interest in other protein or proteinlike hormones. We turned to the examination of oxytocin, the uterine-contracting hormone, and vasopressin, the blood-pressure-raising hormone, of the posterior pituitary gland. There were some indications in the literature that these hormones might be polypeptidelike substances of lower molecular weight than insulin. Furthermore, there was evidence that partially purified preparations of these hormones contained sulfur, but the nature of the sulfur was unknown.

"Kamm and Grote of Parke, Davis and Company kindly placed at our disposal some of their partially purified oxytocin, and we were able to show that, upon hydrolysis, the samples contained approximately 9 percent cystine. Of course, we could not tell at that time whether the cystine was present in the hormone or in the impurities. Nevertheless, in the work with Sealock, we decided to treat the partially purified oxytocin with cysteine and find out whether this hormone lost its activity like insulin. Much to our surprise, the oxytocic activity remained. Oxidation, by aeration of an aqueous solution until the sulfhydryl test was negative, did not cause loss of activity. The question then occurred: Had we really reduced the hormone by the cysteine treatment? It appeared possible to us that if the hormone were a disulfide and had been reduced, treatment with benzyl chloride might cover the sulfhydryl group with a benzyl radical and inactivation might take place. When the reduced oxytocin preparation was treated with benzyl chloride, inactivation did result. On the other hand, treatment of the nonreduced material with benzyl chloride did not cause inactivation. These results made us fairly certain that the oxytocic principle contained sulfur in the form of a disulfide linkage.

"We laid aside the problem during the war for certain assignments, particularly on penicillin, but thereafter the isolation of oxytocin was undertaken in collaboration with Livermore. Since the countercurrent distribution technique developed by Craig for the purification of organic compounds had played a helpful role in our isolation of synthetic penicillin, we naturally thought of using countercurrent distribution on partially purified oxytocin fractions, prepared by the method of Kamm and co-workers. The source material for preparation of the oxytocin fractions was a commercial extract provided by Kamm of Parke, Davis and Company. The countercurrent distribution between 0.05-percent acetic acid and secondary butyl alcohol proved to be highly effective. We obtained a fraction that appeared to behave like a pure compound by this criterion, and, through application of the elegant starch-column chromatographic method of Moore and Stein, we were able, with Pierce, to show that an acid hydrolyzate of oxytocin consisted of eight amino acids and ammonia.

"During the course of these studies on the oxytocic hormone, the pressor hormone, vasopressin, was also isolated from beef glands and shown to contain six of the same amino acids as oxytocin. In place of the leucine and isoleucine in oxytocin, vasopressin contained phenylalanine and arginine.

"With the isolation of what appeared to be the pure hormones and the establishment of their composition, we were for the first time in a position, on a chemical basis, to be quite certain that the oxytocin was free of vasopressin, and therefore it was possible to ascertain the biological effects of oxytocin itself.

"With the purified oxytocin at hand and its composition established, we then turned to the problem of how the component amino acids were linked. Of course there were many structures that could be written involving the eight amino acids and ammonia. The greatest difficulty in the degradative work was the scarcity of material. To obtain enough purified hormones was truly a prodigious task, as has already been mentioned. The various degradative steps were perforce carried out on milligrams of material, and in most instances, the methods had to be adapted to this scale.

"These researches over the course of several years with Pierce, Mueller, Turner, Davoll, Taylor, and Kunkel, and the final decisive experiments with Ressler and Triplett on the cleavage of performic acid-oxidized oxytocin with bromine water and on the partial hydrolysis and identification of peptide fragments, brought us to a clearcut concept of the structure of oxytocin, a new type of cyclic polypeptide amide shown in **Fig. 3**.

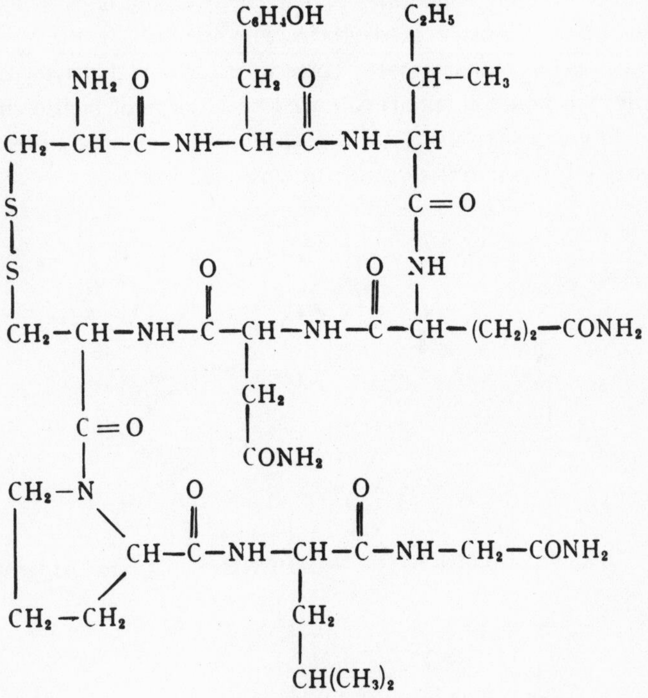

Fig. 3. Oxytocin.

"Although this structure was the only one that we could arrive at through the rationalization of our data, we felt that proof of this structure by synthesis of the compound was mandatory because of certain assumptions involved in postulating it.

BACKGROUND OF SYNTHETICAL APPROACH

"The clue to approaching a synthesis of this compound rested on our work with Sealock, carried out in the 1930's, on the reduction of oxytocin and the oxidation of the reduced oxytocin without appreciable inactivation at either step, which has already been discussed. On the basis of our postulated structure for oxytocin (**Fig. 3**), the reduction of oxytocin and subsequent oxidation could be interpreted as involving the opening and closing of the 20-membered ring. The reduced oxytocin would then have a linear structure containing two sulfhydryl groupings in place of the disulfide linkage in oxytocin. Furthermore, if the proposed structure for oxytocin were correct, reduction of oxytocin with sodium in liquid ammonia followed by addition of benzyl chloride should give rise to the S,S'-dibenzyl derivative of reduced oxytocin, possessing the structure shown in Fig. 4.

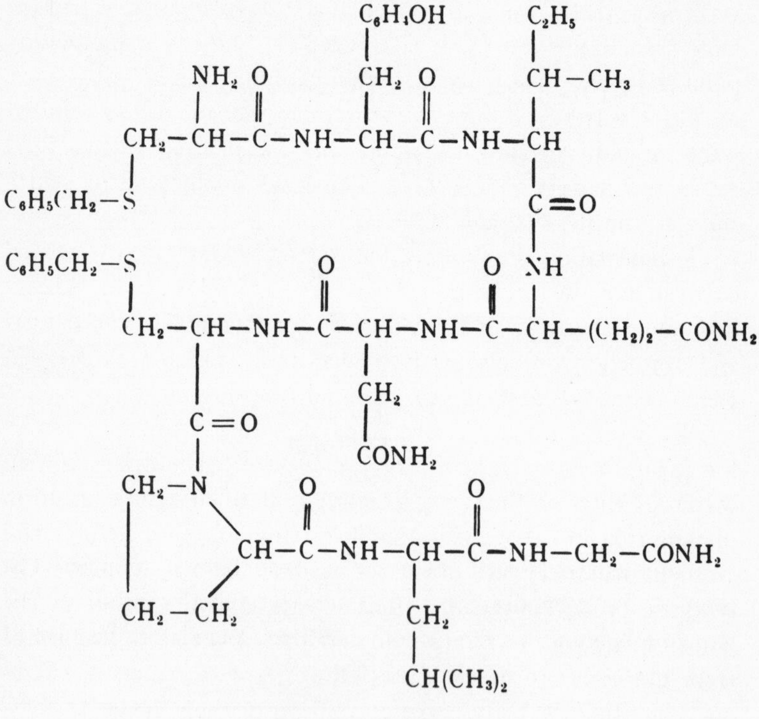

Fig. 4. Benzylated derivative of reduced oxytocin.

SYNTHETIC OXYTOCIN

"The purified synthetic product, isolated by countercurrent distribution, and our best samples of natural oxytocin were assayed against each other following rigorously the procedures outlined by the *United States Pharmacopeia*. The results indicated that the activity of the synthetic material was indeed very close to that of the natural oxytocin.

"This synthetic material and natural oxytocin were then compared by a battery of physical and chemical tests. They had the same amino acid composition. They showed, within experimental error, the same optical activity, partition coefficient (in two different solvent systems), electrophoretic mobility (at two different hydrogen-ion concentrations), infrared pattern, ultraviolet spectrum, and effluent pattern from an IRC-50 resin.

"The synthetic material formed an active flavianate that had the same crystalline form (fine, silky needles) and the same melting point as the flavianate obtained from natural oxytocin.

"On treatment with bromine water, the synthetic material underwent the cleavage into two fragments encountered with natural oxytocin, both giving rise to β-sulfoalanyldibromotyrosine and a sulfonic acid heptapeptide.

"Sedimentation studies on the molecular weight of natural oxytocin and the synthetic material were kindly made by Schachman and Harrington of the University of California. The natural and synthetic materials behaved identically, and the values that were obtained were in the expected range.

"We were fortunate at this stage to have the collaboration of the Lying-In Hospital group of the New York Hospital-Cornell Medical Center on the use of our highly purified natural oxytocin in induction of labor and in milk ejection, for the natural and synthetic material were now compared on human subjects. The synthetic product was fully effective in stimulating labor in the human being and in milk ejection and could not be distinguished from the natural oxytocin in its action. Approximately 1 microgram of either the natural oxytocin or the synthetic material given intravenously to recently parturient women induced milk ejection in 20 to 30 seconds.

"These comparisons of the physical, chemical, and biological properties of the synthetic product with those of the purified, natural oxytocin justified in our estimation the conclusion that the synthetic octapeptide amide is oxytocin and that the structure shown in Fig. 3 represents that of the hormone."

CONSEQUENCES IN THEORY
AND PRACTICE

The source of oxytocin and of vasopressin is the pituitary gland, or hypophysis, situated at the base of the brain. Bernardo Alberto Houssay received the Nobel Prize in Physiology and Medicine in 1947 for his studies on the hormones from the anterior pituitary lobe, which he started in 1907. In 1923, John J. Abel prepared from the posterior lobe a substance with an action on the uterus that was more than a thousand times stronger than that of histamin. The separation of this substance from another one responsible for raising the blood pressure was much debated. Fritz Lieben wrote in his "Geschichte der physiologischen Chemie," published in 1935: "The controversies are explainable by the fact that we are still far from having as much as one of these hormones of the posterior hypophysis, or the Pars intermedia, available in anything approaching purity." (My translation)

Twenty years later, at least 2 of these hormones were available not only in crystallized form, but their constitution was elaborated and one of them was reproduced by chemical synthesis. Further efforts, based upon these results, may proceed in the direction of building somewhat simplified molecules that still have the same clinical effect.

Cystine, which had first lured du Vigneaud on his "trail of sulfur research" and deep into the chemistry of insulin, was also found in certain enzymes. Among them is cytochrome c, one of the iron-porphyrin complexes that regulate biological oxidations.

1 9 5 6
Cyril Norman Hinshelwood
(1897-   )

Nikolaj Nikolajevitj Semenov
(1896-   )

"For their research on the mechanism of chemical reactions."

BIOGRAPHICAL SKETCH
HINSHELWOOD

SIR CYRIL HINSHELWOOD (KNIGHTED 1948) WAS BORN IN London, June 19, 1897. He was a Fellow of Balliol 1920-21, a Fellow and Tutor at Trinity College, Oxford, from 1921 to 1937, and from then on, he has been professor of chemistry at the University of Oxford.

He published his first book on "Kinetics of Chemical Change" in 1926, which saw many subsequent editions. In the Introduction to "The Structure of Physical Chemistry," Oxford, 1951, he wrote of his intentions in this book: "The treatment would be neither historical, nor formally deductive, but at each stage I would try to indicate the route by which an inquiring mind might most simply and naturally proceed in the attempts to understand that part of the nature of things included in physical chemistry. This approach I have ventured to designate humanistic." Among his other books is one on "The Chemical Kinetics of the Bacterial Cell," 1946.

He received many honors and awards in his country, in France, Italy and Norway. He was president of the Chemical Society, 1946-48, and of the Royal Society, London, 1960.

SEMENOV

Nikolaj Nikalajevitj Semenov was born in Saratov, 1896. He began his studies with physics at the University of Petrograd (now Leningrad) in 1913. Under the direction of Abram F. Joffee he worked on dielectrics and molecular bonds. His ideas on chain reactions grew out of investigation of phosphorus oxidation, which he started in 1924 and summarized in a book in 1928. In this year, he became director for chemical physics at the physico-chemical institute. Since 1944, he has been head of the department of chemical kinetics which he had organized at the University of Moscow.

In 1928 he was elected corresponding member, four years later full member, of the Academy of Sciences, USSR. Many other honors followed soon.

His book on "Problems of Chemical Kinetics and Reactivity" first appeared in Russian in 1954. Its second edition, 1958, was also published in English (Princeton, 1958).

DESCRIPTION OF THE PRIZE-WINNING WORK *

HINSHELWOOD

"The reaction

$$2H_2 + O_2 \rightarrow 2H_2O$$

from one point of view perhaps among the most elementary in chemistry, proved to offer a wealth of complex and intriguing behavior, not all details of which are even yet fully understood. Victor Meyer had thought it an interesting reaction to study, but found it, apparently, intractable. Bodenstein showed that at certain

---

* From *Les Prix Nobel en 1956*.

temperatures the union took place on the walls of the vessel. The work in Oxford started from the simple idea that, in the region of temperature between that used by Bodenstein and the inflammation temperature, homogeneous processes must come into play.

"The now well-known phenomena of the lower and upper explosion limits were observed. Semenov, then in Leningrad, had just explained the sharp transition from negligibly slow reaction to inflammation (a 'lower limit') of phosphorus vapor by the theory of chain branching. It was soon clear that the lower limit with hydrogen and oxygen was of a similar nature. The branching was shown here to be controlled by the deactivation of chain carriers at the vessel wall, and the 'upper limit' was proved to depend on the removal of chain carriers by three-body collisions in the gas phase.

"The study of the hydrogen-oxygen reaction was the first point at which the work in Oxford came into close contact with that of Semenov. Our indebtedness to his ideas was at once recognized, and the early exchanges opened friendly relations between Semenov and myself which have lasted ever since. I should like at this point to mention also my personal debt to an earlier great pioneer of chemical kinetics, Max Bodenstein, who himself plays a part in the curious history of the hydrogen-oxygen reaction.

"The phenomena involved in the initiation, propagation, and termination of chains are now among the commonplaces of physical chemistry. Each process may be separately influenced by the conditions, so that the variety and complexity of the experimentally observable effects can no longer be wondered at. The detailed explanation of numerous examples continues to be of importance especially in connection with the control of the polymerization reactions that are widely used in the modern plastics industry.

"The importance of thermal-decomposition reactions of organic molecules in connection with the fundamental theory of chemical reactions has already been mentioned. Once chain processes were discovered, it was obviously necessary to know whether they were involved in the thermal decomposition processes. If so, the rather elaborate theoretical studies for which some of the results had been used would need considerable revision. A decision on this point was not quite simple. Work on the occurrence of free atoms and radicals, notably by R. W. Wood and Paneth, did indeed suggest the possibility of their intervention in such reactions as the ether decomposition, and Rice and Herzfeld formulated theoretical reaction schemes on this basis. On the other hand, tests for the actual presence of free radicals in the reacting systems which Patat and Sachsse made by the application of the o–p hydrogen method seemed at first to negate the idea.

"Definite evidence was at length forthcoming when Staveley and Hinshelwood began to study the influence of nitric oxide on these reactions. The idea which initiated the work was simply that an odd electron molecule such as NO might well produce some interesting effects. Quite how interesting the effects would prove was not altogether foreseen. The pronounced inhibition caused by relatively minute quantities of this substance in a whole series of reactions which could conceivably involve the intervention of alkyl radicals left no doubt that the radical chain mechanism was in fact operative.

"I must turn now to a quite different field of investigation, that namely of the relation between reactivity and structure. Here, perhaps, we may distinguish two main groups of problem. The first is one of a rather broad, indeed almost philosophical character. In the equation for a reaction rate constant

$$k = Ae^{-E/RT}$$
$$\text{or } \ln k = \ln A - E/RT$$

ln k is the kinetic analogue of a free energy, E of a total energy and ln A of an entropy. E does indeed represent the energy required to lift molecules to the transition state, A is concerned with the probability that all other requisites for reaction are fulfilled. Structural changes in reacting substances can affect both A and E. Sometimes, as is beautifully exemplified by the benzoylation of a whole series of aniline derivatives containing different substituents, only E is affected. Sometimes, however, there is a deep inner correlation between the changes in E and the changes in ln A, the completer understanding of which is now being sought, and it is to be hoped may reveal some more of the fundamental harmonies of nature.

"The other great group of problems is that of the relation between changes in rate, whether expressed through E, ln A or both, and electron displacements within molecules, the theory of which has been largely developed by organic chemists, and only very partially interpreted in terms of the quantum mechanical theory of valency.

"Perhaps as typical of the interesting relations in the structural field I may mention one or two examples. The oxidation of hydrocarbon vapors, a very typical chain reaction, offers a rather remarkable one. The oxidation rate for n-octane is many powers of ten greater than that of ethane, and detailed investigation shows the major influence governing the variations to be a most astonishing stabilizing influence of methyl groups which strongly discourage attack at any point of a hydrocarbon chain adjacent to them. This is indeed an elegant problem for theoretical structural chemistry.

"Here are two more such problems for modern valency theory which experiment presents. In a reaction involving a benzene derivative the rate is influenced by substituents in the ring, but to widely varying extents in different examples, and intriguing questions arise about the factors determining the ease of transmission of the substituent influence to the reaction-center. The benzoylation of aniline is slowed down hundreds of times by a nitro-group, while the dissociation of nitrobenzaldehyde bisulphite compound differs little in rate from that of the parent substance.

"When several substituents are introduced into aniline their effects on the free energy of activation of the benzoylation are almost strictly additive: in other examples the additivity is not nearly so evident, offering once again an interesting exercise for the theoretical chemist.

"I am now going to turn briefly to a still more mysterious field, that of the living cell. With a subject like chemical kinetics whose ramifications and details multiply without end, the individual worker is always confronted with the choice whether to repeat, perfect, amplify and consolidate, or whether to press forward into the completely unknown. In one respect, at any rate, a small group in Oxford has pursued the second course. The direction of this further exploration has been to seek an understanding of some of the kinetic phenomena of the living cell.

"In some chemical systems, especially suitable for illustrating the elementary principles of kinetics, simple one-stage systems are met with, though less rarely than might have been hoped. In most of the systems easily accessible to experiment, reactions proceed by more or less complicated combinations of steps. In the living cell, a multiplicity of reactions is not just an unfortunate complication, but the essential condition for the phenomena of life to be possible at all.

"Bacterial cells (and some other unicellular organisms) grow in very simple media at defined rates. They synthesize by long sequences of reactions all the complex components of their structure. When the chemical environment is changed, the growth rate alters. Gradually, however, by what is called an adaptive process, the cells undergo an internal reorganization in such a way that the rate, which may initially be very small, rises to a steady maximum. The detailed study of this process gives interesting information about the way in which the chemical reactions are linked into what we term the reaction pattern of the cell.

"Inhibitory substances, such as drugs, frequently impede growth very seriously, but gradually the cells appear to learn to overcome this inhibition. Detailed study of this process shows it to be capable of a kinetic explanation about which, needless to say, some biologists are skeptical, but which helps to build up the picture of the cell's internal economy and to show how much this is determined by kinetic principles.

"There are many other problems which can be envisaged in terms of the reaction pattern of the cell. Cells contain numerous specific enzymes. The way in which these are built up as the cells multiply has some curious aspects, of which the explanation is certainly linked with the mode of coordination of the reaction pattern. When cells are provided with nutrient, they grow and divide. The division seems to be determined by the moment at which a more or less critical amount of deoxyribonucleic acid has been built up. Here is a fact relating kinetic phenomena closely to structural considerations."

SEMENOV *

"The role of mechanical currents in a gas, and especially of turbulence, during the propagation of a flame has long been observed. It was particularly elucidated in our Institute. For example, it was shown for a mixture of carbon monoxide and air in a glass tube, that the velocity of flame propagation was increased about one thousand fold when a wire in form of a spiral was inserted along the inner glass wall.

"When the flame proceeds in sufficiently long tubes, an acceleration is caused by the turbulization of the original mixture. The acceleration of the flame develops a regime of detonation in combustion, occasioned by the high temperatures that develop when the gas is compressed in the shock wave.

"That the ability to be detonated depends on the chemical kinetics was very clearly shown in our Institute for the mixture of CO and air. It is known that the velocity of this reaction increases strongly when traces of hydrogen are present. Actually, mixtures of CO and air do not detonate, but the addition of 1% hydrogen makes the mixtures explosive.

"Of great interest is the problem of competition between chain reactions and ordinary molecular reactions that are not accompanied by the formation of radicals. Chain propagation (a reaction between molecules and radicals) usually occurs with rather high velocity, at least at higher temperature. The slowest event is the new formation of a chain, which often requires an increased activation energy. Therefore, when the chain is artificially induced, e.g. in photochemical processes or through the effect of addition agents, the speed of reaction is practically higher than for any molecular reaction. When such an artificial chain induction does not occur, the formation of free radicals by molecules participating in the reaction must be considered highly important. The simplest possibility of forming free radicals consists in the decay of the weakest bond in the molecule.

---

* Translated parts of Semenov's Nobel Prize Lecture, from *Les Prix Nobel en 1956.*

"In other cases, the decay into radicals is slower than the decay into molecules. An example is the decomposition of certain chloro- and bromo-derivatives of hydrocarbons. The competition between the two kinds of molecular decomposition is governed by the constitution. For example, propylene bromide, C_3H_5Br, and propylene chloride, C_3H_5Cl, primarily liberate a halogen atom, whereas the ethyl compounds C_2H_5Br and C_2H_5Cl directly split off hydrogen halide with concurrent formation of olefins. Methyl bromide, CH_3Br, splits off a bromine atom, and for chloroform we proved the immediate decomposition into hydrogen chloride and the bi-radical $C\ Cl_2$.

"From research on the relationship between molecular structure and decay mechanism, carried out in our Institute and, independently, by A. Maccoll and others, we can draw some interesting conclusions. A good example is the decomposition of two bromides, n-propylbromide and isopropylbromide. The first decomposes by a chain reaction, the second directly into molecules of hydrogen bromide and propylene. This can be explained as follows: The reactions are, for normal propylbromide:

a) $C_3H_7Br \longrightarrow \dot{C}_3H_7 + \dot{B}r$

b) $\dot{B}r + CH_3-CH_2-CH_2Br \longrightarrow HBr + CH_3-\dot{C}H-CH_2Br$

c) $CH_3-\dot{C}H-CH_2Br \longrightarrow CH_3-CH = CH_2 + \dot{B}r$
$$etc.$$

for isopropylbromide:

1) $\dot{B}r + (CH_3)_2 = CHBr \longrightarrow HBr + (CH_3)_2 = \dot{C}Br$

where the radical $(CH_3)_2C\ Br$ cannot decay, which stops the chain reaction.

"Of the more complicated reactions, we have lately given most of our attention to the slow oxidation processes. For this work, it is particularly characteristic that the kinetics by which all principal reaction products accumulate is investigated, and that balances are calculated for the course of the reactions. In the gas phase, the thermic oxidation of propylene and propane were thoroughly studied. The formulated reaction scheme assumes two competing possibilities in which the intermediately formed radical RO_2 can react—a bimolecular transformation, in which hydrogen superoxides are formed with hydrogen released from the hydrocarbon, and a monomolecular isomerization of RO_2 which is followed by a decomposition of the carbon skeleton and the formation of carbonyl compounds without peroxides.

"In the liquid phase, the oxidation of cyclohexane and n-decane was thoroughly studied by N. M. Emanuel. In this work, the sequence of the stable reaction products was established and, perhaps for the first time, it was shown for paraffins and cycloparaffins that all reaction products follow upon the formation of a primary intermediate hydrogen superoxide. It is interesting to notice that the events are somewhat different when the reaction is carried out in a metal apparatus. According to preliminary results, hydrogen superoxide formation does not occur when cyclohexane is oxidized in a steel apparatus. Since the formation of alkyl superoxides is known to be a homogeneous chain reaction, the change in the reaction mechanism shows that the container walls influence the chain propagation.

"For these studies, M. B. Neuman's kinetic method of using radioactive isotopes was highly important. This method made it possible to measure the speeds of formation and disappearance of stable intermediary products and thus to determine the sequence of their formation.

"Some processes of hydrocarbon oxidation have the character of chain reactions with abnormal branching, which often causes considerable periods of induction. In the liquid phase, e.g. in the oxidation of paraffins, such periods often extend to several hundred hours. It is known that the introduction of nitrogen oxides in small quantities reduces the induction periods in the oxidation of hydrocarbons at elevated temperatures; which is caused by the accelerated formation of radicals through the interaction of the nitrogen oxides with the hydrocarbons. N. M. Emanuel and his associates have recently shown that nitrogen oxides act similarly also at relatively low temperatures. To start the reaction, it is sufficient to pass air with a small NO_2-content through liquid paraffin for a short time. After such a start of the reactions, its continuation is secured by the superoxides formed. At this stage, pure air can be used; additions of nitrogen oxide then rather reduce the speed of reaction somewhat, perhaps by decomposing the superoxides.

"According to A. W. Toptchieff, methane can be easily nitrated or chlorinated only by simultaneous action of NO_2 and Cl_2; chlorination without NO_2 or nitration without Cl_2 are much slower. This can perhaps be explained by the formation of NOCl, which generates chlorine atoms.

"A remarkable phenomenon of chain induction was recently discovered by N. M. Emanuel in his work on the oxidation of propane to acetone at 180-200° in the presence of H Br. He found that in the first few seconds of this propane oxidation a reaction occurs, in which only minute quantities of propane are converted. But it is just during this reaction that certain active particles are formed, which govern the principal course of the process during many minutes.

"At present, there are no direct experimental results to confirm the radical mechanism, or the ion-radical mechanism, of redox processes. However, there are indirectly confirming observations. We must particularly emphasize the fact that the majority of redox catalysts are semiconductors or metals. On the other hand, there are many results from comparative investigations of electric conductivity and catalytic effects of semiconductors, showing that these two properties are closely connected.

"N. M. Tschirkoff has found connections between electric conductivity and catalytic properties, of a different kind, for acid-base catalysts. In 1947, we have shown that plates of mica, quartz, and glass become distinct acid-base catalysts, when small amounts of hydrogen chloride and water vapor are present. Esterifications and the decomposition of paraldehyde were particularly studied. In these reactions, the electric conductivity of the solid surfaces changed in parallel with the catalytic activity.

"One of the next tasks is the application of the theory of chains to the development of the new technology of direct oxidations and hydrocarbon cracking.

"Chemical conversion processes are certainly not limited to radical-chain reactions, which proceed by means of free radicals; many processes occur by means of quite different labile structures.

"I am convinced that it is fundamental to enlarge research on the mechanism of different types of chemical reactions. Without knowledge in this field, it is scarcely possible to enrich chemical technology or to achieve decisive successes in biology.

"In the solution of this most important problem, more than anywhere else, the joint efforts of scholars of all nations are required, so as to discover the secrets of chemical and biological events with a view to the peaceful development and well-being of mankind."

CONSEQUENCES IN THEORY AND PRACTICE

The classical chemical formulas were developed to symbolize the state of substances in the beginning and at the end of chemical processes. These formulas proved insufficient for describing the processes themselves. Intermediate stages between start and end of a reaction had to be assumed. About one hundred years ago, Kekulé sought them in addition compounds:

$$
\begin{array}{c} A \\ | \\ B \end{array} + \begin{array}{c} C \\ | \\ D \end{array} \longrightarrow \left(\begin{array}{cc} A & C \\ | & | \\ B & D \end{array} \right) \longrightarrow \begin{array}{c} A\text{---}C \\ + \\ B\text{---}D \end{array}
$$

Such a scheme was ingenious but arbitrary, and it did not go far in explaining, how an addition would take place, or why the split occurred in the new direction. At least it gave a visual presentation for the necessary close approach between the partners.

The first breach in the classical concepts was the theory of ionization by Arrhenius (see p. 12). At least in solution, substances were there represented to be in a new stage of combination with electrical charges. The electron theory explained this more precisely as capture or release of electrons. But even that was not sufficient, it had to be enlarged by recognizing "abnormal" valence states. The historical name for a substance in an abnormal value state was: radical. It was retained with a new meaning, which stated that it was short-lived, in the order of thousandths of a second, and in transition to several possible stabilizations. With this historical background, the concept of radical as the root of a chemical compound loses the meaning of the word radical as reckless and revolutionary.

The theoretical frame work of radicals and chains, of initiation, propagation and stoppage of reactions is wide enough for many programs of further research. Specificity of chemical structures is observed in many unexpected ways and calls for explanations. The theories and the experimental findings, e.g. concerning the influence of reactor materials and "wall"-effects, have been used industrially in preparing synthetic resins and chemical derivatives from the hydrocarbons of natural gas and mineral oils, while others of the scientific results are still waiting to be used in large-scale operations.

1957
ALEXANDER R. TODD
(1907-   )

"For his works on nucleotides and nucleotidic coenzymes."

BIOGRAPHICAL SKETCH

ALEXANDER ROBERTUS TODD WAS BORN IN GLASGOW ON October 2, 1907. He studied chemistry at the University of Glasgow and at Frankfurt a. Main, where he received his first doctor's degree in 1931 with a thesis on bile acids. Returned to England, he continued his studies with Sir Robert Robinson and acquired the second doctor's degree at Oxford in 1933. After work at the Lister Institute of Preventive Medicine at Chelsea, he moved to the University of London as Reader in Biochemistry, 1937. He was professor of chemistry at Manchester from 1938 to 1944, and since then he has been professor of organic chemistry at Cambridge and Fellow of Christ College. He was visiting professor at several universities in the United States at various times, and at the University of Sidney in 1950.

"He has taken a considerable interest in international scientific affairs and is chairman of the British National Committee for Chemistry. He has served on many Government committees and since 1952 has been chairman of the British Government's Advisory Council on Scientific Policy. He is also a Managing Trustee of the Nuffield Foundation. He was knighted in 1954. Todd's researches have ranged over a number of fields but have been in the main concerned with the chemistry of natural products of

275

biological importance. His main topics of research have been, in addition to nucleotide and nucleotide coenzyme studies described in his Nobel lecture, the chemistry of vitamins B_1, E and B_{12}, the constituents of Cannabis species, insect colouring matters, factors influencing obligate parasitism and various mould products." *

DESCRIPTION OF THE PRIZE-WINNING WORK†

"The term *nucleotide* requires definition, for, like many other terms, it is now used in a much broader sense than when it was first introduced. Originally it was applied only to the phosphate esters of certain N-glycosides of purine and pyrimidine bases (the nucleosides) obtained on hydrolyzing nucleic acids. Today it is applied generally and rather loosely to phosphates of N-glycosides of heterocyclic bases, and it includes not merely the simple nucleotides of the original definition but also the nucleic acids (polynucleotides) and such substances as nicotinamide nucleotide (5'-phosphate of the quaternary N-ribofuranosylnicotinamide), and adenosine triphosphate (ATP). The nucleotide coenzymes are, in general, characterized by the presence in them of at least one simple nucleotide residue and, although derivatives of riboflavin phosphate (FMN) are not glycosidic in nature, they are commonly listed among the nucleotides because of their close similarity to, and association with, true nucleotides.

"In 1939 when I first began experiments in this field the fundamental substances of the group—the nucleosides obtained by hydrolyzing nucleic acids—had long been known and had been the subject of study by various workers. The early studies of Fischer had been followed by those of a few other investigators, among whom one thinks particularly of Levene. As a result it was established that the four nucleosides derived from ribonucleic acids were N-D-ribosides of adenine, guanine, uracil, and cytosine, respectively, but the size of the lactol ring in the sugar residue and

* From the autobiographical note in *Les Prix Nobel en 1957*, p. 84.

† From *Les Prix Nobel en 1957*.

the configuration at the glycosidic linkage were unknown while the point of attachment of the sugar residue in the purine nucleosides was still in dispute, although the spectroscopic evidence of Gulland and Holiday indicated with a high degree of probability that it was N_9. Of the nucleosides from deoxyribonucleic acids, all that was known with any certainty was that they were 2-deoxy-D-ribosides of the bases adenine, guanine, thymine, and cytosine, and it was assumed that they were structurally analogous to the ribonucleosides.

"The chemistry of the nucleotides—the phosphates of the nucleosides—was in a correspondingly primitive state.

· "I decided that we should seek to clarify the nucleotide field beginning with the simplest units—the nucleosides. To do so we applied primarily the method of synthesis since the amount of preliminary information available from earlier work had at least given sufficient indication of the nature of the nucleosides to make such an attack appropriate. This phase of our work, although providing, I believe, an interesting example of the power of synthetic methods in structural work, would take an entire lecture to describe in itself, and I shall not, therefore, discuss it here. Suffice to say that this work led to the rigid establishment of the structure of the individual ribonucleosides as the 9-β-D-ribofuranosides of adenine and guanine and the 3-β-D-ribofuranosides of uracil and cytosine and to the total synthesis of all of them. The deoxyribonucleosides were similarly shown to be 9-β-2-deoxy-D-ribofuranosides in the case of the purine, and 3-β-2-deoxy-D-ribofuranosides in the pyrimidine members.

"The difficulty of obtaining and of handling derivatives of 2-deoxy-D-ribose has hampered synthesis of the natural deoxyribonucleosides, but deoxyuridine has recently been synthesized and it is likely that synthesis of the others will shortly follow. For reference the structural formulae of two typical nucleosides, the ribonucleoside adenosine (I) and the deoxyribonucleoside deoxycytidine (II), are given in Fig. 1.

"The simple nucleotides are phosphates of the nucleosides, the phosphate residue being attached to one or other of the hydroxyls in the sugar portion of the molecule. Phosphorylation of the nucleosides was thus a second essential phase in our studies. Although organic phosphates and polyphosphates are of widespread occurrence in living matter, relatively little attention had been paid in the past to their synthesis and still less to their chemical behavior. True, a number of organic phosphates had been prepared, usually by rather crude procedures not well suited to use with sensitive molecules, and we found it necessary to undertake a general study of phosphorylation in all its aspects so as to make available methods which might be satisfactory in dealing with the rather wide range of delicate structural features to be encountered in the nucleotide and nucleotide coenzyme field.

The most widely employed phosphorylating agent which emerged from these studies is dibenzyl phosphorochloridate $(C_6H_5CH_2O)_2POCl$.

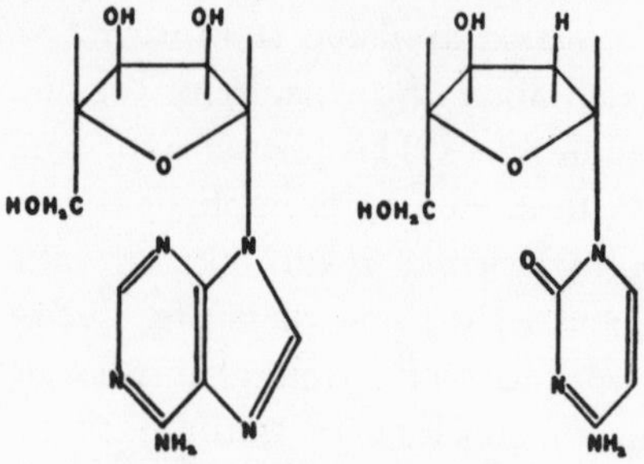

Fig. 1. Structural formulae of two typical nucleosides, ribonucleoside adenosine (I) and the deoxyribonucleoside deoxycytidine (II).

NUCLEOTIDE COENZYMES

"The term nucleotide coenzyme is applied to a large and growing group of substances which are vital components of many enzyme systems involved in metabolic processes. They function in association with specific proteins or apoenzymes, the complete enzyme system being made up of the combination apoenzyme + coenzyme (v. Euler). Historically, the first member of the group is cozymase or diphosphopyridine nucleotide (DPN) whose existence was recognised in 1906 by Harden and Young, although it was not in fact isolated in a pure state until 1936 (v. Euler and

Schlenk); it functions as coenzyme in a group of oxidation-reduction enzymes belonging to the pyridinoprotein group. Other examples are flavin-adenine-dinucleotide (FAD) found in many flavoproteins, adenosine triphosphate (ATP) acting as a cophosphorylase and also as a provider of the energy used in muscular contraction and many others. All known members of the group belong to one or other of two types (a) monoesters of polyphosphoric acids in which the esterifying group is a nucleoside derivative or (b) unsymmetrical P^1P^2-diesters of pyrophosphoric acid in which at least one of the esterifying groups is a nucleoside derivative. Adenosine triphosphate (III) is an example of type (a) and cozymase or DPN (IV) of type (b).

"An examination of structures (III) and (IV) at once reveals the three basic problems of nucleotide coenzyme synthesis—(1) the synthesis of nucleosides, (2) the phosphorylation and polyphosphorylation of nucleosides and (3) the linkage of dissimilar molecules one to another by pyrophosphate residues. Of these problems solutions to (1) and to the simple phosphorylation part of (2) were available to us from the work I have already described. Here I shall discuss only the synthesis of polyphosphates and of unsymmetrical diesters of pyrophosphoric acid leading to actual coenzyme synthesis.

"Starting from our most frequently used phosphorylating agent the simplest and most direct route to pyrophosphates is the reaction between dibenzyl phosphorochloridate and the salt of a phosphodiester. With the variety of procedures open to us for partial or complete removal of benzyl groups the scheme shown schematically below can give not only monoesters of phosphoric and pyrophosphoric acids but also, by simple extension, either mono- or diesters of polyphosphoric acids in general.

"This simple method of polyphosphate synthesis was used by us in the first total syntheses of adenosine-5′ pyrophosphate (ADP) and adenosine-5′ triphosphate (ATP). The yields obtained in these early syntheses were usually poor for reasons which shortly became apparent to us as efforts to discover other and better procedures increased our knowledge of the properties and reactions of esters of pyrophosphoric acid.

"In this field of nucleotide coenzyme synthesis, we are thus still seeking an ideal method for unsymmetrical pyrophosphate synthesis, although, having already developed five distinct types of synthetic method, we have reached a point at which the synthesis of any coenzyme molecule can be undertaken with reasonable certainty of success. Our practical interest in the field today lies very much in the methods of pyrophosphate formation and in the behavior of our pyrophosphates and mixed anhydride intermediates. For in the properties of such anhydrides lies the secret of many biological processes, and it is noteworthy that in our search for new methods we are in many ways coming closer and closer to the methods of nature—not only by working in aqueous media but also by using in some of our synthetic routes intermediates which bear a striking resemblance to some of the reactive phosphate derivatives such as enol-phosphates which are widespread in living.organisms."

CONSEQUENCES IN THEORY AND PRACTICE

With the advance in our detailed knowledge of the nucleotides through the work of Sir Alexander Todd, it has become possible to develop ideas about the biochemistry of growth. These important substances in the nucleus of organismic cells form templates, which guide the process of multiplication and keep it to the exact pattern conforming to the individual species. While providing answers to previous questions, the new work permits to formulate specific new ones. The new methods for introducing phosphate groups at well defined places of complex molecules open up further possibilities of organic chemical synthesis. The achievement of making some of the coenzymes synthetically, although by processes very far from those considered possible in an organism, will provide new ways to the knowledge and synthesis of other enzymes. As usual, the knowledge of chemical structure can be expected to make possible deeper insight into chemical processes.

1 9 5 8
FREDERICK SANGER
(1918-   )

"For his work on the structure of proteins, especially insulin."

BIOGRAPHICAL SKETCH

FREDERICK SANGER WAS BORN ON AUGUST 13, 1918 AT READ-combe, in Gloustershire, England. He studied at Cambridge and did research work on the metabolism of lysine, for which he earned the Ph.D. degree in 1943. Since then, he has been continuing his research, first under a fellowship later on as a member of the External Staff of the Medical Research Center. His work was soon recognized as outstanding. In 1954, he became a Fellow of the Royal Society and a Fellow at King's College, Cambridge. The American Academy in Arts and Sciences elected him an Honorary Foreign Member. He prefers working in the laboratory, with his own hands and in a small group, to teaching and administrative work.

Note: The standard symbols for the amino acids in alphabetical order are as follows:

Ala	— alanine	Leu	— leucine
Arg	— arginine	Lys	— lysine
Asp	— aspartic acid	Phe	— phenylalanine
Cy	— cystine	Pro	— proline
Glu	— glutamic acid	Ser	— serine
Gly	— glycine	Thr	— threonine
His	— histidine	Tyr	— tyrosine
Ileu	— isoleucine	Val	— valine

DESCRIPTION OF THE PRIZE-WINNING WORK*

"In order to study in more detail the free amino groups of insulin and other proteins, a general method for labeling them was worked out. This was the dinitrophenyl (or DNP) method. The reagent used was 1,2,4-fluorodinitrobenzene (FDNB), which reacts with the free amino groups of a protein or peptide to form a DNP derivative.

$$NO_2 \underset{NO_2}{\overset{F}{\bigcirc}} \quad + \quad \underset{R}{\overset{NH_2 \cdot CH \cdot CO \sim}{|}} \quad \rightarrow$$

FDNB   protein

$$NO_2 \underset{NO_2}{\overset{NH \cdot \overset{R}{\overset{|}{C}} H \cdot CO}{\bigcirc}} \quad + \quad HF$$

DNP-protein

"The reaction takes place under mildly alkaline conditions which normally do not cause any breakage of the peptide bonds.

"The DNP-protein is then subjected to hydrolysis with acid which splits the peptide bonds in the chain, leaving the N-terminal residue in the form of its DNP-derivative.

"The DNP-amino acids are bright yellow substances and can be separated from the unsubstituted amino acids by extraction with ether. They could be fractionated by partition chromatography, a method which had just been introduced by Gordon, Martin and Synge at that time. The DNP-amino acids could then be identified by comparison of their chromatographic rates with those

* From *Les Prix Nobel en 1958*.

of synthetic DNP-derivatives. In the original work on insulin, silica gel chromatography was used, though more recently other systems, particularly paper chromatography, have been found more satisfactory. When the DNP derivatives had been separated and identified they could be estimated colorimetrically.

$$
\begin{array}{c}
R \\
| \\
NH \cdot CH \cdot CO \sim
\end{array}
$$

NO₂ ⬡
NO₂
DNP-protein

$\xrightarrow{HCl}$

$$
\begin{array}{c}
R \\
| \\
NH \cdot CH \cdot COOH
\end{array}
$$

NO₂ ⬡
NO₂
DNP-amino acid

+   amino acids

"When the method was applied to insulin, three yellow DNP-derivatives were found in the hydrolyzate of the DNP-insulin. One of these was not extracted into ether; this was ε-DNP-lysine, which was formed by reaction of the FDNB with the free ε-amino group of lysine residues which are bound normally within the polypeptide chain. The others were identified as DNP-phenylalanine and DNP-glycine, and estimation on the basis of an assumed molecular weight of 12,000 showed that there were two residues of each. This suggested to us that insulin was composed of four polypeptide chains, two with phenylalanine and two with glycine end groups. This method has now been applied widely to many proteins and peptides and, together with the Edman phenylisothiocyanate method, is the standard method for studying N-terminal residues. In general it has been found that the chains of other proteins are much longer than those of insulin. All pure proteins appear to have only one or two N-terminal residues.

SEPARATING THE PEPTIDE CHAINS

"It seemed probable that the chains of insulin were joined together by the disulfide bridges of cystine residues. Insulin is relatively rich in cystine, and this was the only type of cross linkage
that was definitely known to occur in proteins. It was thus next
attempted to separate the peptide chains by splitting the disulfide
bridges. Earlier attempts to do this by reduction to —SH derivatives had not proved successful and had given rise to insoluble
products which were probably the result of some type of polymerization. More satisfactory results were obtained by oxidation
with performic acid. The cystine residues were converted to cysteic
acid residues, and thus the cross links were broken.

$$
\begin{array}{ccc}
\text{—NH—CH—CO—} & & \text{—NH—CH—CO—} \\
| & & | \\
\text{CH}_2 & & \text{CH}_2 \\
| & & | \\
\text{S} & \xrightarrow{\text{H} \cdot \text{COOOH}} & \text{SO}_3\text{H} \\
| & & \\
\text{S} & & \text{SO}_3\text{H} \\
| & & | \\
\text{CH}_2 & & \text{CH}_2 \\
| & & | \\
\text{—NH—CH—CO—} & & \text{—NH—CH—CO—} \\
\text{Cystine residue} & & \text{Two cysteic acid residues}
\end{array}
$$

Performic acid also reacts with residues of methionine and tryp-
tophan, the two amino acids which fortunately were absent from
insulin.

"From the oxidized insulin two fractions could be separated
by precipitation methods. One (fraction A) contained glycine; the
other (fraction B), phenylalanine N-terminal residues. Fraction A
was acidic and had a simpler composition than insulin in that the
six amino acids lysine, arginine, histidine, phenylalanine, threo-
nine, and proline were absent from it. It thus had no basic amino
acids; these were found only in fraction B. From a quantitative
determination of the end groups it was concluded that fraction A
contained about 20 residues per chain, four of these being cysteic
acid, and that fraction B had 30 residues, two of which were
cysteic acid. Since the yield of each fraction was greater than 50

percent in terms of the N-terminal residues present and since the fractions appeared to be homogeneous, it seemed likely that there was only one type of glycyl chain and one type of phenylalanyl chain. This was confirmed by a study of the N-terminal sequences.

RESULTS OF ACID HYDROLYSIS

"When the DNP derivative of fraction B was subjected to complete acid hydrolysis, DNP-phenylalanine was produced. If, however, it was subjected to a milder acid treatment so that only a fraction of the peptide bonds were split, DNP-phenylalanine peptides were produced which contained the amino acid residues near to the N-terminal end, and by an analysis of these peptides it was possible to determine the N-terminal sequence to four or five residues along the chain. The results for fraction B are shown in Table 1. It was concluded from these results that all the N-terminal phenylalanine residues of insulin were present in the sequence

Phe-Val-Asp-Glu.

This suggested that if there were in fact two phenylalanyl chains, then these two were identical. Similar results were obtained with fraction A, and it was shown that the N-terminal glycine residues were present in the sequence

Gly-Ileu-Val-Glu-Glu.

"These results, besides giving information about the position of certain residues in the polypeptide chains, showed for the first time that the molecule was composed of only two types of chains and that if the molecular weight were 12,000, as was then believed, then the molecule was built up of two identical halves. The alternative conclusion was that the actual molecular weight was 6000, and this was later shown to be the case. At any rate the structural problem was somewhat simplified, since we were now concerned with determining the sequence in two chains containing 20 and 30 residues, respectively.

Table 1.

Peptide	Products of complete hydrolysis of peptide	Products of partial hydrolysis	Structure	Yield from DNP insulin[1]
B1	DNP-phenylalanine	---	DNP-Phe	13
B2	DNP-phenylalanine Valine	B1	DNP-Phe · Val	16
B3	DNP-phenylalanine Valine Aspartic acid	B1, B2	DNP-Phe · Val · Asp	13
B4	DNP-phenylalanine Valine Aspartic acid Glutamic acid	B1, B2, B3	DNP-Phe · Val. Asp · Glu	30
Other Bands giving B4 on partial hydrolysis				20
			Total	92

[1] Moles peptide as per cent of total N-terminal phenylalanine residues of insulin.

"Fraction B was subjected to partial hydrolysis with acid. Since the mixture was too complex for direct analysis by paper chromatography it was necessary to carry out certain preliminary group separations in order to obtain fractions containing 5—20 peptides that could then be separated on paper. This was accomplished by ionophoresis, ion exchange chromatography and adsorption on charcoal. These simplified mixtures were then fractionated by two-dimensional paper chromatography. The peptide spots were cut out and the material eluted from the paper, subjected to complete hydrolysis and analysed for its constituent amino acids. Another sample of the peptide was then investigated by the DNP technique to determine the N-terminal residue. Table 2 illustrates the results obtained with a very acidic fraction obtained by ion-exchange chromatography. This contained only peptides of cysteic acid. Since there are only two such residues in fraction B all these peptides must fit into two sequences. The way in which the two sequences Leu · CySO$_3$H · Gly and Leu · Val · CySO$_3$H · Gly were deduced from the results obtained with the peptides is illustrated in the table.

"When the structures of the two chains of insulin had been determined, the only remaining problem was to find how the

Table 2. *Cysteic acid peptides identified in a partial acid hydrolysate of fraction B*

(The inclusion of residues in brackets indicates that their relative order is not known.)		
	$CySO_3H \cdot Gly$	$CySO_3H \cdot Gly$
	$Val \cdot CySO_3H$	
		$Leu \cdot CySO_3H$
	$Val \cdot (CySO_3H, Gly)$	
		$Leu \cdot (CySO_3H, Gly)$
	$Leu \cdot (Val, CySO_3H)$	
	$Leu \cdot (Val, CySO_3H, Gly)$	
Sequences deduced	$Leu \cdot Val \quad CySO_3H \cdot Gly$	$Leu \cdot CySO_3H \cdot Gly$

disulfide bridges were arranged. About this time it was shown by Harfenist and Craig that the molecular weight of insulin was of the order of 6000 and thus that the molecule consisted of two chains containing three disulfide bridges, and not of four chains as we had originally thought. The fact that fraction A contained four cysteic acid residues whereas fraction B had only two indicated that two bridges must connect the two chains together and that one must form an intrachain bridge connecting one part of the A chain with another part of the same chain.

"In order to determine the distribution of the disulfide bridges, it was necessary to isolate, from unoxidized insulin, peptides containing intact cystine residues. These could then be oxidized to give cysteic acid peptides, which could be recognized since they had been found in the hydrolyzates of the oxidized chains. However, an unexpected difficulty arose in that, during hydrolysis, a reaction occurred which caused a random rearrangement of the disulfide bonds, so that cystine peptides were isolated which were not actual fragments of the original insulin, and it would have appeared from the results that every half-cystine was combined to every other half-cystine residue.

"The disulfide interchange reaction that occurred in acid solution was found to be different from that occurring in neutral and alkaline solution and instead of being catalyzed by —SH compounds was actually inhibited by them. This not only showed that a different reaction was involved but it also made it possible to prevent its occurring during acid hydrolysis. Thus, when insulin was treated with concentrated acid to which a small amount of thioglycolic acid was added, cystine peptides could be isolated which were in fact true breakdown products and from which the distribution of the remaining two disulfide bonds could be deduced. These are shown in Fig. 2, which shows the complete structure of insulin.

"Of the various theories concerned with protein chemistry, our results supported only the classical peptide hypothesis of Hofmeister and Fischer. The fact that all our results could be explained on this theory added further proof, if any were necessary, of its validity. The results also showed that proteins are definite chemical substances possessing a unique structure in which each position in the chain is occupied by one, and only one, amino acid residue."

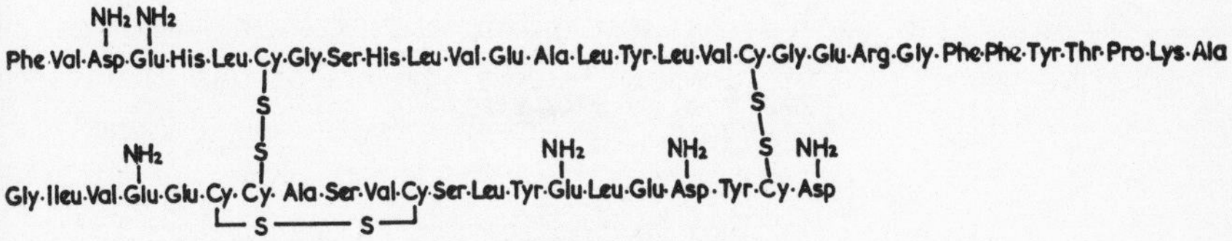

Fig. 2. Structure of insulin.

CONSEQUENCES IN THEORY
AND PRACTICE

Insulin, of which normal blood contains about four millionths of a gram per liter, is one of the life-regulating hormones. Two Nobel prizes in medicine and physiology had previously been given for the discoveries of insulin and its mode of influencing sugar metabolism: in 1923 to Frederick G. Banting and John J. R. Macleod, in 1947 to Bernardo Albert Houssay together with Carl F. and Gerty T. Cori.

Many intensive studies of the chemical nature of insulin culminated in Sanger's work. The methods he developed have been used for other high-molecular proteins, e.g. those of the hormones in the adrenal cortex, the corticotropic hormones. Further applications and expansions are to be expected for the still more complex molecules of hemoglobin, which contains a protein of about ten times the size of insulin. The new knowledge will most likely also have consequences for insulin therapy.

1 9 5 9
JAROSLAV HEYROVSKY
(1890-   )

*"For inventing and developing the polarographic
method of analysis."*

BIOGRAPHICAL SKETCH

JAROSLAV HEYROVSKY WAS BORN IN PRAGUE ON DECEMBER 20,
1890. He studied at the Czech University of Prague from 1909
to 1910 and then went to the University College, London, where
F. G. Donnan aroused his interest in electrochemistry. During the
war, he served in a military hospital. He obtained his Ph.D. degree
in Prague, 1918, and a D.Sc. in London, 1921. Then he returned
to Charles University in Prague and became its first full professor
of physical chemistry in 1926. The development of his invention,
on which he has been working since 1922, led to the creation
of a Polarographic Institute under his direction, in 1950. He was
Vice President of the International Union of Physics from 1951
to 57 and received many honors in his country and abroad.

His several books on polarographical practice (Springer Verlag,
Berlin, 1948; with P. Zuman, Verlag Technik, Berlin, 1959)
have been translated into many languages.

DESCRIPTION OF THE PRIZE-WINNING WORK *

"For some 38 years I have carried on electromechanical research with the dropping-mercury electrode because of its exquisite properties as electrode material. Its physical conditions of dropping as well as the chemical changes that occur during the passage of the electric current are well defined, and the phenomena displayed at the dropping-mercury electrode proceed with strict reproducibility. Owing to the latter property the processes of the electrode can be exactly expressed mathematically. According to the registering apparatus, called a "polarograph," which automatically draws curves characteristic of the electrode processes, the electrochemical studies with the dropping-mercury electrode and the analytical method developed on the basis of these investigations have been called "polarography.""

"The capillary electrode is normally a tube 8 centimeters long and 5 to 6 millimeters wide with an inner bore of 0.05 to 0.1 millimeter (Fig. 1), from which the drops of mercury fall off every 3 to 6 seconds, according to the height of the mercury reservoir, which is about 40 centimeters above the tip of the capillary.

"In order that the current passing through this electrode may be entirely governed by the composition of the solution surrounding it, the second electrode has to be indifferent, unpolarizable, and of a constant potential; most suitably, it is the layer of mercury at the bottom of the electrolytic vessel (Fig. 2).

"To apply the external voltage to the cell we use a potentiometric arrangement, shown in Fig. 2. From a 2- or 4-volt lead accumulator, an increasing voltage E is branched off, and the

Fig. 2.

corresponding current is determined by the deflection of the galvanometer. In such an arrangement the whole applied voltage E acts at the small polarizable electrode and determines its potential. The solution has to be conductive by an indifferent electrolyte (about 0.1 normal).

---

* From *Les Prix Nobel en 1959*.

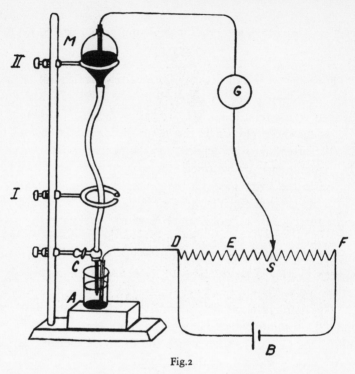

Fig.2

"Until the year 1924 the galvanometer deflections were plotted by hand on the ordinate against the voltage applied by pushing the wheel of the Kohlrausch drum to different values. It took a couple of hours to obtain a full graph, point by point, from 0 to 2 volts. To accelerate the plotting of the curves, Shikata and I constructed in 1924 an automatic device, the "polarograph," by rotating the Kohlrausch drum mechanically and by synchronously moving a photographic paper. This mechanism drew the current-voltage diagram—the "polarogram"—in less than 10 minutes, with all the advantages of automatic recording. The galvanometer has to be damped to register the mean current, instead of the instantaneous current, during each drop. It is not advisable to damp the motion of the galvanometer mirror so far that the oscillations disappear; the regularity of the oscillations provides a good check of the correct functioning of the apparatus (Fig. 4).

"Next, the forms of the current-voltage curves were classified according to the various processes occurring at the dropping elec-

Fig. 4. The first polarograph.

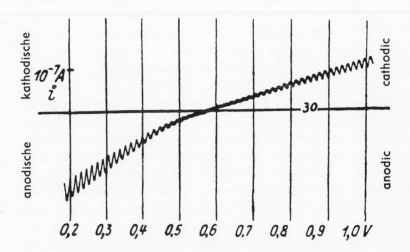

Fig. 5. Capacity current in o,1 M KCl freed from air.

trode. The most fundamental of these is the "charging" current which accompanies every drop formation, conveying to the drop the charge corresponding to the externally applied potential. Since this charge depends on the capacity of the dropping electrode and does not involve any electrolytic changes, the current is also termed "capacity current" or "non-faradic current" (Fig. 5). It is very small, of the order of 10^{-7} ampere per volt, and ordinarily is regarded as negligible. However, the charging current plays an important role in oscillographic polarography, where it is considerably greater. At a certain potential an electrolytic process starts—reduction or oxidation—which is shown by the passage of the current due to electrolysis. In the simplest case, molecules or ions of the reducible or oxidizable substances interchange electrons with the electrode and thereby are removed from the electrode surface. Then new molecules of the electroactive substance—the depolarizer—diffuse from the interior of the solution to the surface of the electrode. Ilkovic has calculated the current governed by diffusion to the surface of the expanding drop, deducing (in 1933) the formula of the "diffusion current":

$$i_d = 0.627 \; nF{\cdot}D \; \tfrac{1}{2} {\cdot} m \; \tfrac{2}{3} {\cdot} t \; \tfrac{1}{6} {\cdot} C$$

where n is the number of electrons involved in the reaction; F, the charge of Faraday; D, the diffusion constant; m, the rate of flow of mercury through the capillary; t, the drop time; and C, the concentration. This is the most exact electrochemical law announced since Faraday's laws in 1833.

"The sensitivity of the polarographic method is high, showing depolarizers in a $5 \times 10^{-6} M$ concentration even in 0.1 cubic centimeter and, in a special vessel, even in 0.005 cubic millimeter, in which 5×10^{-11} gram of a depolarizer may be ascertained. The most sensitive test is that of ruthenium, which is shown in a $5 \times 10^{-10} M$ concentration. With the Barker's "square wave polarograph," where the charging current is practically eliminated and the electrolytic one is strongly amplified, curves of a derivative character are obtained which show 10^{-8} mole per liter.

"Most sensitive of all is polarography combined with measurement of radioactivity. The method consists in measuring the activity of the β and γ radiation of mercury drops on which the radioactive metal has been deposited. Isotopes, of course, cannot be distinguished, but, for example, from a mixture of radioactive zirconium-95 and niobium-95, the daughter substance, zirconium-95, can be separated, because it is deposited at the electrode, whereas niobium remains in solution. This radioactive technique promises wide applications through enabling one not only to carry out quick, accurate analyses and separations of radionuclides but also to learn the basic electrochemistry of very dilute solutions and electrode reactions. The sensitivity is that of radioactive methods.

"A great field that has opened since 1938 is "oscillographic polarography," which substitutes the cathode-ray oscillograph for the galvanometer and voltmeter. This brings the velocity of recording a polarographic curve to 1/50 second, and the accuracy of analytical determinations is about the same as in classical polarography."

CONSEQUENCES IN THEORY AND PRACTICE

The electrical potential between a falling mercury drop and a pool of mercury had long been observed. Walther Nernst discussed its theory in 1896, and Wilhelm Palmaer confirmed it experimentally a few years later. Heyrovsky saw that measuring the electron exchange on the thin interface between the steadily renewed mercury surface and the surrounding solution could reveal much about the composition and processes in the solution. The sensitivity of the polarographic method can be such that concentrations of a millionth of a gram-molecule are measured in less than 0.1 c.c.

Polarographic methods are now being used in the analysis of metals, in the study of electrochemical processes of inorganic and organic compounds, and for following biochemical reactions.*

---

* See: Petr Zuman and Philip J. Elving, Journal of Chemical Education 37, 562 (1960).

1 9 6 0
WILLARD FRANK LIBBY
(1908-   )

"For developing radio carbon dating techniques."

BIOGRAPHICAL SKETCH

WILLARD FRANK LIBBY WAS BORN ON DECEMBER 17, 1908, IN Grand Valley, Colorado. He studied at the University of California, Berkeley, and received his Ph.D. degree there in 1933. He remained at Berkeley as instructor and later as professor until 1941. During the war years, he worked in the Manhattan District project at Columbia University and then joined the Institute for Nuclear Studies (Enrico Fermi Institute) at Chicago University. In 1954, he was appointed a member of the U.S. Atomic Energy Commission. At the end of his term, in 1961, he returned to the University of California.

For his work on natural carbon-14 and on tritium he received many honorary awards. His book on "Radiocarbon Dating" was first published in 1952 and has had subsequent new editions.

DESCRIPTION OF THE PRIZE-WINNING WORK *

"Radiocarbon dating had its origin in a study of the possible effects that cosmic rays might have on the earth and on the earth's atmosphere. We were interested in testing whether any of the various effects which might be predicted could actually be found

---

* From *Les Prix Nobel en 1960.*

and used. Initially the problem seemed rather difficult, for ignorance of billion-electron-volt nuclear physics (cosmic-ray energies are in this range) was so abysmal at the time (and, incidentally, 14 years later is still so abysmal) that it was nearly impossible to predict with any certainty the effects of the collisions of the multi-billion-volt primary cosmic radiation with air.

FORMATION OF RADIOCARBON

"However, in 1939, just before the war, Serge Korff of New York University and others discovered that the cosmic rays produce secondary neutrons in their initial collisions with the top of the atmosphere. The neutrons were found by sending counters, designed to be sensitive to neutrons, up to high altitudes, and they were found to have an intensity which corresponded to the generation of about two neutrons per second for each square centimeter of the earth's surface.

"Whereas it was extremely difficult to predict the types of nuclei that might be produced by the billion-volt primary cosmic rays, the neutrons, being secondaries, were in the million-volt energy range and, therefore, subject to laboratory tests. So at this point the question was: What will million-electron-volt neutrons do if liberated in the air? The answer to this question was already available—in fact, Korff noted in one of the papers announcing the discovery of the neutrons that the principal way in which the neutrons would disappear would be by forming radiocarbon. The reaction involved is a simple one. Oxygen is essentially inert to neutrons, but nitrogen is quite reactive. Nitrogen-14, the abundant nitrogen isotope, reacts essentially quantitatively to form carbon-14 with the elimination of a proton. It also reacts about 1 percent of the time to produce tritium (radioactive hydrogen); this is another story, leading to a method of dating water and wine.

"To return to radiocarbon dating, knowing that there are about two neutrons formed per square centimeter per second, each of which forms a carbon-14 atom, and assuming that the cosmic rays have been bombarding the atmosphere for a very long time in terms of the lifetime of carbon-14 (carbon-14 has a half-life of about 5600 years), we can see that a steady-state condition should have been established, in which the rate of formation of carbon-14 would be equal to the rate at which it disappears to reform nitro-gen-14. This allows us to calculate quantitatively how much carbon-14 should exist on earth (see Fig. 1); and since the two atoms per second per square centimeter go into a mixing reservoir with about 8.5 grams of carbon per square centimeter, this gives an expected specific activity for living matter of 2.0/8.5 disintegrations per second per gram of carbon.

" . . . it is clear from the set of assumptions that have been given that organic matter, while it is alive, is in equilibrium with the cosmic radiation—that is, all the radiocarbon atoms which dis-integrate in our bodies are replaced by the carbon-14 contained in the food we eat, so that while we are alive we are part of a great pool which contains the cosmic-ray-produced radiocarbon. The specific activity is maintained at the level of about 14 dis-integrations per minute per gram by the mixing action of the biosphere and hydrosphere. We assimilate cosmic-ray-produced carbon-14 atoms at just the rate that the carbon-14 atoms in our bodies disappear to form nitrogen-14. At the time of death, how-ever, the assimilation process stops abruptly. There is no longer any process by which the carbon-14 from the atmosphere can enter our bodies. Therefore, at the time of death the radioactive disintegration process takes over in an uncompensated manner and, according to the law of radioactive decay, after 5600 years the carbon that was in our bodies while we were alive will show half the specific carbon-14 radioactivity that it shows now. Since we have evidence that this has been true for tens of thousands of

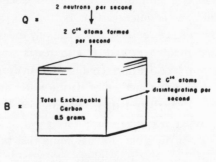

Fig. 1. Radiocarbon genesis and mixing.

years, we should expect to find that a body 5600 years old would be half as radioactive as a currently living organism. This appears to be true. Measurements of old artifacts of historically known age have shown this to be so within the experimental errors of measurement.

INITIAL RESEARCH

"The research on radiocarbon dating was carried out in several stages. In the first place, my collaborator, E. C. Anderson, and I had to determine whether the living material actually had the radioactivity expected. At that time we had no measurement techniques sufficiently sensitive to detect the radioactivities involved directly because these levels are quite low. Later we developed methods for making the measurement, but at that time we did not have them, so we used the method of concentrating the heavy isotope of carbon. An apparatus for this purpose had been built by and was being used by A. V. Grosse of Temple University, then of the Houdry Process Corporation at Marcus Hook, Pennsylvania. Grosse was concentrating the carbon-13 isotope for medical tracer purposes and kindly agreed to try to concentrate some biological methane for the test so crucial to our research. We had to use biological, as contrasted with petroleum, methane, for we had at this point arrived at a distinction between living and dead organic chemicals. We had both "dead" methane and "living" methane in the sense that methane from oil wells in which the oil has been long buried would be expected to be entirely free from radiocarbon while the methane made from the disintegration of living organic matter should contain radiocarbon with an activity of 14 disintegrations per minute per gram of carbon. The task was to take this living methane and concentrate it in the isotope separation column to see whether the heavily enriched product was radioactive. Happily for our research, it was found to be so, and to about the expected degree. The material used was methane gas from the sewage disposal plant of the city of Baltimore.

"The second stage of the research was the development of methods of measurement sufficiently sensitive to eliminate the use of this $10,000 thermal-diffusion isotope column, which was so expensive to operate that it cost thousands of dollars to measure the age of a single mummy. Obviously, radiocarbon dating would have been an impractical method of measuring archeological ages if this phase of the research had been unsuccessful.

COUNTING TECHNIQUE

"The counting method developed involves measuring the radioactivity of the carbon directly. We convert the samples by chemical methods into a suitable form—carbon dioxide or acetylene gas or even solid carbon—which then is placed inside a Geiger or proportional counter, where it itself constitutes the gas or lies on the inner counter wall. This is possible because carbon as lampblack is an electrical conductor, and the gases carbon dioxide and acetylene are satisfactory counter gases. In this way a maximum count rate is achieved.

"The counter itself is shielded from the background radiations in order to accentuate the carbon-14 count. Charcoal is one of the best materials for radiocarbon dating, provided adequate care is taken to see that intrusive rootlets and humic acids are removed before measurements are made."

CONSEQUENCES IN THEORY
AND PRACTICE

In a recent survey, H. Goodwin (Cambridge) stated: "Since Libby first demonstrated the validity of the method and the feasibility of making the rather difficult measurements, some forty radiocarbon-dating laboratories have come into operation, and they are attempting to act in cooperation with one another, publishing their definitive data lists yearly in the American Journal of Science." *

These measurements provide new insights into the "ice ages," the sequences of glacial drifts in America and Europe. Human cultures in California are found to be as old as in other parts of the New World. Sagebrush-bark sandals from Fort Rock Cave, Oregon, have been measured to be about 9,000 years old, with an uncertainty of ± 350 years.

---

* H. Goodwin, Proc. Royal Society, London, *153*, 287/320 (1961).

1 9 6 1

MELVIN CALVIN
(1911-   )

"For his work on photosynthesis."

BIOGRAPHICAL SKETCH

MELVIN CALVIN WAS BORN APRIL 8, 1911, IN ST. PAUL, MINnesota. He received his B.S. degree from the Michigan College of Mining and Technology at Houghton in 1931 and his Ph.D. from the University of Minnesota in 1935. Under a Rockefeller Foundation Grant he studied for two years in Manchester. There, he became interested in the phthalocyanine dyes, which contain copper or other metals in a complex bond to nitrogen atoms, similar to the metal bonds in the molecules of hemoglobin and in chlorophyll. He joined the University of California in 1937 and became director of the Bio-organic Division, Lawrence Radiation Laboratory, at Berkeley in 1946.

He is a member of many committees, including some of the Armed Forces and the National Academy of Science. Among the honors he received are a D.Sc. from the Michigan College, the award of the Richards Medal in 1956, the Nichols Medal in 1958, and election as Foreign Member of the Royal Society of London.

301

DESCRIPTION OF THE PRIZE-WINNING WORK*

"Our own interest in the basic process of solar energy conversion by green plants, which is represented by the overall reaction

$$CO_2 + H_2O \xrightarrow[\text{Chlorophyll}]{\text{Light}} (CH_2O)_n + O_2$$

began some time in the years between 1935 and 1937, during my postdoctoral studies with Professor Michael Polanyi at Manchester. It was there I first became conscious of the remarkable properties of coordinated metal compounds, particularly metalloporphyrins as represented by heme and chlorophyll. A study was begun at that time, which is still continuing, on the electronic behavior of such metalloporphyrins. It was extended and generalized by the stimulus of Professor Gilbert N. Lewis upon my arrival in Berkeley. I hope these continuing studies may one day contribute to our understanding of the precise way in which chlorophyll and its relatives accomplish the primary quantum conversion into chemical potential which is used to drive the carbohydrate synthesis reaction.

"Even before 1940 the idea that the reduction of carbon dioxide to carbohydrate might be a dark reaction separate from the primary quantum conversion act was already extant, stemming most immediately from the comparative biochemical studies of Cornelis van Niel and the much earlier work of F. F. Blackman and its interpretation by Otto Warburg. The photoinduced production of molecular oxygen had been separated chemically and physically from the reduction of carbon dioxide by the demonstration of oxygen evolution by illuminated chloroplasts. This was done by

---

* From Melvin Calvin's Nobel Prize Lecture, December 11, 1962.

Robert Hill using ferric iron as oxidant in the place of carbon dioxide.

"In 1945 it became apparent to us that carbon-14 would be available cheaply and in large amounts by virtue of the nuclear reactors which had been constructed. With the encouragement and support of Professor Ernest O. Lawrence, the Director of the Radiation Laboratory in Berkeley, we undertook to study that part of the energy converting process of photosynthesis represented by the carbon reduction sequence, making use of C^{14} as our principal tool.

DESIGN OF THE EXPERIMENT

"The principle of the experiment was simple. We knew that ultimately the CO_2 which enters the plant appears in all of the plant materials but primarily, and in the first instance, in carbohydrate. It was our intention to shorten the time of travel to such an extent that we might be able to discern the path of carbon from carbon dioxide to carbohydrate as the radioactivity which enters with the CO_2 passes through the successive compounds on its way to carbohydrate.

"Preliminary experiments confirmed the idea that the absorption of CO_2 and its incorporation in organic material was indeed a dark reaction. This was easily established by exposing plants which had first been illuminated in the absence of carbon dioxide so as to store some of the intermediate high energy containing compounds, and then noting that these compounds could be used in the dark to incorporate relatively large amounts of CO_2. However, the products did not proceed very far along the reduction scheme under these conditions, and so we undertook to do the experiment in what we call a steady state of photosynthesis.

"As the precision of our experiments increased, the need for more reproducible biological material also increased, and very soon we found it necessary to grow our own plant material in as highly reproducible manner as possible. A very convenient green plant that had already been the subject of much photosynthetic research was the unicellular green alga, *Chlorella*.

"We developed methods of growing these organisms in a highly reproducible fashion, both in intermittent and continuous cultures, and it is with organisms such as these that most of our work was done. I hasten to add, however, that the essential features of the cycle with which we finally emerged were demonstrated on a wide variety of photosynthetic organisms, ranging from bacteria to the higher plants.

EARLY ANALYTICAL METHODS

"In the early work, the classical methods of organic chemistry were applied in our isolation and identification procedures, but it soon became apparent that these were much too slow and would require extremely large amounts of plant material to provide us with the identification of specific labeled compounds. Here, again, we were able to call upon our experience during the war years in which we had used ion exchange columns for the separation of plutonium and other radioactive elements. We made use of both anion and cation exchange columns, and soon discovered that the principal compounds in which we were interested, that is, those which became C^{14} radioactive in the shorter exposure times, were, indeed, anionic in character.

"Because of the peculiar difficulty we found in eluting the principal radioactive components from anion exchange resins, it became apparent that this radioactive material was a strongly acidic material and very likely had more than one anionic point of attachment to bind to the resin. Among these peculiarities was the fact that an ordinary carboxylic acid could be eluted relatively easily while the principal radioactive material would require either very strong acid or very strong base to bring it off. This, taken together with a number of other chromatographic properties, led to the idea that these early products might very well be phosphate esters as well as carboxylic acids.

"A more detailed analysis of the precise conditions required to elute the material off the ion exchange columns suggested phosphoglyceric acid as a possibility. To a relatively large amount of algae was added as indicator a small amount of the purified radioactive material obtained from a small sample of algae exposed to radioactive carbon for a few seconds. This led to the direct isolation of slightly over nine milligrams of a barium salt which by classical organic procedures we were able to show to be the barium salt of 3-phosphoglyceric acid.

PAPER CHROMATOGRAPHIC METHODS

"About this time Martin and Synge had developed their method of partition chromatography which was particularly adapted for amino acid analysis because of the sensitivity of the colorimetric detection method. We turned to this as our principal analytical tool. It was particularly suited to our needs because, having spread our unknown material from the plant onto a sheet of filter paper by two-dimensional chromatography, we could then find the particular components which we sought, namely, the radioactive ones, without knowing their chemical nature beforehand. This was done by placing the paper in contact with photographic film, thus exposing the film at those points of the paper upon which were located the very compounds in which we were interested.

ORIGIN OF PHOSPHOGLYCERIC ACID

"We now are ready to return to the question of the origin of the PGA itself. Here we were led, by what appeared to be an obvious kind of arithmetic, to seek a compound made of two carbon atoms as a possible acceptor for the radioactive CO_2 to produce the carboxyl-labeled three-carbon compound, phosphoglyceric acid. This search was a vigorous one and extended over a number of years. (Again, a considerable number of students and laboratory visitors were involved.) While free glycolic acid was found under certain very special conditions, these did not correspond to what would be required of the so-called carbon dioxide acceptor. A good many other compounds were identified in the course of this search; particularly among them were a five-carbon sugar, ribulose as its mono- and diphosphate, and a seven-carbon sugar, sedoheptulose as its mono- and diphosphate.*

---

* (Ribulose, as a keto-carbohydrate, has the same relationship to ribose as fructose has to glucose.)

"We can now formulate the cyclic system driven by high energy compounds produced in the light, acting upon phosphoglyceric acid which, in turn, is made as a result of a reaction between ribulose diphosphate and carbon dioxide as shown in Figure 16. The triose phosphate then undergoes a series of condensations and sugar rearrangements, represented by the letters A and B and including the pentose and heptose rearrangement which we have just discussed, leading back again to a ribulose monophosphate which is then phosphorylated to ribulose diphosphate, thus completing the cycle.

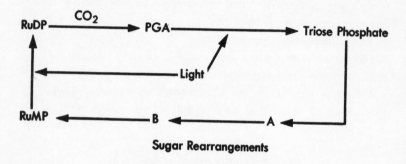

RuMP = ribulose monophosphate
RuDP = ribulose diphosphate
PGA = phosphoglyceric acid

Fig. 16. Formation of five-carbon sugars from ribulose diphosphate.

QUANTUM CONVERSION IN PHOTOSYNTHESIS

"As you can see from the various levels of the schematic drawing of the photosynthetic carbon cycle (Figure 18), the energy required to drive the synthetic sequence from carbon dioxide to carbohydrate and the many other reduced carbon materials which can be derived from the cycle is delivered to it in the form of a number of compounds of relatively high chemical potential in the aerobic aqueous system in which the plant operates. The particular ones with which we can actually drive the photosynthetic carbon cycle in the absence of light but in the presence of all

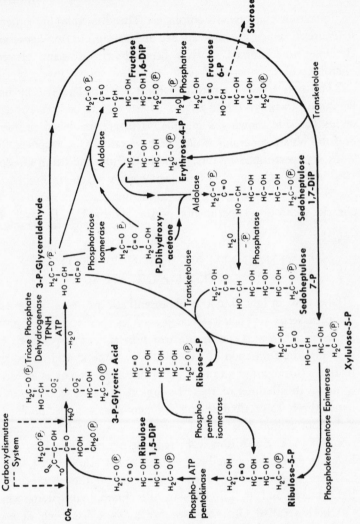

Fig. 18. The photosynthetic carbon cycle.

the initial enzymes and substrates are triphosphopyridine nucleotide (TPNH) and adenosine triphosphate (ATP).

"The apparatus which performs the quantum conversion act in the plant, together with all of the carbon reduction enzymes we now know, can be isolated from the intact chloroplasts in the higher plants. The carbon reduction enzymes are very easily washed off the chloroplasts by water, leaving behind only the chlorophylous quantum conversion equipment. This has a highly ordered structure in which the lamellae are alternating electron-dense and electron-thin materials, as has been shown in many electron micrographs.

"The next level of structure within the lamellae is only now beginning to be visible to us . . . here we can see the lamellae on its flat side showing a granular structure, made up of fairly uniform oblate spheroids which we have called Quantosomes; this work was performed by Drs. Roderic B. Park and Ning G. Pon. Within these Quantosomes the chlorophyll itself is highly organized, as we have been able to demonstrate, particularly by electric dichroism experiments performed by Dr. Kenneth H. Sauer."

CONSEQUENCES IN THEORY AND PRACTICE

The new insight into the photosynthetic processes presents a complex series of chemical reaction cycles. Some of these go by stages which also occur in fermentation and in respiration. For example, the formation of phosphates of glyceric acid and carbohydrates through the action of adenosine triphosphate is a feature common to all three of these biological processes. On the other hand, the roles of ribulose and sedoheptulose are specific for the way from carbon dioxide and water to carbohydrates in assimilation. Of the enzymes responsible for the intermediary steps, some, like a transketolase, have been isolated and crystallized.

These reactions depend for their start on the absorption of light energy and its utilization by the chlorophyll system, which Calvin has called Quantosomes. Much work has been done to elucidate the conversion of quanta of one energy form into the other. Yet, we are far from having solved all the problems in this field. One of them is the formation of the chlorophyll system in the evolution of life, which Calvin is pursuing in continuation of his previous studies on metalloporphyrins. We have gained new tools and methods for approaching answers to the questions, which we are now able to transform into designs for experiments. After his success on the way to such answers, Calvin is now advocating further research on a broad basis.

BIBLIOGRAPHY

After starting with books about Alfred Nobel the bibliography is limited to publications about the Nobel Prize winners in chemistry (section 1) and that part of their work that was closely connected with the object of the prize (section 2). The names of the laureates are in alphabetical order, followed by the year of the award.

IN SECTION 1, the letters (B), (G), and (V) refer to biographical articles, not otherwise listed, in the following collective works:

(B): Buch der Grossen Chemiker, ed. Günther Bugge. Verlag Chemie, Weinheim, vol. 2, 1930, reprinted 1958.

(G): Great Chemists, ed. E. Farber. Interscience Publishers, New York, 1961.

(V): Via regia-Nobelpreisträger auf dem Wege ins Atomzeitalter, and: Via triumphalis-Nobelpreisträger im Kampf gegen den Tod, ed. Rudolf Erckmann. Wilhelm Anderson Verlag, München und Wien, 1955.

IN SECTIONS 1 and 2, frequently cited journals are abbreviated in conformance with the practice of Chemical Abstracts:

Angew. Chem.: (Zeitschrift für) Angewandte Chemie
Ann. chim.: Annales de chimie et de physique (Paris)
Biochem J.: Biochemical Journal (Cambridge University Press)
Biochem. Z.: Biochemische Zeitschrift (Heidelberg)
Chem. Ber.: Chemische Berichte and its predecessor: Berichte der Deutschen Chemischen Gesellschaft
Chem. Eng. News: Chemical & Engineering News (Washington, D.C.)
Compt. rend.: Comptes rendus (Paris)
Helv. Chim. Acta: Helvetica Chimica Acta
Ind. Eng Chem.: Industrial & Engineering Chemistry
J. Am. Chem. Soc.: Journal of the American Chemical Society
J. Biol. Chem.: Journal of Biological Chemistry (Baltimore)
J. Chem. Soc.: Journal of the Chemical Society (London)
J. Chem. Ed.: Journal of Chemical Education
Kolloid Z.: Kolloid Zeitschrift (Darmstadt)
Liebig's Ann.: Liebig's Annalen der Chemie
Phil. Mag.: Philosophical Magazine (London)
Phil. Trans.: Philosophical Transactions of the Royal Society London, Series A and B
Science: Science, American Association for the Advancement of Science
Z. physik. Chem.: Zeitschrift für physikalische Chemie

ALFRED NOBEL

H. Schück and R. Sohlman, "The Life of Alfred Nobel," (Nobelstiftelsen) W. Heinemann, London, 1929.

Michael Evianoff, "Nobel-prize Donor, Inventor of Dynamite, Advocate of Peace," Blackiston, Philadelphia, 1929.

H. Schück, R. Sohlman, A. Österling, G. Liljestrand, A. Westgren, M. Siegbahn, A. Schou, N. K. Stahle, "Nobel, the Man and his Prizes," Ed. Nobel Foundation, Sohlmans Förlag, Stockholm, 1950.

Edith P. Meyer, "Dynamite and Peace, the Story of Alfred Nobel," Little, Brown & Co., Boston, 1958.

ALDER, KURT, 1950

1

Kölner Universitäts-Reden, Heft 22. Scherle Verlag, Krefeld, 1959.
(V)

2

Anwendungen der Diels-Alder Synthese für die Erforschung von Naturstoffen (with Marianne Schumacher), in Fortschritte der Chemie organischer Naturstoffe, vol. 10 (1953), 1-118.

ARRHENIUS, SVANTE, 1903

1

Autobiography: "Aus meiner Jugendzeit," Akademische Verlagsgesellschaft, Leipzig, 1913.
(B) (G)

2

Dissociation der in Wasser gelösten Stoffe, Z. physik. Chem. *1* (1887), 631-648.

Lärobok i teoriskik Elektrokemin, Stockholm, 1900.

ASTON, FRANCIS WILLIAM, 1922

1

(G)

2

The Mass Spectra of Chemical Elements, Phil. Mag. (6) *40* (1920), 628-634.

Constitution of Atmospheric Neon. Phil. Mag. *39* (1920), 449-455.

Masses of Some Light Atoms Measured by Means of a New Mass Spec-
trometer, Nature *137* (1936), 357-358.

BAEYER, ADOLF VON, 1905

1

W. H. Perkins, J. Chem. Soc. *123* (1923), 1520-46.
(B) (G) (V)

2

Verbindungen der Indigogruppe, Chem. Ber. *16* (1883), 2188; *33*
(1900), Sonderheft.
Gesammelte Werke, 2 vols., Vieweg, Braunschweig, 1905.

BERGIUS, FRIEDRICH, 1931

1

K. Schoenemann, Brennstoffchemie *30* (1949), 177-181.
(V)

2

Historical Review of Hydrogenation, World Petroleum Congress 1933,
vol. 2(1934), 282-9.

BOSCH, CARL, 1931

1

C. Krauch, Angew. Chem. *53* (1940), 285-8.
R. Kuhn, Naturwissenschaften *28* (1940), 481-3
A. Mittasch, Z. für Elektrochemie *46* (1940), 333-5.
(G) (V)

2

Erdöl und synthetisches Benzin, Petroleum *29* (1933), No. 27, 1-18.

BUCHNER, EDUARD, 1907

1

C. Harries, Chem. Ber. *50* (1917), 1843-76.
(V)

2

Alkoholische Gärung, Chem. Ber. *31* (1898), 568.
Eduard Buchner, Hans Buchner, and Martin Hahn: "Die Zymasegär-
ung," München, 1903.

BUTENANDT, ADOLF, 1939

1

E. Müller, Chemiker Zeitung 77 (1953), 171.
(V)

2

Chemical Constitution of the Follicular and Testicular Hormones, Nature *130* (1932), 238.
Chemistry of Sterins, J. Soc. Chem. Industry *55* (1936), 753-9; Heart Poisons and Vitamin D. Ib., 891-3.
Neuere Beiträge der biologischen Chemie zum Krebsproblem, Angew. Chem. *53* (1940), 345-52.

CALVIN, MELVIN, 1961

1

Chem. Eng. News *39* (1961), 36.

2

Melvin Calvin, Charles Heidelberger, James C. Reid, Bert M. Tolbert, and Peter E. Yankwich: "Isotopic Carbon," Wiley, New York, 1949.
"The Path of Carbon in Photosynthesis," Prentice-Hall, Englewood Cliffs, 1957.
Evolution of Enzymes and the Photosynthetic Apparatus, Science *130* (1959), 1170-74.
Quantum Conversion in Photosynthesis, J. Theoret. Biol. *2* (1961), 258.
Evolution of Photosynthetic Mechanisms, in Perspectives in Biology and Medicine, *5* (1962), 147.
The Path of Carbon in Photosynthesis (Nobel Prize Lecture), Science 1962 (in print).

CURIE, MARIE SKLODOWSKA, 1911

1

Eve Curie, "Madame Curie," tr. Vincent. Sheean, Garden City Publishing Co, Garden City, N. Y., 1938.
F. Eileen Bigland, "Madame Curie," Criterion Press, New York, 1957.

2

M. Curie: "Traité de Radioactivité," Gauthier-Villars, Paris, 1910.

DEBYE, PETER J. W., 1936

1

J. M. Kolthoff, J. Polymer Science *13* (1954), 2.
M. von Laue, Z. für Elektrochemie *58* (1954), 151-3.

2

"Polar Molecules," Chemical Catalog Co., New York, 1928.
"The Dipole Moment and Chemical Structure," tr. by W. M. Deans, Blakiston, London, 1932.
Energy Absorption in Dielectrics With Polar Molecules, tr. Faraday Society *30* (1934), 679-84.

DIELS, OTTO, 1950

1

W. Klemm, Angew. Chem. *63* (1951), 180.
H. Wieland, Jahrbuch der Bayerischen Akademie der Wissenschaften 1954, 200-2. Olsen Sigurd, Chem. Ber. *95* (1962), V-XLVI. (V)

2

Kohlensuboxyd (with K. Hansen), Chem. Ber. *59* (1926), 2555-60.
Die Dien- Synthese, Angew. Chem. *42* (1929), 911-8.
Organic Compounds Having Hydrogenated Ring Systems, U. S. Patent 1,944,731 of January 23, 1934 (assigned to I. G. Farbenindustrie).

EULER-CHELPIN, HANS VON, 1929

1

W. Franke, Naturwissenschaften *40* (1953), 177-80.
(V)

2

"Chemie der Enzyme," München, 1928.
Water-soluble vitamins, in Annual Review of Biochemistry *5* (1936), 355-78.
Coenzyme und Hemmstoffe, Chem. Ber. *75* (1943), 1876-85.
Beziehungen der Enzyme zu ihren Wirkstoffen, in Ergebnisse der Enzymforschung *10* (1949), 302-57.

FISCHER, EMIL, 1902

1

Autobiography: "Aus meinem Leben," Springer, Berlin, 1922.

Martin Onslow Forster, J. Chem. Soc. *117* (1920), 1157-1201.
Kurt Hoesch, Chem. Ber. Sonderheft *54* (1921).
(B) (G) (V)

2

Synthesen in der Zuckergruppe, Chem. Ber. *23* (1890), 2115-41.
Synthesen in der Puringruppe, Chem. Ber. *32* (1899,) 435-504.
Proteine und Polypeptide, Angew. Chem. *20* (1907), 913.

FISCHER, HANS, 1930

1

Alfred Treibs, Z. Naturforschung *1* (1946), 476-9.
S. F. MacDonald, Nature *160* (1947), 494.
(G) (V)

2

Porphyrine und ihre Synthese, Chem. Ber. *60* (1927), 2611-51.
Liebig's Ann. *502* (1933), 175.
Zur Konstitution des Chlorophylls, Liebig's Ann. *486* (1931), 107-90.

GIAUQUE, WILLIAM FRANCIS, 1949

1

Hans Holtan, Tidskrift Kjemi, Bergvesen, Met. *9* (1949), 185-8.
Ind. Eng. Chem. *28* (1936), 743.

2

Thermodynamic Treatment of Certain Magnetic Effects, A Proposed Method of Producing Temperatures Considerably Below 1° Absolute, J. Am. Chem. Soc. *49* (1927), 1864-70.
Temperatures Below 1° Absolute, Ind. Eng. Chem. *28* (1936), 743-50.

GRIGNARD, VICTOR, 1912

1

(G)

2

Combinaisons Organo-Magnésiennes Mixtes et Leur Application à la Synthèse d'Acides, d'Alcohols, et d'Hydrocarbons, Ann. chim. (7) *24* (1901), 433-90.
Compt. rend. *198* (1934), 625-8.

HABER, FRITZ, 1918

1

Autobiography: "Aus Leben und Beruf," Berlin, 1928.
M. Bodenstein, Z. Elektrochemie 40 (1934)
(G) (V)

2

Thermodynamik technischer Gasreaktionen, München, 1905; English edition by Arthur B. Lamb, New York, 1908.
Das Ammoniak-Gleichgewicht, Chem. Ber. 40 (1907), 2144-54 (with R. le Rossignol).

HAHN, OTTO, 1944

1

L. Meitner, Naturwissenschaften 41 (1954), 97-9.
E. Regener, Mitteilungen der Max Planck Gesellschaft 1954, 3-10. (V)

2

"Applied Radiochemistry," New York, 1936.
Künstliche radioaktive Atomarten aus Uranium und Thorium, Angew. Chem. 40 (1936), 127.
Neue Umwandlungsprodukte bei Neutronenbestrahlung des Uraniums, Chem. Ber. 69 (1936), 905-19.
Künstliche Umwandlungen bei Bestrahlung des Thoriums mit Neutronen, Z. Physik 109 (1938), 538-52.
Zur Geschichte der Uran-Spaltung, Naturwissenschaften 46 (1959), 158-63.

HARDEN, ARTHUR, 1929

1

Karl Josephson, Svensk Kem. Tidskrift 41 (1929), 275-81.

2

"Alcoholic Fermentation," Longmans, Green & Co., New York, 1911 (4th ed. 1932).
Biochem. J. 21 (1927), 23 (1929), 230-6.

HAWORTH, WALTER NORMAN, 1937

1

E. L. Hirst, J. Chem. Soc. 1951, 2790-2806.

2

"The Constitution of Sugars," Edward Arnold & Co., London, 1929.

HEVESY, GEORGE DE, 1943

1

Autobiography, in Perspectives in Biology and Medicine, University of Chicago Press, Chicago 1958, vol. 1, 345-65.
(V)

2

"Das Alter der Grundstoffe," Speyer und Karner, Freiburg, 1929.
"Chemical Analysis by X-rays and its Applications," McGraw-Hill, New York, 1932.

HEYROVSKY, JAROSLAV, 1959

1

M. von Stackelberg, Z. Elektrochemie 60 (1956), 105-6.

2

Méthode Analytique d'Électrolyse à Gouttes de Mercure, Bull. Soc. Chim. de France 41 (1927), 1224-41.
Analysis of Petroleum and Its Distillates for Reducible Substances and Adsorbable Matter by Means of the Polarographic Method With the Dropping Mercury Cathode, Trans. Am. Electrochem. Soc. 59 (1931).
"Oszillographische Polarographie" (mit R. Kalvoda). Akademie-Verlag, Berlin, 1959.

HINSHELWOOD, CYRIL, 1956

Homogeneous Reactions, in Chemical Reviews 3 (1926), 227-56.
Present-Day Chemical Kinetics, J. Chem. Soc. 1947, 694-701.
"Chemical Kinetics in the Bacterial Cell," Oxford University Press, London, 1947.

HOFF, JACOBUS HENRICUS VAN'T, 1901

1

Ernst Cohen, "J. H. van't Hoff," Akademische Verlagsgesellschaft, Leipzig, 1912.
W. Ostwald, Chem. Ber. *44* (1911), 2219-52.
(B) (G)

2

"Etudes de Dynamique Chimique," Amsterdam, 1884.
"Dix Années dans l'histoire d'une Théorie," Amsterdam, 1887.

JOLIOT, FRÉDÉRIC, and JOLIOT-CURIE, IRÈNE, 1935

1

G. Teillac, "Irène Joliot-Curie," Nuclear Physics *4* (1957), 497-502.
Louis de Broglie, "Frédéric Joliot," Compt. rend. *247,* 25 April, 1958.

2

"La Projection de Noyaux Atomiques par un Rayonnement Très Pénétrant. L'Existence du Neutron," Hermann & Cie., Paris, 1932.
Production Artificielle d'Éléments Radioactives, Journal de Physique et Le Radium (7) *5* (1934), 153-6.

KARRER, PAUL, 1937

1

Chem. Eng. News *33* (1955), 2820.

2

Vitamin A (with K. Morf), Helv. Chim. Acta *16* (1933), 625.
Chemie der Vitamine A und C, Chemical Reviews *14* (1934), 17-30.
"Die Carotenoide" (with Ernst Jucker). Birkhäuser, Basel, 1948; trans., Van Nostrand, New York, 1955.

KUHN, RICHARD, 1938

1

(V)

2

Plant Pigments, in Annual Review of Biochemistry *4* (1935), 479-96.
Lactoflavin (Vitamin B_2), Angew. Chem. *49* (1936), 6-10.
Adermin, Vitamin B_6 (with A. Wendt), Chem. Ber. *71* (1938), 780; 1118.

LANGMUIR, IRVING, 1932

1

Eric K. Rideal, Chem. Soc. Proceedings 1959, 80-3.
Albert Rosenfeld, "Langmuir, the Man and Scientist," vol. 12 of Collected Works, ed. C. Guy Smith et al., Pergamon Press, New York, 1961.
(G)

2

"Electrochemical Interactions of Tungsten, Thorium, Caesium, and Oxygen," Columbia University Press, New York, 1930.

LIBBY, WILLARD FRANK, 1960

1

Chem. Eng. News 32 (1954), 3994-6.

2

"Radiocarbon Dating," Chicago University Press, Chicago, 1952.
Chicago Radiocarbon Dates, Science 120 (1954), 733-42.

McMILLAN, EDWIN M., 1951

1

Chem. Eng. News 30 (1952), 238.

2

Radioactive Element 93 (with Philip Hauge Abelson), Physical Review 57 (1940), 1185.
The Synchroton, Physical Review 68 (1945), 143-5.
Lecture Series in Nuclear Physics (with E. Segré, E. Teller, F. Bloch et al.), Government Printing Office, Washington, D.C., 1947.

MARTIN, ARCHER JOHN PORTER, 1952

Partition Chromatography, in Annual Reports Progress in Chem. 45 (1949), 267-83.

MOISSAN, HENRI, 1906

1

P. Lebeau, Bull. Soc. Chim. de France 1953, 135-8.
(G)

2

Études des Carbures Métalliques, Proceedings Royal Soc. London, 60 (1897), 156-60.
"Le Four Electric," Paris, 1897; The Electric Furnace, Easton, Pa., 1920.
Le Fluor et ses Composés," Paris, 1904; trans. by Th. Zettel, Berlin, 1906.

NERNST, WALTHER, 1920

1

M. Bodenstein, Chem. Ber. 75 A (1942), 79-104.
Nature 149 (1942), 375.
  (G)   (V)

2

"Applications of Thermodynamics to Chemistry" (Silliman Lectures), Scribner, New York, 1907.
"Die theoretischen und experimentellen Grundlagen des neuen Wärmesatzes," Knapp, Halle, 1918.
"The New Heat Theorem, Its Foundations in Theory and Experiment," trans. by G. Barr, London, 1926.

NORTHROP, JOHN HOWARD, 1946

1

Autobiographical: Biochemists, biologists, and William of Occam, in Annual Review of Biochemistry 30 (1961), 1-10.

2

Crystalline Pepsin, J. General Physiology 13 (1930), 14 (1931).
"Crystalline Enzymes" (with M. Kunitz and R. M. Heriot), Columbia University Press, New York, 1948.

OSTWALD, WILHELM, 1909

1

Autobiography: "Lebenslinien," Klasing & Co., Berlin, 1926, 1933.
Grete Ostwald: "Wilhelm Ostwald, Mein Vater," Berliner Union, Stuttgart, 1953.
F. G. Donnan, J. Chem. Soc. 1933, 316-32.
E. Farber, J. Chem. Ed. 30 (1953), 600-2.
  (G)   (V)

2

Beschleunigung eines langsam verlaufenden chemischen Vorgangs durch die Gegenwart eines fremden Stoffes, Z. Physik. Chem. *15* (1894), 705.

"Prinzipien der Chemie, eine Einleitung in alle chemischen Lehrbücher," Akademische Verlagsgesellschaft, Leipzig, 1907.

"Outline of General Chemistry," trans. W. W. Taylor, 3rd ed., New York, 1912.

"Grundriss der allgemeinen Chemie," Engelmann, Leipzig, 1889.

PAULING, LINUS, 1954

1

M. L. Hoggins, Chem. Eng. News *33* (1955), 242-4.

2

The Nature of the Chemical Bond; Application of Results Obtained From the Quantum Mechanics and From a Theory of Paramagnetic Susceptibility to the Structure of Molecules, J. Am. Chem. Soc. *53* (1930), 1367-1400; *54* (1932), 988.

"The Nature of the Chemical Bond," Cornell University Press, Ithaca, New York, 1938; 3rd ed., 1960.

"Introduction to Quantum Mechanics with Applications to Chemistry" (with E. Bright Wilson, Jr., and Martin Karplus), McGraw-Hill, New York, 2nd ed., 1960.

PREGL, FRITZ, 1923

1

(G)   (V)

2

"Die quantitative organische Mikroanalyse," Springer, Berlin, 1917; 5th ed. by H. Roth, 1947.

RAMSAY, WILLIAM, 1904

1

Th. W. Richards, Proc. Am. Philosophical Soc. *56* (1916).

Harry F. Keller, J. Franklin Institute *182* (1916), 267-70.

Benjamin Harrow, Scientific Monthly 1919, 167-78.

(G)

2

"The Gases of the Atmosphere, the History of their Discovery," Macmillan, London, 1896; 4th ed., 1915.
The Homogeneity of Helium and of Argon (with J. Norman Collie), Proc. Roy. Soc. 60 (1897), 206-15.
Gaseous Contents of Certain Mineral Substances and Natural Waters, (with Morris W. Travers), ibid., 442-8.
"Elements and Electrons," Harper & Bros., New York, 1913.

RICHARDS, THEODORE WILLIAM, 1914

1

G. P. Baxter, Science 68 (1928), 333-9.
H. Hartley, J. Chem. Soc. 1930, 1937-69.
(G)

2

Determinations of Atomic Weights, Carnegie Institution of Washington, Publication No. 125, 1910.
"Experimentelle Untersuchungen über Atomgewichte 1887-1908."
Deutsche Ausgabe von J. Koppel. Voss, Hamburg, Leipzig, 1909.
Ideals of Chemical Investigation, Science 44 (1916), 37-45.

ROBINSON, ROBERT, 1947

1

Chem. Eng. News 31 (1953), 3844.

2

Synthesis in Biochemistry, J. Chem. Soc. 1936, 1079-90.
Brazilin and Haematoxylin, part VIII. (with W. H. Parkin, Jun.), J. Chem. Soc. 93 (1908), 491-517.
Molecular Structure of Strychnine and Brucine, Proc. Roy. Soc. Ser. A, 130 (1931), 431-52.
"The Structural Relations of Natural Products," Clarendon Press, Oxford, 1955.

RUTHERFORD, ERNEST, 1908

1

A. S. Eve, "Rutherford 1871-1937, Being the Life and Letters of the Rt. Hon. Lord Rutherford," Macmillan, New York, 1939.
E. Marsden, Proc. Roy. Soc. Ser. A, 226 (1954), 283-305. (G)

2

Radioactivity, Cambridge University Press, Cambridge, 1904; 2nd ed., 1905.

"Radioactive Substances and Their Radiations," Cambridge University Press, London, C. P. Putnam Sons, New York, 1912.

RUZICKA, LEOPOLD, 1939

1

Mladen Dezelic, Archiv za Hemija i Technologija (Kemijski Vjestnik) *13* (1939), 73-97.

2

Zur Kenntnis der Wagner'schen Umlagerung II, Uber die Bildung des Santens (with Fr. Liebl), Helv. Chim. Acta 6 (1923), 267-81.

Höhere Terpenverbindungen XXXVI, Uber die Konstitution des Zingiberens (with A. G. van Veen), Liebig's Ann. *468* (1929), 143-62.

Bedeutung der theoretischen organischen Chemie für die Chemie der Terpenverbindungen, in "Perspectives in Organic Chemistry," ed. A. R. Todd, Interscience, New York, 1956, 265-314.

SABATIER, PAUL, 1912

1

J. R. Partington, Nature *174* (1954), 859-60.

Charles Camichel, Georges Champetier, and Gabriel Bertrand, Bull. Soc. Chim. de France 1955, 465-75.

2

"La Catalyse en Chimie Organique," C. Bréanger, Paris et Liège, 1913; 2nd ed. 1920; trans. by Emmet Reid, Van Nostrand, New York, 1922.

SANGER, FREDERICK, 1958

Amino Acid Sequence in the Glycyl Chain of Insulin:
  I. Identification of Lower Peptides From Partial Hydrolyzates (with E. O. P. Thompson), Biochem. J. *53* (1953), 353-65.
  II. Peptides From Enzymic Hydrolyzates, ibid., 366-74.

The Structure of Insulin, in "Currents in Biochemical Research," 1956, ed. David E. Green, Interscience, New York, 1956, 434-59.

SEABORG, GLENN T., 1951

1

Chem. Eng. News *26* (1948), 740-1.

2

The Transuranium Elements, Science *104* (1946), 379-86.
The Transuranium Elements, Research Papers, ed. with Joseph J. Katz and Winston M. Manning, McGraw-Hill, New York, 1949.
"The Transuranium Elements," Yale University Press, New Haven, 1958.

SEMENOV, NIKOLAJ NIKOLAJEVITJ, 1956

1

N. M. Chirkov and V. V. Voavodskii, Zhurnal Fizichskoi Khimii *30* (1956), 722-8.

2

"Some Problems in Chemical Kinetics and Reactivity," Moscow, 1954; trans. by Michel Boudart, 2nd ed., Princeton University Press, Princeton, 1958; by J. C. S. Bradley, Pergamon Press, New York, 1958.

SODDY, FREDERICK, 1921

1

Muriel Howorth, "Pioneer Research on the Atom—the Life Story of F. Soddy," New World Publications, London, 1958.
(G)

2

"The Chemistry of the Radio-elements," Longmans, Green & Co., London, 1911; 2nd ed., 1914.
"The Interpretations of Radium," G. P. Putnam's Sons, New York, 4th ed., 1922.

STANLEY, WENDELL MEREDITH, 1946

1

R. S. Shriner, Chem. Eng. News *24* (1946), 750-2.
Vincent du Vigneaud, ibid., 752-5.

2

The Virus of Tobacco Mosaic. VII. The Isolation of a Crystalline Protein Possessing the Properties of Aucuba Mosaic Virus, J. Biol. Chem. *117* (1937), 325-40.
Biochemical Studies on Influenza Virus, Chem. Eng. News *24* (1946), 755-8.

STAUDINGER, HERMANN, 1953

1

H. A. Bruson and H. Mark, J. Polymer Science *19* (1956), 387.
Autobiography: "Arbeitserinnerungen," Heidelberg, 1961.
(V)

2

Der Aufbau der hochmolekularen organischen Verbindungen, Naturwissenschaften *22* (1934), 65-71, 84-9.
Die Chemie der Cellulose, ibid., 797-803, 813-9.
Uber die Polymerisation als Kettenreaktion, Chem. Ber. *68* (1935), 2351-6.
Der Begriff des Molekular-Gewichts bei nieder- und hochmolekularen Verbindungen, ibid., 2357-62.

SUMNER, JAMES B., 1946

1

L. A. Maynard, National Academy of Sciences, Washington, D.C., Biographical Memoirs *31* (1958), 376-96.

2

Isolation and Crystallization of the Enzyme Urease, J. Biol. Chem. *69* (1926), 435-41; *79* (1928), 489 (with R. G. Holloway).
"Chemistry and Methods of Enzymes" (with Fred G. Somers), Academic Press, New York, 1943; 2nd ed., 1953.

SVEDBERG, THEODOR,. 1926

1

J. Arvid Hedvall, in "The Svedberg 1884-1944," ed. Arne Tiselius et al., 681-725.

2

"Die Methoden zur Herstellung kolloider Lösungen anorganischer

Stoffe," Steinkopf, Dresden, 1909; 2nd ed., 1920.

The Ultracentrifuge, a New Instrument for the Determination of Size and Distribution of Size of Particles in Ultramicroscopic Colloids (with Hermann Rinde), J. Am. Chem. Soc. *45* (1923), 943-54; (with J. B. Nichols) 2910-7.

Cataphoresis of Proteins (with Eric R. Jette), ibid., 954-7.

"Die Ultrazentrifuge," Steinkopff, Dresden, 1940.

SYNGE, RICHARD LAURENCE MILLINGTON, 1952

Synthesis of Some Dipeptides Related to Gramicidin S, Biochem. J. *42* (1948), 94-104.

Physico-Chemical Studies of Gramicidin and Some Implications for the Study of Proteins, in Cold Spring Harbor Symposia on Quantitative Biology *14* (1949), 191-8.

General Review of the Applicability of the Method, in Biochemical Society Symposia *3* (1950), Partition Chromatography, 90-103.

TISELIUS, ARNE, 1948

1

Ralph E. Oesper, J. Chem. Ed. *28* (1951), 538.

2

Berechnung thermodynamischer Eigenschaften von kolloiden Lösungen und Messungen mit der Ultrazentrifuge, Z. physik. Chem. *124* (1926), 449-63.

Bestimmung der Beweglichkeit und Ladung kolloider Teilchen, in Handbuch biologischer Arbeits-Methoden, ed. E. Abderhalden, Vol. III B, 1929.

TODD, ALEXANDER, 1957

1

Chem. Eng. News *29* (1951), 3466.

2

The Chemistry of the Nucleotides, Proc. Roy. Soc. Ser. A, 226 (1954), 70-82.

Phosphates in Vital Processes, Chemistry & Industry, Aug. 11, 1956, 802-7.

UREY, HAROLD C., 1934

1

Viktor K. La Mer, Scientific Monthly *38* (1934), 387-90.

2

Natural System of Atomic Nuclei, J. Am. Chem. Soc. *53* (1931), 2872-80.

A Heavy Isotope of Mass 2 and Its Concentration (with F. G. Brickwedde and G. M. Murphy), Physical Review *40* (1932), 1-15; 464-5.

Significance of the Hydrogen Isotopes, Ind. Eng. Chem. *26* (1934), 803-6.

Separation of Isotopes by Chemical Means, J. Washington Academy of Sciences *30* (1940), 277-94.

DU VIGNEAUD, VINCENT, 1955

1

E. C. Kendall, Chem. Eng. News *33* (1955), 5587-8.

2

High Potency Oxytocic Material From Beef Posterior Pituitary Lobes (with John J. Pierce), J. Biol. Chem. *186* (1950), 77-89.

"A Trail of Research in Sulfur Chemistry and Metabolism and Related Fields," Cornell University Press, Ithaca, 1952.

The Synthesis of an Octapeptide Amide with the Hormonal Activity of Oxytocin, J. Am. Chem. Soc. *75* (1953), 4879.

VIRTANEN, ARTTURI ILMARI, 1945

Lactic Acid Fermentation III (with H. Karström), Z. physiol. Chem. *155* (1926), 251-8.

British Patents, with Voinvienti-Osuuslike Valio:

   Storage and Preserving of Fodder, No. 370,685 (1931), 385,212 (1932); Preserving Animal and Vegetable Substances, No. 391, 331 (1933).

"Cattle Fodder and Human Nutrition, with Special Reference to Biological Nitrogen Fixation," Cambridge University Press, Cambridge, 1938.

WALLACH, OTTO, 1910

1

Leopold Ruzicka, J. Chem. Soc. 1933, 165-80.

Walter Hückel, Chem. Ber. *94* A, VII-CVIII, 1961.
(G)   (V)

2

"Terpene und Campher," Veit & Co., Leipzig, 1909; 2nd ed., 1914.

WERNER, ALFRED, 1913

1

P. Karrer, Helv. Chim. Acta *3* (1920), 196.
G. T. Morgan, J. Chem. Soc. *117* (1920), 1639.
(G)   (V)

2

"Neuere Anschauungen auf dem Gebiete der anorganischen Chemie,"
Vieweg, Braunschweig, 1909; trans. as New Ideas in Inorganic
Chemistry, by E. P. Hadley. Wiley, New York, 1911.

WIELAND, HEINRICH, 1927

1

Rolf Huisgen, Chem. Soc. Proceedings, August, 1958, 210-9.
(G)   (V)

2

"Die Knallsäure," Sammlung chemischer und chemisch-technischer Vor-
träge, Vieweg, Braunschweig, vol. 14, 1909.
The Bile Acids, XXIII (with Richard Jacobi), Z. physiol. Chem. *148*
(1925), 232-44.
Biological Oxidations, J. Chem. Soc. 1931, 1055-64.
"On the Mechanism of Oxidations," Yale University Press, New Haven,
1932.
Die Konstitution der Gallensäuren, Chem. Ber. *67* A (1934), 27-39.

WILLSTATTER, RICHARD, 1915

1

Autobiography: "Aus meinem Leben," Verlag Chemie, Weinheim,
1949.
R. Kuhn, Naturwissenschaften *36* (1949), 1.
R. Robinson, Obituary Notices of Fellows of the Royal Society, No.
22 (1953), 609-34.
(G)   (V)

2

"Untersuchungen über Chlorophyll" (with Arthur Stoll), Springer, Berlin, 1913.

Chlorophyll, J. Am. Chem. Soc. *37* (1915), 323-45.

"Untersuchungen über die Assimilation der Pflanzen," Springer, Berlin, 1918.

Pflanzenfarbstoffe, Chem. Ber. *47* (1914), 2831-74.

Untersuchungen über die Anthocyane, Liebig's Ann. *408* (1916), 1-162.

WINDAUS, ADOLF, 1928

1

Gulbrand Lunde, J. Chem. Ed. 7 (1930), 1771-7.

A. Butenandt, The Windaus Memorial Lecture, Proceedings of the Chemical Soc., April, 1961, 131-8.
(V)

2

Die Konstitution des Cholesterins, Gesellschaft d. Wissenschaften, Göttingen, Nachrichten, 1919.

Anwendungen der Spannungstheorie, ibid., 1921.

Ultra-violet Bestrahlung von Ergosterin (with K. Westphal, F. v. Werden, and O. Rygh), ibid., Math.-physik. Klasse, 1929, 45-59.

Abbau und Aufbau im Gebiete der Sterine, in Handbuch biologischer Arbeitsmethoden, ed. E. Abderhalden, Abt. 1: Chemische Methoden, vol. 6 (1925), 169-210.

Chemistry of Irradiated Ergosterol, Proc. Roy. Soc. Ser. B, *108* (1931), 568-75.

ZSIGMONDY, RICHARD, 1925

1

H. Freundlich, Chem. Ber. *63* (1930), 1912.
(V)

2

"Colloids and the Ultramicroscope, a Manual of Colloidchemistry and Ultramicroscopy," trans. Jerome Alexander, Wiley, New York, 1909.

Reduktionsgeschwindigkeit und das Wachstum kleiner Goldteilchen bei der Herstellung kolloidaler Goldlösungen (with E. Hückel), Z. physik. Chem. *116* (1925), 291-303.

"Kolloidchemie," Spamer, Leipzig, 5th ed., 1925-7.

AUTHOR INDEX

SUBJECT INDEX